Man
under the Sea

By the same author:

THE GREAT IRON SHIP

Man
under the Sea

by James Dugan

Illustrated

Harper & Brothers · Publishers · New York

This book is published in England
under the title of *Man Explores the Sea*

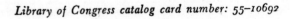

Library of Congress catalog card number: 55-10692

To Ruth and Simone

Table of Contents

Acknowledgments

I WANT to thank Mrs. Joan St. George Saunders of London and Leslie Schenk of Paris, who found much material and provided additional interviews for this book. I am grateful for generous aid and advice to Sir Robert H. Davis, Captain G. C. C. Damant, R.N. (Ret.), Captain W. O. Shelford, R.N. (Ret.), Frédéric Dumas, Jacques-Yves Cousteau, Auguste Boutan, Dr. Harold E. Edgerton, Beaumont Newhall and Thomas A. Manar.

In Britain I wish to thank also David Woodward, Commander Ian Fleming, R.N.V.R., Sir Arthur Elton, J. A. Jerome of Admiralty Information; Mrs. Joan Bright Astley, O.B.E., Dr. R. E. Davies, Dr. H. G. Vevers, Dr. Harold Barnes, Donald Burke, Frederick Burr Opper, H. Neville Davies, W. Maconachie, C. B. Towill, Ronald Tritton, Professor J. B. S. Haldane, Mrs. Elaine Greene; the Misses Dilys Powell, Olwen Vaughan and Margaret Bean; Drs. H. J. Taylor, Cyril Rashbass and H. V. Hempleman; Bernard Ashmole, A. L. Butcher and the following organizations: Siebe, Gorman and Company, Ltd.; British Marconi (Marine), Ltd.; Kelvin & Hughes Marine, Ltd.; Pye, Ltd.; British Petroleum, Ltd.; London Electrotype Agency, Ltd.; the National Institute of Oceanography; the Scottish Marine Biological Association; the Marine Biological Association of the United Kingdom; the British Sub-Aqua Club; the *Sunday Times*; the *London Illustrated News*; The Manchester *Evening News*; the Central Office of Information; Director of Information, Admiralty; the Royal Navy Physiological Laboratory, the National Maritime Museum, Greenwich; the Imperial War Museum; Underwater Surveys, Ltd.; and Writer's & Speaker's Research. I thank Dr. Robert S. Dietz, Scientific Liaison Officer, U.S. Embassy, London, and those who furnished pictures reproduced in the book, which are each acknowledged beneath the plates.

In France I am indebted to MM. Jacques Augustin-Normand, Henri Broussard, Daniel P. Cousteau, Dmitri Rebikoff, Professor Pierre Drach, Professor Louis Fage, Commandant Jules Rouch, François Vilarem, Professor Paul Portier, Jean-Loup Berger, André Portelatine, Louis Lehoux, Dr. Alexandre Ivanoff, Norbert Casteret, Ferdinand Lallemand, Serge de

Sazo, André Galerne, Georges Barnier, Commandant Georges S. Houot, Lieutenant Pierre-Henri Willm, Armand Frémont, Henri Coanda, Professor Georges Petit, Henri Maleville, Jean Delmas and Louis Malle. And Dr. and Mme. Edmund Mauric, Anthony Guinness, George T. Moody, Ginette Goharghi, Commandant Maurice Delpeuch, M. and Mme. Jean Bisch, Lieutenants Jean Alinat and Guy Morandière, Roger Gary, and Mme. Pierre Amandry. Aid was kindly given by the Musée de la Marine, the Bibliothèque Nationale, Éditions Larousse and the Club de la Mer.

In Italy, I thank Roberto Galeazzi and Professor Nino Lamboglia; in Algeria, Dr. René Dieuzeide and the Musée Alaoui at Bardo; and in Greece, Dr. Georges Daux of the French School of Athens and Dr. C. W. J. Eliot of the American School of Classical Studies. I owe special thanks for submarine archeological information to Professor George Karo. The Swiss savants, Professor Auguste Piccard and his son Jacques, were most helpful. Australian information was volunteered by Robert Lord, Noel Monkman and Clive Ogilvie, and from Norway by Dr. Gunnar Rollefsen. John E. Williamson of Nassau and Park Breck of Bermuda furnished ready data.

In the United States I thank Lucien L. Pohl, William Ryan, John Lochhead, Kip Ross, Walter M. Edwards, Commander F. D. Fane, U.S.N.; David M. Owen, Colonel John D. Craig, Jon Lindbergh, Donald Gerue and Professor Delwin L. Covey, Robert F. Dill, Dr. Preston E. Cloud, Jr., Jim Auxier, René Bussoz, Dr. Robert Owen, Henry S. Moncrief, Commander Fenimore Johnson, Dr. John F. Storr, Owen Churchill, Edwin E. Turner, John Lyman, Gustav dalla Valle, Robert Carse, Jerry Greenberg, Emil Corwin, Raynor T. McMullen, Max Gene Nohl, Paul Cherney, William Westell, Ralph N. Davis, Herman J. A. C. Arens, Luis Marden, Dr. Jerome M. Schweitzer, Henry Schwanda, John Weilberg, Dr. George Grisinger, Dr. Maurice Ewing, Jack W. Hale, Robert S. Lyle, Jeremy North, Mrs. Roderick Cox, A. A. Hoehling, John Ryan, Lila Parrish Lyman, Donald Shepard, Nathaniel Klasky, Jan Hahn, Admiral J. A. Furer, U.S.N. (Ret.), Commander J. V. Dwyer, U.S.N., and the naval lieutenants Edward H. Lanphier, Kenneth Ploof, Herbert E. Hetu and William Maley. I am grateful to Edward R. Sammis, Noel McLean and Dr. William J. Clench. The following were unusually co-operative: the Edo Corporation, the Electric Boat Division of General Dynamics Corp., Socony Mobil Oil, the Medical and Pharmaceutical Information Bureau, the Collins Construction Co., the National Geographic Society, the American Museum of Natural History, Navy Information of the Department of Defense, the Experimental Diving Unit, the United Nations Press Services, The Mariner's Museum, Newport News, the Submarine Library, Groton, Connecticut, and the Oakland (California) *Tribune*.

My reliance on leading underwater writers may be seen in text. I am especially grateful to Sir Robert Davis, J. Valerio Borghese, Edward L. Beach, Georges S. Houot and Pierre Willm, C. E. T. Warren and James Benson, Simon Lake and Herbert Corey, T. J. Waldron and James Gleeson, Jacques-Yves Cousteau and Frédéric Dumas, William Beebe, Otis Barton, Kenneth Edwards, David Masters, Eugenie Clark, Philippe Tailliez, John E. Williamson and John D. Craig. What you will read is an introduction to a subject I hope you will explore in their books.

JAMES DUGAN

Man
under the Sea

1

Naked in the Sea

A LEAN, straw-haired man, wearing a loincloth and carrying a long spear, walked along the beach in the sun. He waded into the green water and swam lazily far into the blue water. He floated face down for a while, surveying the scene below, then abruptly lifted his head and held his spear upright. He filled his lungs and swept a cupped hand into the water. He bounced out to his waist, blew the air from his lungs and sank rapidly, feet first. Underwater, he turned head down and drove with rapid kicks straight for the bottom with his empty lungs squeezing toward the crushing point. Forty feet down he addressed a big brown grouper with his spear. The fish looked at him with curiosity but no fear. The man lunged like a fencer and drove his shaft clean through the fish. There was a puff of gray-green blood. The fish turned white. The man pulled himself along the spear, closer to the flipping fish, and steered it ahead of him to the surface.

It was the first act of the drama of amateur diving and undersea hunting. The place—Cap d'Antibes. Time—the 1920's. The hunter—Guy Gilpatric. The scene could have occurred in many places and times, but this was its inauguration as a sport. Gilpatric, writer and *bon viveur*, had devised the adventure to amuse himself. In the mornings he sat on a terrace by the warm blue sea, typewriting about Mr. Glencannon and a rusty tramp steamer ploughing gray, cold seas. In the afternoon he sallied out with his spear. The fish had known nets, hooks, tridents and blinding lights at night, but they had never met a *Saturday Evening Post* author coming at them with a spear.

Around 1929 Gilpatric puttied shut a pair of flying goggles to look beneath the surface and the sea led him down. He beckoned to his polyglot acquaintance of idle fellows—émigré Russians, unaccountable Balks and merry-andrews from here and there who ate his free lunch and were game to follow. They evolved the primitive ballast-blowing technique as artlessly as the Pacific islanders who also dived with empty lungs. In his frolicsome book, *The Compleat Goggler,* the first on sport diving, Gilpatric tells of days when he made fifty such dives with his "little group of serious sinkers." They swam to sea without boats or other floats and stayed there diving for hours. They were possessed by a virgin adventure, away from politics, newspapers, economics and domestic affairs. They lived in dangers they knew nothing of and the sea was kind to them, welcoming home a species that had left her long ago.

Gilpatric wrote a *Post* piece on his wonderful new pastime. It rallied solitary divers in many parts, each of whom thought himself alone in the rare sport. Gilpatric's book came out in 1938. I saw a copy recently in Captain Jacques-Yves Cousteau's quarters in the *Calypso,* the marine research ship. It was inscribed from Philippe Tailliez, another leader of contemporary French free diving. Gilpatric was the inspiration of Cousteau, Tailliez and many others, who were to pass him in technique, but never exceed the bold ardor he took into the secret sea. The war drove the divers from the Mediterranean and Gilpatric's happy opera closed in tragedy. When his wife was told she had a hopeless cancer, they killed themselves together.

Mighty hunters plunged in the blue sea in the Gilpatric days. Photographs of the early hunters stalking *merous* remind you of George Catlin's drawings of Sioux spearmen advancing on bearpaw snowshoes toward the buffalo a hundred years ago. When amateur diving revived after the war, the great *merou* was almost gone, due to wartime dynamiting. André Portelatine and Louis Lehoux, the seasoned hunters of the Club de la Mer at Juan-les-Pins, now study the habits of a big sedentary rock fish for two or three days before they go down for a shot. The proudest hunters pit themselves against the big running ocean nomads, tunas and liches. Such a diver is Albert Falco, a quiet Hercules from Sormieu, a cove village east of Marseille which huddles under such steep rock that it can only be reached by sea.

As a favor to a friend, Falco entered the first International Undersea Hunting Competition in Antibes in 1948. Despite the fact that he had lost the thumb and forefinger of his left hand from a mine clearance job, Falco speared as many fish as all the other contestants combined. That was his last competition. He comes from a place where people eat fish and don't expect medals for killing them in the name of sport. I saw Falco in action one day off the west coast of Corsica where the *Calypso* had stopped for a peaceful lunch out of the wind. I was swimming off the stern when I heard yells on deck. A crowd arrived at the diving ladder, yelling and pointing. They had seen something coming from the bow. Falco broke through, grabbing a spear gun, fins and mask, and seemed to have put them on while skinning down the ladder. I looked down and saw the first of a pride of liches streaming slowly and insolently past the ship about twenty-five feet down. It was the first time I had seen this species—little known to marine biologists and unknown to anglers and trawlmen. They were long silvery animals with large dark eyes, slick as jet fighters. Falco's big brown body drove into the pack. He shot his *arbalète*. A five-foot liche fell out of the formation with a squirt of brown blood. The others accelerated without perceptible motion and vanished on course. The stricken fish jerked, dislodged the arrow and sped after the pack. Falco surfaced, grinning. He looked off across the Ligurian Sea. It had been a sporting chance. He admired the liche.

Falco is not a new type in the Mediterranean, although Gilpatric was. Naked divers have been inside this sea since ages beyond writing. Mother-of-pearl, which cannot be gathered in any quantity without diving for the shells, has been found in carved ornaments in excavations of Sixth Dynasty Thebes, about 3200 B.C., and also turned up in Mesopotamian diggings dating to 4500 B.C. Greek mythology is a web of undersea tales. Crippled Hephaestus was dropped from Olympus and set up a smithy in a submerged cave. He is the god of submarine engineers. Aphrodite, goddess of desire, arose foam-borne on a scallop shell and stepped ashore on Kythera Island. She married Hephaestus. Aristotle, the first scientific naturalist, wrote so accurately on fishes that you suspect he was a diver. He describes Alexander the Great descending in a diving bell. Xerxes employed combat divers. It is not even necessary to look at these scraps of allusion. The evidence of ancient diving is obvious in the marine products used by the ancient Greeks, including animals attached to the bottom that could be harvested properly only by divers. Imperial purple dye came from a shellfish. Sponges were widely used by the Greeks. Roman soldiers soaked them with water and carried them as canteens. Divers plunged in choppy water with oil-soaked sponges in their mouths. They bit the sponges and sent up oil to lay the water and cut down on dancing beams of sunlight. Red coral was a mystical substance, exported as far as China to make the badge of office of the mandarins. Today it is still worn by superstitious women in southern Italy as a charm against the evil eye. The Golden Fleece was the long silky byssus of the big pinna clam, the threads it exuded from its shell to anchor it to a rock. Aphrodite's "waterski"—best seen in Botticelli's famous painting—became the *Coquille St. Jacques,* the badge of medieval pilgrims who had made the journey to the shrine of St. James in Campostella, Spain. Shells of the great tridacna clam were built into medieval

The chap sitting on the bale of cordage is Alexander the Great, an early submariner. From a medieval French painting.

cathedrals as holy water fonts. Free diving in the Mediterranean cradle of civilization is a long unbroken story.

In all warm seas people without histories have been diving for thousands of years, not necessarily without apparatus. Frédéric Dumas found a seventeenth-century French print of naked red coral divers with goggles on their eyes. Wall paintings in Arnhem Land, in aboriginal north Australia, show the "living stone age men" swimming with spears and strings of fish. An eighteenth-century French engraving shows a free salvage diver wearing air bottles on his back. Da Vinci sketched several independent diving rigs in the fifteenth century. Diving bells were invented so often down through history that I decided I could not double the size of this book with a short sketch of their development.

The original inhabitants of the Bahama Islands, a gentle, peaceful people called the Lucayans, were accomplished fish spearmen and pearl divers. My friend, Hilary St. George Saunders, who was writing a history of the Bahamas when he died there a few years ago, recorded the fearful end of the Lucayans in a manuscript which Mrs. Saunders has kindly showed me. In 1509, Nicolás de Ovando, Spanish governor of Santo Domingo, having killed most of the aborigines of that island by forced labor, bethought himself of the Bahamas, undisturbed since Columbus' call seventeen years before. Don Nicolás sailed his fleet to the Bahamas, where he was received innocently. He announced that he had come from heaven and all who wished to return with him were welcome. Over thirty thousand people crowded aboard the Spanish ships; the population was only forty thousand. Don Nicolás battened them below and sailed for Santo Domingo. The following ships did not need navigators—they simply followed the track of floating bodies behind the flagship. The survivors were culled for the best divers and the rest were herded into the mines and worked to death. The divers were sent to Hispaniola (Haiti) and Juana (Cuba), where pearl divers brought as high as 150 gold pieces on the Spanish slave market. Soon they were all dead, along with all the rest of the Lucayans taken in later raids. The island race was completely extinguished and is known only from potsherds and Spanish documents.

Ancient divers knew there were limits and dangers beneath the sea, but a scientific explanation of man in pressure did not come until a mere seventy-five years ago, when Paul Bert looked into the breathing problems of high balloonists and, in thoroughly checking altitude physiology, arrived in the treacherous and fascinating pressures of the sea. The main problem of primitive naked diving was simply holding the breath long enough to do some task on the bottom. There are authentic records of naked dives to two hundred feet and of men who stayed under, without exercising, in shallow water for over four minutes. In 1913 a Greek sponge diver named Stotti Georghios put a line on the lost anchor of the Italian battleship *Regina Margharita* at a depth of two hundred feet. He wore no breathing apparatus, fins or eyeglasses. At that depth, his lungs were squeezed by seven atmospheres of pressure into the circumference of a thigh.

Such profound dives often resulted in decompression accidents. Dr. Alphonse Gal, pioneer medical observer of divers' ailments in 1868, found the Greeks had hemorrhages from the eyes, nose and mouth on surfacing. In Japan the *Amas* professional women divers of the Mikimoto culture pearl industry, still dive, wearing nothing but goggles, as deep as 145 feet. Each woman goes down sixty to ninety times a day. There are no male divers in the pearl farms. The Japanese believe diving causes male sterility. The belief is strongest among lazy men.

Pressure itself has very little to do with diving, despite the fact that pressure is doubled thirty-three feet down, tripled at sixty-six feet, quadrupled at ninety-nine, and so on down. The human body, except for its hollow parts, is almost incompressible. It has nearly the same density as the salt water from which came the primitive animals that turned into men. Fish or flesh has no pressure problems, except preventing their hollow organs from collapse, or training them, as have professional naked divers, to contract nearly to collapse for a brief time.

The diving mask, a single plate of glass set in watertight rubber over both eyes and nose, is the one indispensable item of modern free diving. It opened man's eyes to the underwater world, bringing his naked blurred vision there into focus. Light in water is refracted in such a fashion that the naked human eyeball loses most of its resolving power. Images do not converge properly on the retina. If human corneas were flat they would work all right. Naked South Sea divers who plunge a hundred feet without masks say their vision is greatly improved at the bottom. That is because pressure flattens their eyeballs.

The mask, however, makes objects appear a quarter larger and nearer, because of the different refraction index of water and air. You become quickly accustomed to the new relationship of objects in space, but it is queer at first. The modern pioneers started out with two-lens goggles, which long-distance swimmers wore to prevent salt inflammation of the eyes. Diving goggles are very old, going back to the time before marine peoples had glass. The medieval Moroccan traveler, Ibn-Batuta, visited the pearl fishery of the Persian Gulf in 1331, and wrote, "Before diving the diver puts on his face a sort of tortoise-shell mask and a tortoise-shell clip on his nose." Sea-turtle shell can be polished to near-perfect transparency. Probably Polynesian divers used tortoise shell before European mariners brought glass to the islands.

By 1936 Fernez diving goggles were being manufactured in France. The trouble was keeping the two lenses in the same plane. You saw double most of the time. Gilpatric first heard of single plane *lunettes,* or diving masks, from a Yugoslav on the Riviera. This party had heard from a Greek in Italy that Japanese divers at Naples were wearing them. The masks had come from Mikimoto divers in Japan. Gilpatric imparted the news to Commandant Yves Le Prieur, the brilliant inventor of much early free-diving paraphernalia. Le Prieur laughed. "The Japanese copied a mask I designed for a submarine escape apparatus years ago. I sold some of them in Japan."

The idea of sealing off both eyes behind a single plate of glass occurs in early diving helmets, but undoubtedly the first modern mask was produced in 1865 by Benoît Rouquayrol and August Denayrouze to wear with their compressed-air apparatus, the *aérophore*. Fourteen years later, when Henry Fleuss built his oxygen rebreathing unit, he used the inferior goggle system. The inventor worked alone, ignorant of what was going on in the next shire, let alone a foreign country. What little patent searching he did was confined to his own country.

One of the heroes of Riviera diving in the 1930's, Alec Kramarenko, built a single-plane mask, but it did not cover the nose. Such masks flatten against the eyes in pressure. Kramarenko provided internal pressure by tapping into his mask with a rubber bulb and squeezing in air as needed. He had seen Japanese divers so equipped, but the principle dates at least to the 1890's when Louis Boutan used external balloons to pressurize underwater camera cases. It took Riviera divers years to realize that the human nose is admirably suited to do the work of such bulbs. All they had to do was seal the nose inside the mask, and snort as much air as needed.

Apparently no solitary individual broke through the problem. Everybody on the Riviera seems to have thought of tucking the nose inside at the same time. Philippe Tailliez had a *lunette* in 1938. Dumas copied his from Tailliez' mask. Recently Dumas brought the original model aboard the *Calypso* to re-enact in film an experience of naked diving days. It was made of a round hunk of plate glass clamped to a section of truck inner tube cut out to provide a head strap. Dumas put it on and dived. It worked just as well as the scientifically engineered commercial masks. One Italian firm sells forty-seven varieties of diving masks, some with comic noses and some with two rampant breathing tubes, which make the diver look like a billy goat. The flood of diving gadgetry by the midfifties has assumed eerie proportions. The novice is beset with breathing tubes containing ping-pong balls supposed to close the tube automatically when submerged. There are hand, and even elbow fins. You can puzzle over dozens of different flippers and buy yourself a mask with a yellow plastic faceplate, certain to mist over from the breath. The maker says you can de-mist by wiping the inside with a raw potato.

Glass is the only substance yet found that works in diving masks. It mists over if one fails to apply to the inside a magic, wonder-working solution. Tailliez discovered the secret antimisting formula and divulged it to Cousteau and Dumas: before you don the mask, dip it in the water and empty it, then expectorate on the inside and spread saliva over the glass with your fingers, rinse again in water and the mask will stay perfectly clear under water.

Owing to the rubber setting of the faceplate, a diver loses his lower and side fields of visibility. Oblique light rays distort objects at the edges of the

glass itself and you see only things directly ahead. Cousteau estimates that
the mask diver loses 90 per cent of his normal field of sight. He feels that
man-fish evolution has been very retarded. "We should have eyes where
our ears are located," he once said. "And the eyes should be designed in
a flat plane with hundreds of individual retinas, like bee's eyes."

Commandant Tailliez was one of the first mask divers to devise a breathing tube. He made his *tuba* from a heavy garden hose, which remained

Leonardo da Vinci's design for hand fins, sixteenth century.

upright, but bent if it struck something under water. Manufactured plastic
tubes have not improved on this simple idea, and some of them are sold
in hook shapes that are easily fouled on underwater obstacles.

Gilpatric's generation wore nose clips, as the Persian Gulf divers still
do. Several submarine escape lungs provide pince-nez. When the nose-
enveloping *lunette* came along these were no longer necessary, but they
did add to an escapee's sense of security. The list of things Gilpatric's band
did wrong, in the light of later discovery, is a long one and it includes
plugging the ears. Diving physiologists unanimously condemn ear plugs.
In pressure the plug can be driven into the ear drum.

One of the greatest aids to underwater swimming is the rubber foot
fin, which imparts about 40 per cent more motive power than the naked
foot and releases the diver's hands from propulsive strokes. Such an obvious

idea would seem to be ancient, but it is quite contemporary and can be unquestionably settled on a single inventor, Louis de Corlieu. There were embryonic fin ideas in the past. Alfonso Borelli, an Italian, designed an independent diving dress in 1679, which included clawlike footwear, but his diver walked on the floor. Leonardo da Vinci's notebooks contain sketches of free divers wearing hand paddles. They are of little use under water. When that accomplished diver and all-round gadgeteer, Benjamin Franklin, was a sprout in Boston, he constructed artificial flukes which he described late in his life to Barbeu Dubourg:

"When I was a boy I made two oval pallettes each about ten inches long and six broad, with a hole for the thumb, in order to retain it fast in the palm of my hand. They much resembled a painter's palette. In swimming I pushed the edges of these forward, and struck the water with their flat surfaces as I drew them back. I remember I swam faster by means of these palettes, but they fatigued my wrists. I also fitted to the soles of my feet a kind of sandals: but I was not satisfied with them, because I observed that the stroke is partly given by the inside of the feet and the ankles and not entirely with the soles of the feet."

The modern pioneers of the Mediterranean dived with bare feet until de Corlieu put his rubber foot fins on the market in 1935. The French patent dates from 1933 and the prototype from 1929. Although vulcanization of rubber had been known for a half century, the perfect material was not used until de Corlieu. His fins trickled around the world. A tall blond Olympic yachtsman from Los Angeles named Owen Churchill sailed to the South Seas and leased a plantation on Tahiti Island in 1938. "While there," Churchill told me, "I saw some natives using crude fins on their feet when spearfishing, which helped their speed in the water considerably. I purchased a pair, used them, and showed them to a yachtsman friend who had spent years cruising in the islands. He told me that he had seen natives of the Marquesas Islands using fins made of palm fronds or woven pandanus leaves." Churchill brought the crepe-rubber fins home to California and spent eight months improving the design, testing them with the swimmers Johnny Weismuller and Buster Crabbe. Churchill discovered that the Tahitian fins were patented in the United States by de Corlieu. Churchill is an honest man. Although France was at war, he searched for the inventor and found him in Algiers as an officer in the French Air Force. The Frenchman licensed their manufacture to Churchill, who patented his own improvements on the design. Since then Churchill has paid one hundred thousand dollars to de Corlieu in royalties, an indication of the enormous sale of fins, particularly when one considers that none of the other fin makers have paid de Corlieu one sou. French divers, who know the history of diving devices, have a favorite American named Owen Churchill.

Churchill sold 946 pairs in 1940. He manufactured 25,000 pairs for Allied swimmers during the war. Italians were first to use fins in combat—copies of the de Corlieu *palmes*. Churchill's patent searches showed no Italian designs prior to de Corlieu. When Britain's underwater infantry operations were planned at Lord Louis Mountbatten's secret Combined Operations Development Center at Southsea, a Canadian corvette skipper, Lieutenant Bruce Wright, recalled prewar dives on the Côte d'Azur and said, "We've got to get those fins for our people." They could not find a pair in England. They couldn't capture enough Italian swimmers with right foot sizes. Captain W. O. Shelford, chief of the planning group, came across a clue in a movie-fan magazine. He told me, "There was a picture of a gorgeous Hollywood dish at a swimming bath, posing with fins on the wrong feet." It led to placing an order with Owen Churchill. The initial consignment of fins was torpedoed and sunk in the Atlantic. The second lot got through. When British and American underwater demolition teams cleared the way on the Norman beaches in 1944, the French invention arrived home from its world tour. Churchill estimated there were two million pairs of fins sold in the United States by 1954, in the great diving boom.

The first amateur air-lung divers appeared in Gilpatric's day. They used an independent lung devised in 1933 by Commandant Yves le Prieur, a French naval officer. The apparatus consisted of a compressed-air bottle slung on the chest with an air pipe to a full face mask. The diver hand-valved air during submersions of twenty minutes at twenty-five feet and ten minutes at forty feet. He was not yet a fish. He walked on the bottom. Le Prieur trained dozens of novices in swimming pools. With Jean Painlevé, the film producer, he founded the first French sport diving society in 1934—the *Club des Sous-l'Eau*. Soon the group adopted de Corlieu fins and were liberated into space. Thousands saw them in *l'Aquarium Humain* at the 1937 Paris Fair, an underwater ballet in a glass tank, in the play of changing colored lights.

Georges Comheines carried the air lung a step further with a semiautomatic regulator, with which he dived to 166 feet at Marseille in 1943. He was killed the next year in the liberation of Strasbourg. In June 1943, Cousteau made the first successful sea tests of the fully automatic Aqualung, created by himself and the engineer Émile Gagnan. It supplied compressed air on demand to the human respiratory system at the correct depth pressure. The invention came from a small clandestine group in an occupied country. It was conceived not as a military tool but as a means of exploration of the sea. It proved to be the passport to inner space.

2

Workshop of Hephaestus

O N A WINTER day last year I took a train in London to meet the Old Man of the Sea, Sir Robert Henry Davis, eighty-five, who had been a submarine engineer for seventy-four years. His driver was waiting in the station plaza at Surbiton, Surrey, and carried me through a maze of suburban roads to the Neptunia Works of Siebe, Gorman and Company, Ltd., the world's largest and oldest diving equipment firm. The one-storey saw-tooth roofs of the plant sprawled in misty rain, and sad, gray light fell into the paneled, book-lined office of the board chairman as though it were fathoms down in a northern ocean. At a teak desk sat an old man with white hair falling to his gates-ajar collar. His skin was pink, his chin jutted like a scow and his large blue eyes gleamed under icicles of eyebrows.

Sir Robert gave me a chair by a bare green baize table that formed an el to his big desk, and said in a high vibrato voice, "Did you have a good crossing?" My trip in February on the *Liberté* had been phenomenally smooth the whole way from New York to Plymouth. I described it to him. That gave Sir Robert time to pull his trick. I heard a whirring sound and saw him staring past me at the green table. I turned to look. From the middle of the green cloth a tiny helmet diver arose, turned and offered a chest of life-size cigarettes. Sir Robert laughed, gestured at the doll with a big hand and said, "They call him my toy."

The toy wore a miniature Davis self-contained injector dress, the latest variation of the world's first practical helmet diving suit invented in 1839 by the founder of Sir Robert's company, Augustus Siebe. The history of the firm and my host traces the development of mechanical diving from Siebe's time to the present. The first independent diving lung was built by Henry Fleuss of Siebe, Gorman in 1879. The Aqualung, manufactured under the Cousteau-Gagnan patents, is its latest product. Sir Robert worked with both Fleuss and Cousteau. He is also the historian of diving. He wrote the *Encyclopaedia Britannica* article on the topic. His mammoth treatise, *Deep Diving and Submarine Operations*, which he has revised occasionally during fifty years, covers underwater technology and includes a section of marvelous yarns. No one could write an undersea book without raiding Sir Robert's treasure chest. This writer is the remotest man on a long queue who have done so.

Sir Robert Davis, 74 years a submarine engineer.

Neptunia Works is not merely a factory; it is an underwater college with classrooms, laboratories, experimental animals pens and even a museum of diving. Siebe, Gorman does most of its business in breathing sets for firemen, miners, aviators and chemical workers. The bible of this field is Sir Robert's other tome, *Breathing in Irrespirable Atmospheres*. Siebe, Gorman has built oxygen sets for the British Everest expeditions since 1922. Hillary and Tensing wore them on the top in 1953. A few steps from Sir Robert's book-lined study are the compression chambers and the pressure pots in which British scientists found the means for free divers to attack the Nazis in World War II. Here they equipped and trained submerged infantry, sappers, and cavalry, who went by gaudy names such as "Gamma Parties" or "Frogmen" (an inexcusable misnomer), "Locku Boys"—Landing Craft Obstruction Clearance men, and "X-craft," or midget submarines.

Sir Robert said, "My life has been spent here, almost wholly. I went into the shops when I was eleven years old, in a very minor capacity. The firm was then in London off Westminster Bridge Road. I received all my engineering training with the firm. My family lived south of the river and I got to work at six in the morning and went home at five. I attended night school, and after a while they changed my working hours to seven in the morning until six at night. On account of my youth, I suppose.

"I was virtually the manager when I was twenty. We had twenty-five employees. Now there are about six hundred. I made my first dive as a youngster in the deep end of Westminster baths, about sixteen feet. We had no diving tanks in the works then. I gave a lot of thought to diving bells. I remember my first try for a big order was in Dover. Sir Ernest Moir was doing a harbor job and I thought I had a better bell than he was using. He said, in effect, come down and convince me. I was given an appointment and took the steam train. The Southeastern Railway was then known for its slowness. They used to say that a man one time lay down on the tracks to commit suicide and starved to death. My train finally arrived. The superintendent met me and said, 'You're miles late. Sir Ernest is already in the bell.' It did not look favorable for my sale. I went out on the head of the gantry and Sir Ernest came up in the bell. He rowed over to me and was very short, 'Come along here now, I can't wait all day.' We got in the bell and went down. I unrolled my drawings and we discussed the problem. He actually gave me my first order at the bottom of the harbor."

Sir Robert often descended in bells and diving dresses in those days, and dived while he was developing the revolutionary Davis Submarine Escape Apparatus (D.S.E.A.), an oxygen lung in which the diver's exhalations were passed through caustic soda or oxylithe, which removed the carbon dioxide and returned pure oxygen to him. In 1931, a submarine which had D.S.E.A. equipment sank. She was H.M.S. *Poseidon,* named for the Greek god of the sea. The *Poseidon* was rammed on the surface by the steamer *Yuta* in the China Sea. All but six men bailed out of the conning tower and were picked up alive. The others—two petty officers, three seamen and a Chinese mess attendant—were trapped in a forward compartment as the *Poseidon* plunged 125 feet to the bottom. Going down, CPO Patrick Willis got them to work closing a watertight door in a bulkhead warped by the collision. They forced it shut, but water leaked in. By flashlight CPO Willis had them put on the Davis lung. Able Seamen Vincent Nagle helped the Chinese, Ah Hai, with the unfamiliar nose clip and goggles, strapped on his mouthpiece and harnessed the rebreathing bag on his chest. They waited for incoming water to build up pressure to that of the sea without so they could open the escape hatch. A sailor told Willis his oxygen bottle was empty; he could not hear it bubbling.

Willis tested his own. It too was empty. Casually he said, "That's all right. I can't hear anything in mine either and it's full."

After two hours the water was up to their knees. Willis figured the inside air pressure was enough to open the hatch. By this time ships had rallied on the surface. With great exertion the entombed men opened the hatch. Seamen Lovock and Holt got out, but Lovock struck his head against the outer casing and arrived dead in Holt's arms on the surface. The sea clamped the hatch tight on the other four. Willis continued flooding to restore inside pressure. An hour passed and the water came up to their necks. Willis ordered another try. The hatch opened and they all soared up to life. Davis won his knighthood as a result of the *Poseidon* escapes. He sent gifts to the survivors. Hanging on his wall is a thank-you note from Hong Kong:

This letter is for your great inspection. I thank you very much for the silver cigaret case you have given me as a present. I am sending you by post your younger brother's photo and beg you will accept this present favorably. I write this specially to inform you and offer you new year's congratulations. Your younger brother, Ah Hai, respectfully writing this.

The first diving engineer with whom Sir Robert worked was Henry Fleuss, a thin, lively Wiltshire man who invented the first fully independent diving lung. Fleuss, an officer in the merchant marine, became curious about what was under the sea. In 1876, while still sailing, he started working on an oxygen rebreathing device and in 1879 tested it in a tank at the Old Polytechnic in Regent Street, London. He stayed a few feet down for an hour on his first dive. He continued his tests, admitting the public, and studying everything he could find on pressure physiology. It was not much. Paul Bert published his classic *La Pression Barométrique* that same year, but it was some time before Fleuss knew about Bert's discovery that oxygen, when breathed at two or more atmospheres of pressure, induced convulsions and blackout. Fleuss' first apparatus was a stiffened rubber mask fitted watertight over the face. Into it ran two breathing tubes from a flexible bag worn on the diver's back. The bag was connected to a copper tank of oxygen compressed to thirty atmospheres. The diver's exhalations returned through the bag, where an absorbent removed the carbon dioxide product of breathing. The absorbent was a solution of caustic potash soaked in rope yarns.

Fleuss' first dive in open water was in Wootten Creek, Isle of Wight. He was rowed out wearing bathing drawers and his breathing set. To sink himself he put lead and iron weights on his belt and chains around his ankles. He did not even intend to use a safety line until his friends insisted that he be tethered to the rowboat. The medical texts he had read stated that breathing large excesses of oxygen would cause "excita-bility or feverish rise in temperature." Fleuss figured he might reduce the risk by inflating the breathing bag with air before donning the mask and then hand-valve oxygen as needed to keep the pressure in the bag.

Henry Fleuss dropped feet first into the water. He landed on the creek bed and strolled about eighteen feet down. His anxious friends in the boat felt reassuring tension from below and paid out more line. Fleuss was an incurable experimenter. He was not content to revel in his liberty as the first free-lung diver; he wondered what would happen if he shut off his oxygen entirely. He did so. He blacked out immediately. In the boat the lifeline went limp and the tenders got no response on the signal line. They rapidly hauled him up. He appeared to be dead. Fleuss came back to life. He said his first sensation was a nightmare of men smashing his ribs with rocks. He convulsed and tried to jump out of the boat. They held him down. He sat up and vomited gushers of blood. The pain ceased and he became rational. In his quick rise, the air under depth-pressure in his lungs had expanded and ruptured his lung linings.

A few weeks later he was diving again. It occurred to him that his gear would be useful in entering flooded mines, or those filled with noxious gases after an explosion. He went to Augustus Siebe's diving equipment firm, where his device was taken up for commercial production. It is the direct ancestor of mine safety devices, firemen's respirators, submarine escape apparatus and the breathing units of World War II underwater swimmers.

As a boy Sir Robert met big Alexander Lambert, the most celebrated diver of the nineteenth century. "He did the Severn Tunnel, you know," Sir Robert reminded me. In the mid-Victorian age "Severn Tunnel" was a heroic term like "Grace Darling" or "Mafeking." In 1880 a tunnel being driven under the River Severn in Gloucestershire flooded from a river breakthrough. The engineers could not pump it dry unless a heavy iron door were closed deep inside the tunnel. It was inaccessible to a helmet diver, trailing his air hose and lines; the diver would have to go two hundred feet down a verticle shaft and then proceed a thousand feet in the tunnel.

Henry Fleuss offered his new oxygen lung to Lambert. The great man had never seen the gadget before, but he said, "I'll give 'er a go." It was absolutely crazy. Since then physiologists have shown that oxygen can be fatal more than thirty-three feet down, but Fleuss and Lambert didn't know that. Lambert dropped into the black pit, got into the tunnel and lumbered along the builder's railway to the open door in total darkness. He put his back to the door and heaved it. The door stopped ajar and would not close. He got down and groped. He found that the builder's rails ran over the sill. He ripped up one rail with his bare hands. The other would not yield. Lambert plodded to the shaft, climbed up and borrowed a wrecking bar. He went back in, upheaved the second rail, slammed the door and bolted the dogs.

The renown of Lambert's salvage of Severn Tunnel still echoed three years later when the builders came along and said the tunnel was flooded up again; would Mr. Lambert please fix? He went back and nearly died on oxygen before he made his way out, heavily poisoned. He took overnight to shake it off and then called for his trusty Siebe helmet dress. Two divers went down with him to pay out and haul his lines. Lambert marched into the tunnel on his twenty-pound boots, carrying his forty-pound breast weight and his sixty-pound helmet and dragging his lines. He slammed the door again.

Lambert went where jobs were toughest. Sir Robert said, "I saw him stripped when he was about forty-five and he was built like Eugene Sandow." Once he was coppering the bottom of a coaling hulk at Diego Garcia in the Indian Ocean in fine bright water. A nosy shark hung around day after day, growing more familiar. Lambert valved noisy clouds of bubbles from his helmet to send it skittering, but the shark always came back to superintend the job. Lambert tired of this animal. He held up his bare left hand as bait and lured the shark to arm's length. He lunged with a knife and ripped the shark's belly several satisfying times. He fastened the shot rope to its tail, signaled to have the kibitzer removed and went back to nailing copper plates on the collier.

In 1885 Lambert singlehandedly recovered nearly a half million dollars in gold bullion from the *Alphonse XII,* sunk at 162 feet at the Grand Canary. He blasted his way down through the main deck, A deck, and B deck to breach the strong room. Sir Robert said, "He got a case of bends from that and had to retire. Then he worked for us as salvage officer. I remember him fondly. He was a great ladies' man and hail-fellow. We took a stand at the Chelsea Naval Exhibition in 1891, a tank with glass sides so people could see the divers. Lambert was in charge of the show. A helmet man went into the tank. Then came a chap Lambert had found somewhere, who called himself Professor Newman. I think he was a Greek sponge diver. He went into the tank practically naked, without apparatus, and swam around the helmet diver. He had remarkable powers of holding his breath. It was quite a jolly thing. We posted the tank with navy recruiting appeals. I remember one of them said: WANTED, STOUT HEALTHY BOYS!" Sir Robert leaned back and laughed about the stout healthy boys.

Airy reminiscence was on him and the day outside seemed brighter. "Have you heard about the time the goats blew up?" he asked. I applied for the tale. "We have pig and goat pens for animals used in research. One time—oh, thirty years back—Professor Leonard Hill, the great physiologist, put some goats in the big chamber under oxygen pressure. We strung an electric lamp into the chamber to see the behavior of the goats. You know how goats are. One of them chewed the electric cord. A good deal of oxygen had been introduced. The goat made a spark and the oxygen started burning. Professor Hill and my son, Robbie, took to their heels, shouting to everyone that the tank was going to explode. A pressurized tank can build up quite an explosion, you know—big plates ripping out and making a shambles of the place. We were lucky. A single bolt gave way and released the force. The bolt chased Professor Hill. He danced a regular hornpipe to avoid it."

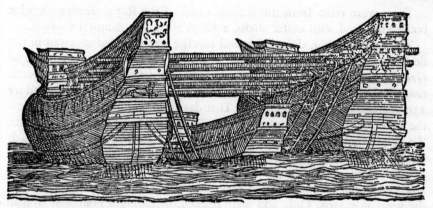

A sixteenth-century Italian plan by Nicolo Tartaglia for raising wrecks with pontoon ships. The method is still used.

Sir Robert showed me the Siebe, Gorman museum down the corridor from his office. Along the walls and an island in the center were glass cases with devices and finds of diving. There was Augustus Siebe's first open helmet of 1819, which led to his classical closed dress; Henry Fleuss' crude elephantine oxygen mask that Lambert wore in Severn Tunnel; and Sir Robert's own D.S.E.A. which saved the lives of a hundred submariners. There were beautifully modeled miniature bells, caissons, deep-diving chambers. On the walls were prints, photographs and the superb diagrammatic drawings of G. H. Davis (no relation), of the London *Illustrated News*, who was commissioned for decades by Sir Robert to draw pictures of undersea operations.

The relics were old and unlovely; their only meaning had been given by divers: this ship, sunk on this date, salvaged on another—a carpenter's plane from one of the wrecks of the Spanish Armada, 1588; a deadeye from the wreck of the *Mary Rose* overturned at Spithead in 1545; an earthenware mustard pot from the German battleship *Hindenburg* scuttled at Scapa Flow in 1918.

I saw objects recovered from the oddest field of diving, men going down in dry land, below the water table, to replace the foundations of ancient buildings. There was a skull brought up from a shaft under Winchester Cathedral built in 1202. A Siebe, Gorman man had dived to shore up the rotting beech log platforms laid down 750 years ago. In the well he also found a Roman tile and a legionnaire's spur. The newest recovery was the oldest: a Delian amphora encrusted with marine skeletons, brought up on 1954 by the *Calypso* expeditions from a ship sunk in 205 B.C.

There were relics from the famous wreck of the *Royal George*—a wine bottle encrusted with oyster shells, a thigh bone, the Admiral's sword.

The art of diving, demolition and salvage was founded in 1839 in the fleet anchorage at Spithead on the wreck of the first-rate 108-gun *Royal George*. She had been one of the garish marine disasters of the eighteenth century. She was at anchor in 1782 with 1,300 persons aboard, including 250 visiting women and children. That day they found a small leak below the waterline of the aged man-of-war. To bring it out of water for repair, the *Royal George* was heeled by trundling her guns to the other side. It placed a critical strain on the creaking timbers. The ship careened dangerously low. At that moment the lighter *Lark* came up to the heavy side and began to put aboard a cargo of rum. The ports went under and the great ship sank. Only 300 were rescued, including a bum-boat woman who had just sold her goods on credit and lost her account book in the water. Admiral Richard Kempenfelt was trapped by a jammed cabin door, and went down with his ship.

The *Royal George* came to rest upright sixty-five feet down with her top poles sticking through the surface. There were immediate attempts to deal with this menace to the busy anchorage. The Navy tried to raise her by a cat's cradle of cables from two straddling ships, but she was far too heavy. They tried to blow her to pieces and failed. Primitive diving apparatus was used on the *Royal George,* and finally a diving bell. The bell arrived in 1839 in charge of Commandant-Colonel Charles Pasley, of the Corps of Royal Sappers and Miners. He was a remarkable engineer in a corps famous for its ingenuity. A consciously intellectual British soldier in the nineteenth century was automatically assumed to be a sapper. The corps was brave, donnish, eccentric and close-knit; "mad, married or Methodist," as the byword was. It had a give-and-take between ranks and officers that would have scandalized another branch of the army. Sapper

NCO's habitually assumed responsibilities of field grade officers, and officers joined the work of tradesman-artificers.

Colonel Pasley brought to Spithead four officers, twenty-three sappers and nine men from the private army of a private navy, the Sapper Corps of the East India Company. It was not sailors, but these soldiers who carried out the first industrial salvage, founded the first navy diving school and learned the techniques of helmet diving. They were a merry, combative band, with bravery to match their skills—traits which were soon called forth. The diving bell failed. Pasley turned to three newfangled types of helmet diving suits that were offered. One was rejected before it got anybody in trouble, the second nearly drowned a diver and the third proved very practical. It was the design of Augustus Siebe, a German-born instrument maker and gunsmith, who had settled in England in 1816. Siebe's route to England had been by way of the battles of Leipzig and Waterloo, where he served against Napoleon as an artillery lieutenant. His diving outfit was the first closed type, a helmet sealed to a watertight suit. The suit could be inflated to provide counterpressure. Previously Siebe had designed an open helmet, similar to a diving bell, but one had to stay rigidly upright to keep the water level below the chin. With the closed dress, divers could bend over to some extent and had much more security. Siebe had also built efficient hand pumps to force compressed air down the diver's pipe. The equipment was classic—only refinements have been added to the closed helmet suit since Siebe took it to Colonel Pasley at Spithead in 1840.

The Siebe suit was tested by the boldest spirit of the sappers, Lance-Corporal Richard Pillman Jones. Delighted with the gear, after several dives he wondered how long a diver could remain conscious without air. He experimented on deck with the air pipe closed. He endured ten minutes. A witness said, "That's all very well, but it would be certain death below if the air pipe failed." Jones differed. He said, "I'll go down and you stop pumping. Don't pump again until I give the signal." He dived. The noisy pump fell silent. A minute passed. The signal line hung lifeless for another minute. Long and anxious seconds ticked past . . . three minutes . . . four. His friends rushed for the pump, convinced he was unconscious. As they grabbed the pump bars there came strenuous pulls on the line. Jones had lasted five minutes. The jolly experimenters were ignorant of the laws of pressure or of the physiological effects of diving. They jumped in to find out.

The wooden wreck, after fifty-seven years, was diminished by worms and bacteriological action. The *Royal George* stood clothed in weed and burdened with silt. Starfish and clams lived on Admiral Kempenfelt's once holystoned decks. Iron ballast and big brass guns had burst through deck and sides and were buried in mud. The sappers dived in pairs, thus establishing the golden rule of underwater safety. Their task was to demolish the hulk with gunpowder, send the broken timbers up in slings and recover the valuable cannon and fittings. There was about $25,000 worth of brass as an economic goal. Privates were paid 25 cents a day and noncommissioned officers 50 cents. Professional divers charged over a dollar a day and none of them cared to work on a job like that. It was too deep.

Colonel Pasley used an early means of underwater demolition explosion—an oaken hogshead, sheathed in lead, containing a couple of hundred pounds of powder. The divers placed the barrelhead against the wreck and were hauled up. From the barrel ran a wire to a voltaic battery on deck, used to explode the charge. The wire was coated with Sergeant-Major Jenkin Jones' waterproof composition of pitch softened with beeswax and tallow. On deck, they loaded the barrel with gunpowder through a narrow brass spout and welded it shut *after it was filled with powder*. The first time the sappers loaded a barrel, Pasley sent for a Portsmouth dockyard artificer to solder the disc. This worthy arrived, reeled back from the barrel, and announced, "I would not attempt it for a thousand pounds!" Private John Skelton, who had never soldered anything in his life, stepped forward and welded the tube. Once they found a leak in the barrel after it was loaded. They had to remove the powder. Sergeant David Harris cut a manhole in the side and crawled in with a copper shovel. The scraping of the shovel was a high hazard. To minimize other risks they surrounded the area with wet tarpaulins, doused galley fires and wore soft slippers. Harris shoveled out the loose powder. He found some caked around the leak. He called out for a wooden wedge and hammer and knocked the powder loose. Then he popped out, blackened like a chimney sweep.

Harris and Corporal Jones proved the best divers, Harris for his patient fatherly teaching of the youngsters and Jones for his prodigious labors in the wreck. Jones went down with his chum, Private Roderick Cameron. They dug dog-fashion under the great keel and slung up a section thirty-four feet long. Colonel Pasley shrewdly encouraged competition for the biggest slingloads. The divers basked in the attentions of numerous press correspondents aboard, who sent dispatches that "filled the public with wonder." It was perhaps the first time newspapermen had lived with soldiers and reported their daily heroic deeds with names in full and a sense of the individual character. Siebe seized the opportunity to publicize his diving suit. He issued a big color lithograph showing the operation above and below the surface, and England bought thousands at printsellers. It was actually an advertisement; the legend did not omit the address of Siebe's shop.

Private William Crowdy made a sensation by bringing up a gold guinea. Private Alexander Cleghorn sent up an eighteen-pound iron gun. Corporal Jones retaliated by slinging five heavy pigs of iron ballast on a chain hoist. To tighten his sling, he climbed on top of the load and jumped up and down on it with his heavy boots. The load whirled under him, fouled his air pipe and safety line and twisted them with the chain and bull rope. He was hopelessly entangled with his air line choked off sixty feet down. The great Jones leaned back and slashed off his pipe and line. He kicked off his weighted boots and soared to the surface, using his hands as hydrofoils and exhaling continuously as he passed through lessening pressures. I have found no earlier record of an escape in which the diver knew how to avoid ballooning and prevented his lungs from bursting as the air expanded in the dangerous surface zone. One day Jones was downstairs when he felt wet. A faucet of water was pouring on his head. He surfaced, nearly swamped. The nonreturn valve in the helmet, which vented his exhalations into the water, was jammed by a pebble.

The first medical record of diver's "squeeze" was made on the *Royal George* salvage. This abominable accident occurs when a diver's air pipe ruptures and the pressure in his suit is released up the broken pipe. Sometimes the collapse is complete; the flesh is sucked off his bones and goes streaming up the pipe and the skeleton is jammed into the helmet. Sapper Private John Williams' pipe broke. He felt "a sudden shock which struck him motionless and then followed a tremendous pressure as if he were being crushed to death." As soon as they saw the pipe had broken, the tenders hauled him up swiftly. His face and neck were swollen and livid. His eyeball capillaries were ruptured, blood flowed from his ears and he was retching gore. Williams spent a month in hospital and reported back for duty, but he was unable to dive again. The *Royal George* divers were subject to air-pipe failure all the time. No one yet knew how to vulcanize rubber and make strong air hose. They used web tubes smeared with Jenkin Jones' waterproof compound.

Corporal Jones' record hauls of the slippery bones of the *Royal George* were challenged by a hulking private named John Girvan. They grabbed opposite ends of a timber one day. Jones tied his bull rope on it and Girvan lunged for him. Jones declined combat with the furious private. He started climbing the bull rope. Girvan grabbed his legs. Jones kicked to free himself and put a boot through Girvan's faceplate. On deck, the tenders suspected something amiss from the thrashing of the lines. They hauled them both up, Jones clinging to the distressed man. Henry Siebe, son of the inventor, witnessed the incident and reported, "These two submarine combatants ever afterward carried on their duties with the greatest cordiality." As a matter of fact they divorced their respective diving mates and formed the unbeatable team of Jones and Girvan.

As objects were fished from the wreck, Sergeant Samuel March sketched them with a camera lucida. Among them was a human skull, a musket and a dog collar inscribed "Thomas Little, H.M.S. Victory, 1781." Corporal Jones was in the ruin one day, slinging one of his spectacular loads when a three hundred pound ballast pig bumbled out and crashed on his helmet. It left a dent and knocked out several of his teeth, but did not impair his efficiency. A six-ton sailboat, one of the many sightseers which hung around the two salvage barges, blundered into their moorings and capsized, carrying away a diving ladder as she sank. Jones went down to put lines on the boat and was caught in a changing tide. The sailboat rolled over and the mast, sails and rigging fell on the diver. Jones did not panic. He wriggled out of the web of canvas and shrouds, freed his lines and resumed work. A thunderstorm broke and the tenders hoisted him up, protesting. He went down again and slung the sailboat.

Jones was working on a cannon barrel one day, when a sixteen-inch lobster flew up "like a bird" and hovered about him. He stood still to "learn a fact or two in the history of its habits." He and the crustacean stared at each other. The lobster "darted off like an arrow, using its fanlike tail as a rudder to shape its course." The lobster flew around him for a bit and settled in the mud. Jones tensed himself and pinned the lobster with his pricker, or wrecking bar, and brought the giant up for dinner. Another time he found the head of a conger sticking out of a cannon muzzle. He whacked at it with his pricker. The conger withdrew to the interior. Jones took up a tampion and plugged the muzzle. He made a fast trip up the rope ladder to see the fun when the eel popped out.

He lifted a brass twenty-four-pounder ten feet long, dated 1748, the most valuable gun they had found. It started such a passion for cannon that Colonel Pasley had to take steps to prevent underwater fratricide. He divided the wreck into plots, each assigned to a team. Jones and Sergeant Harris were neighbors. Harris' section turned out to be the mother lode; he got three brass and one iron cannon. One day, while he was resting on deck, Jones ambled into Harris' territory and saw a gun muzzle sticking out of the floor. He explained later, "It seemed to invite the favor of instant removal." He dug out the gun and signaled to hoist it. Harris noticed that the sling line came out of the water over his beat and went down the ladder to defend it. Visibility was always very poor. He found the intruder had reduced it to zero with his tramping. Harris groped around and felt the breech of a cannon slipping through his fingers. In the meantime Jones had surfaced to see a fine twelve-pounder, dated 1739, coming aboard. He kept his eye on Harris' signal line. When it tugged, he dived. They passed in the water, without seeing each other. On deck, Harris lost his customary benignity and went about vowing revenge on the poacher. Jones was below slinging another of Harris' guns.

Colonel Pasley took a serious view of the prank. While Jones was his star salvor, Harris was his steady man, the patient instructor who broke in the novices and helped them get cannons without laying claim to them. The commandant transferred Jones to other duties. By this time the salvage had gone on for four seasons and sailors envied the soldiers who had become famous in the sea. Pasley mustered thirteen petty officers and men from H.M.S. *Excellent* and set up the first Navy diving school under Professor Jones. H.M.S. *Excellent* has remained the Royal Navy's diving school in several reincarnations. Jones and his pupils were assigned a lighter and sent on a practical course to demolish H.M.S. *Edgar*, another wreck in the fleet anchorage. The senior service's students were receptive, but when it came to slinging cannon, Professor Jones followed the rule of every ruddy blighter for hisself. He took *all* the artillery from the *Edgar* but graciously permitted his *summa cum laude* graduate a credit of one half a cannon.

Once Jones stayed down five hours. It was a marvel that these trail blazers survived their gay obliviousness to pressure dangers. In thousands of dives on the *Royal George,* the *Edgar,* and the *Perdita* during five years, not a man lost his life, although several were incapacitated for further diving. The brainy artificers of the Royal Sappers and Miners discovered strange and delightful things in the sea. Jones was down one day when he heard unearthly singing. He walked to his companion, Private John Skelton, to find if he heard it too. He looked into Skelton's helmet and saw that he was singing. Up till then, none of them had known the sound-conducting power of water. Jones, always the experimenter, beckoned to Skelton to keep up the recital and moved away, listening. At a considerable distance, he still heard the words. On the surface he was able to sing them back to Skelton:

> Bright, bright are the beams of the morning sky
> And sweet are the dews the red blossoms sip.

The discovery of submerged vocalization started many a ribald duet, unsuitable for the sightseers on the surface.

Jones was working in the *Edgar* one day when a blast went off in the *Royal George.* It nearly deafened him, but was unheard in the lighter directly over the *Royal George.* Private Girvan laid a charge in the *Edgar* and was still under the surface when it went off prematurely directly beneath. He was hauled out with a wrenched back and a slight case of shock. The only time Jones was defeated under water was in a thick murk. He encountered a smooth cylindrical resilient object, half floating off the floor. He felt a sort of grating running along its length and froze with fright. He was counting the vertebrae in a drowned human body. The great Jones went up the ladder like a comet and would not dive again until another sapper went down and removed the corpse.

Colonel Pasley reported, "Whatever success has attended our operations, is chiefly to be attributed to the exertions of Corporal Jones, of whom as a diver I cannot speak too highly." When the historic operations at Spithead were finished in 1845, Jones went to China with "the reputation of being the best diver in Europe." He was promoted to sergeant for leadership in an attack on the Canton forts, and busted to private for one of his jokes. He won his stripes again, helped blow up the Bomarsund forts in the Aland Islands in 1854 and served in the Crimea. An MP named Goldsworthy Gurney invented a powerful light to play at night on the Russians in the earthworks at Sevastopol and Jones volunteered to carry the gadget into no man's land and shine it on the foe. Fortunately for the great Jones' hide, the War Office realized in time that the light would also reveal the British positions. Apparently Jones never dived again.

After the *Royal George,* salvage divers gathered to the oystering port of Whitstable and hung out in public houses around the sea-coal docks of the Southeastern Railway. When the *Lutine* bell tolled at Lloyd's for a sunken ship that was within diving range, then not much more than one hundred feet, Lloyd's agents took the laggard steam trains to Whitstable and went round the locals, raising divers. Henry Siebe, son of the founder, said, "A good diver will earn a pound a day." The diver also charged two or three pounds a week for hire of his dresses, pumps and tenders. Sometimes he could get risk pay or salvage shares out of Lloyd's man, but only when the wreck was very hard, rich and dangerous. John Dean's ordinary was the principal "house of call" in Whitstable. There diver John Gann listened to a lot of pub talk about an Armada wreck off Galway and finally deduced there was something to it. He went over to Ireland, hired a dragger and swept the area. One day the net hauled a lump of Spanish gold dollars stacked in a barrel shape. John Gann went back to Whitstable and put his helmet in the attic. He built a row of rental houses and sat down and collected from his rent agent. The people called it Dollar Row.

During the construction of the eight-pier Westminster Bridge in the sixties (the one that runs by Big Ben and the Houses of Parliament), there was a lot of steady work for divers. Whitstable men went up to the city and made a hiring hall in the licensed premise of an ex-diver named Phillips, in Lower Marsh Street, Lambeth. Phillips was a poet. The National Trust ought to lovingly restore his pub back of Waterloo Station. Phillips called the place The Diver's Arms. Outside he slung a beautiful standard, a big polished brass diver's helmet with a red lamp shaped like a diver, and inside he hung undersea engravings and lithographs. Phillips was extinguished by conviviality, but his successor was a righteous and matey soul named Jemmy Armstrong. Henry Siebe once entered The Diver's Arms and introduced himself to the landlord. Armstrong slung his bar rag and spoke, "I am a diver m'self. And by no means a bad one, either, though I say it m'self. Which is how I ought not. I can lay me hand within a half hour on any kind of diver you may require. Aye, even wrecking, although that is no longer our style of business. And if it comes to the push, why I'll do it m'self, and I *can* do it, too, for I have been down a well, in a gas tank, laid pipes across the river, sunk cylinders, screwed piles, visited the *Great Eastern's* bottom, and even done a little wrecking, although as how I don't profess that high branch of the business. But, Lord, sir, if you want to know about divers, come here some evening when they are havin' a bit of harmony, and then you will hear some rum tales. I don't know as how they're all true, but you *will* hear how all our mates are doing in the foreign parts."

During my visit to Neptunia Works, Sir Robert Davis' staff showed off the plant itself. In one department there were row after row of diving helmets coming off the benches. There seemed enough to replace all the gear in the world, but I was told it was normal production. Siebe, Gorman makes a dozen models of helmets, which differ only superficially, usually in the number of bolts on the corselet. It seems that in Hong Kong they prefer twelve bolts and simply would not feel safe in the ten-bolt South American model. Helmet divers are traditionalists.

Back upstairs to say good-by to Sir Robert, I asked him what, from his long perspective, he thought were the most promising developments in submarine engineering. "Television," he said. "Submersible TV did wonderful things on the *Affray* search and the Comet that fell in the sea at Elba. We have been working closely with the Marconi people on underwater television. The bathyscaphes are also an outstanding idea that will go far."

In the corridor, after leaving Sir Robert, his aide said, "The old man won't quit. You know, he was the managing director until a few years ago. We made him board chairman to try to lessen his responsibilities. But he comes to the plant practically every day and knows everything that is going on."

3

The Viper's Eye

M EN OF PURE curiosity, who experimented with natural phenomena without "practical" aims broke paths into the mystery of what happened to the human body under water. One was the Englishman, Robert Boyle, who was engrossed with the invisible air itself. In 1660 he wrote *New Experiments, physico-mechanicall, touching the spring of air, and its effects,* the book that contained Boyle's Law and explained the barometer. Boyle built a compression chamber and studied animals in it. One day in 1670, watching a decompressed viper, he saw its eye glint with aeroembolism, the "bends," which was to cripple and kill undersea workers for centuries to come. There was a tiny air bubble in the pupil of the snake's eye. It was a bubble of nitrogen, one of the myriads that break out of solution into froth when a diver comes up. The enemy entered in the air he breathed. Underwater man waited two hundred years for a great scientist, Paul Bert, to explain the bubble.

Boyle's compressed-air chamber was not to aid divers; instead, his slick contemporary, Mr. Henshaw, found a commercial angle. He built a pressure chamber to heal what ailed people and called it an "air bath." Fashionable doctors built big air tanks like waiting rooms with seats for patients. In the early nineteenth century the French Academy of Science approved a grand quack named Dr. Pravaz, who sold air baths on the scale of Florida sunshine. He advertised cures of tuberculosis, catarrhal deafness, chest deformities and prolonged menstrual periods in young girls by clamping victims in air pressure. The poor souls actually obtained relief. As long as they were under pressure it tightened worn lungs, joints and Eustachian systems. The misery returned afterward, but they could coast a bit on the memory of a painless hour.

Viennese doctors got in on it, and air baths were installed at Baden-Baden and Munich. The latter compressed fifty patients at a time. At Brussels there was a Pneumotherapeutic Institute that compressed seventy sufferers at a sitting. By 1879 air specialists were bottling people for asthma, emphysema, bronchitis and whooping cough. The air bath overtook the discovery of diseases as fast as researchers named them. The air cure had reached Canada and the U.S.A. by 1867. There were not enough licensed doctors in the United States to compress the inmates. Laymen and "empirics" took over. In 1903 at Reichenhall, a plant that compressed eighty-six souls at a time, fooled people with croup, hypochrondria and hysteria. French quacks retaliated to this German threat with an air bath on wheels, which rumbled around the provinces. Air baths were the biggest thing since bleeding, and just as healing. A Frenchman, J.-A. Fontaine, designed a pressurized surgical theater to compress three hundred doctors, nurses, patients and audience. An American physician said, "Raised pressures induce a rich flow of ideas with a tendency of verse-making." There is no record that Walt Whitman, Baudelaire and Francis Thompson needed it. Air-bath promoters claimed the conquest of eczema, small pox and viper bites. Only one chamber was used to save the life of a distressed undersea workman, when Dr. Andrew Smith recompressed Brooklyn Bridge sandhogs in 1873. In the 1870's a scientist took over diving physiology where Robert Boyle had left off when he saw the bubble in the viper's eye.

He was a volatile, black-eyed Burgundian named Paul Bert, born in 1833. He was primarily a physiologist, but also worked in marine biology. He was the first to make skin grafts and show the possibilities of plastic surgery. Bert marched with his Scottish wife under the original banners of female suffrage, and founded and taught for many years a free course in science for adolescent girls, who were not allowed to take science courses in French schools. He thought they were just as intelligent as boys, an unfashionable notion in his time, especially among men. Bert was a member of the bar, a licensed physician and an active Radical politician, when the French party of that name was actually radical. He is called "the father of aviation medicine," although he never saw an airplane. His masterwork, *La Pression Barométrique,* published in 1878, was last reprinted in English in 1943 as a textbook for the U.S. Army Air Force—all 1055 pages of it.

Bert was a scientist of the vanguard. He became interested in the breathing problems of balloonists and alpinists in the low pressures of the high thin air. This led him to study the other extreme of pressure, the depths of the sea. He did not have the money to build a compression chamber, so he boomed out a public challenge: "Who will come forward to do for this study of respiration under diminished or augmented pressure what the King of Bavaria did for Pettenkofer, when he supplied the apparatus necessary for the study of normal respiration?" A wealthy physician, M. Jourdanet, came forward with the apparatus. The scientist and his wife decompressed themselves in the tank along with sparrows and rats. They took their own temperatures and pulses as the air thinned out. Once Bert decompressed himself in seventy-five minutes to the altitude of Mount Everest. Turning to investigations of high pressures, Bert gathered medical reports on bends victims from bridge pier caissons in France, the great Eads Bridge across the Mississippi at St. Louis and the Brooklyn Bridge, where the sandhogs worked eighty feet below water level on the New York pier.

He was struck by the experiences of young Dr. Alphonse Gal, the first medical man who actually dived to study man under water. In 1866 Gal accompanied a French sponge-diving expedition to the Aegean, which introduced the first diving suits to the Greek *sphoungarades*. The gear was the extraordinary *aérophore*, invented by a mining engineer, Benoît Rouquayrol, and a French Navy officer, Lieutenant Auguste Denayrouze. In *Twenty Thousand Leagues Under the Sea*, Captain Nemo says to Professor Aronnax: "You know as well as I do, Professor, that man can live under water, providing he carries a sufficient supply of breathable air. The workman, clad in impervious dress, with his head in a metal helmet, receives air from above by means of forcing pumps and regulators." Aronnax says brightly, "That is a diving apparatus." "Just so," says Nemo, "but under these conditions the man is not at liberty; he is attached to the pump which sends him air through an india-rubber tube, and if we were obliged to be thus held to the *Nautilus*, we could not go far." Asks Aronnax, "And the means of getting free?" Nemo answers, "It is to use the Rouquayrol apparatus, invented by two of your own countrymen."

Verne's readers thought this was one of his choicest flights of imagination, and indeed, in his old age, the author himself came to believe he had dreamed it. The fact is that the Rouquayrol-Denayrouze device was in service by 1865, four years before the publication of Verne's masterpiece. The diver wore an air reservoir strapped to his back, which received air forced down through a pipe. On the tank was a regulator which released air through a rubber tube into a mouthpiece. The compressed air came out at the hydrostatic pressure the man required for his depth. Moreover, he could detach the pump line and walk about freely for short periods, sucking on the reservoir. The *aérophore* was the ancestor of the Le Prieur independent gear of the 1930's, the Aqualung of the forties and the Cousteau-Gagnan jet *Mistral* lung of the fifties.

Dr. Gal's expedition carried French divers and recruited Greeks, who were supplied with Rouquayrol's diving manual in Greek. When the group brought in a phenomenal sponge harvest, the traditional divers broke out in Luddite riots, smashing *aérophores* and beating up the mechanical divers. But a decade later three hundred *aérophores* were in use in Greece. Siebe's helmet suit was introduced in the Aegean soon after the *aérophore*. While it was dependable, it lacked the regulator which furnished air pressure as needed. There also seems to have been less instruction and training involved with users of the English dress. In 1867, of twenty-four men who used Siebe suits, ten died. The number of incapacitated men wasn't even

The semi-independent diving gear Jules Verne described in *Twenty Thousand Leagues Under the Sea.* It was invented by Rouquayrol and Denayrouze five years before the book.

counted. The French company knew no more about pressure effects than the English, but they cautiously alternated three men in each outfit, which reduced individual immersion time. The Greeks stayed down for hours with the magical breathing apparatus, sometimes at 150 feet! Dr. Gal went down to more than eighty feet to record his sensations and watch divers pick sponges. He counted their breaths per minute by the sharply defined bursts of exhalations from the mouthpiece. They averaged eighteen per minute. He took his own pulse as best he could and said, "I think that its rate never dropped." Bert studied Gal's clinical reports on divers who were maimed or killed in the sea, and then set to work in a former monastery to find out why. His father had bought the place from the revolutionary government in 1789 after the expropriation of religious property. The Jesuits tried to oust Bert and recover the building. Bert sued one cleric for slander, collected and gave the money for public-school scholarships.

His findings demolished all previous diving theories, such as those of a poobah named von Vivenot, who said that compressed air diminished the circulation of blood in the veins and capillaries. Bert remarked, "The strangest part of his experiments, so oddly conceived and so poorly carried out, is that they have been accepted and praised on both sides of the Rhine. 'Vivenot has made an experiment!' they said. And that is enough for many people; for there is a whole school of medicine, the followers of which, of course, have never frequented laboratories, for whom the word 'experiment' answers for everything, like the custard pie in the comedy."

Bert found the truth. He said: "Pressure acts on living beings not as a direct physical agent, but as a chemical agent changing the proportions of oxygen contained in the blood, and causing asphyxia when there is not enough of it, or toxic symptoms where there is too much." He found that breathing pure oxygen was fatal in high pressure. To carry out his enormously detailed experiments, Bert invented many apparatuses. His double-valve gadget for sampling human exhalations had a rubber mouthpiece exactly like that of the modern diving lung.

His most important discovery was the effect of nitrogen breathed under pressure, which explained bends for the first time. Nitrogen is roughly four-fifths of the air we breathe. A diver thirty-three feet down breathes twice as much nitrogen as he does on the surface, because he breathes twice as much air to maintain his external pressure against the sea. At sixty-six feet he breathes three times as much nitrogen, at ninety-nine feet four times and so on down. This heavy inert gas does not pass off with the other gas products of respiration, but goes into solution in the blood and tissues, particularly in fat and cartilage. As long as the diver stays in pressure, he is okay, but when he goes up into lighter pressures nitrogen comes out of solution in the form of minute bubbles, such as the one Boyle saw in the viper's eye. These bubbles expand more and more as the diver rises, until they start blocking off capillaries, then veins, then arteries. They damage the nervous system and throttle the spinal cord. The "black froth" in its mildest form causes intense pains in the joints, so that the diver contorts grotesquely to relieve them. Thus the word "bends."

Bert saw two answers to the black froth—to raise the diver very slowly so his body could gradually pass off nitrogen under water, called "decompression." And, if a diver was seized afterward, he should be artificially returned to the depths in a compressed-air chamber, which forced the froth back into solution. That was "recompression," and he could be slowly decompressed, at the rate of twenty minutes of decompression for each atmosphere of pressure. This meant, for instance, that a diver who had been working at a hundred feet—or four atmospheres—would be hauled up very slowly for sixty minutes.

After his work was published, Bert became Minister of Public Instruction in Gambetta's government, and in 1886 was sent to Indo-China to reorganize the provincial government of Tonkin. He burst upon sleepy Hanoi, the capital, and started a cleanup. After only five months he died suddenly of dysentery at the age of fifty-three.

The full application of Bert's discoveries waited for a deep-eyed Scotsman with a powerful nose, jutting chin and a great scraggly mustache, John Scott Haldane of Cloan, peak climber, humanitarian, and one of the greatest of physiologists. Doctor (of medicine) Haldane did not start out to help divers. He was concerned with what foul air did to people in slums, factories, sewers and mines. Modern mine safety practices are built on Haldane's studies of black damp and the deadly afterdamp, the inflammable mixture of coal dust and air blown through the galleries after a mine explosion. At the Tylorstown disaster of 1896, Haldane examined the bodies of the fifty-seven victims and found that only four had been killed by violence, the rest by carbon monoxide poisoning. He inhaled carbon monoxide, recorded his own symptoms and drew blood samples to find the proportion of CO in the hemoglobin. Haldane devised a simple instrument for such analysis. He also invented a small apparatus with which he could tell from a small blood sample exactly what volume of blood a person had in his body.

Haldane taught miners to carry mice, where deadly carbon monoxide was suspected, as an index of danger. Mice have high metabolism and give warning of deadly gases long before men are afflicted. Haldane discovered that deaths of miners in afterdamp was often due to shock from superficial burns. He introduced quick application of life-saving tannic acid for flash burns. The compassionate physiologist believed in the direct way; he rode the cage into the pits. In 1903 the Home Office asked him to find the cause of anemia among Cornish tin miners, which was suspected to be bad ventilation. Haldane went into the deep mines, where the humidity was terrific and where 93° F. heat was generated by the oxidation of iron pyrites in the ore face. Haldane found that the air was not harmful. The miners had hookworm and silicosis. He wanted to know how the body regulated its central temperature in such extremes, and took his apparatus into Turkish baths for long experiments.

To refine Bert's work on men in high altitudes, Haldane led an expedition which camped on the top of Pike's Peak, Colorado. He was morose on the 14,100-foot summit because he had to get up at sunrise. At home he worked into the night and slept till noon. One day he got up smiling to greet the dawn and his surprised companions. He waved his watch and said, "Everything is all right now. I'm keeping the same hours. You see, it is noon in England." His work on rarefied air helped the British Everest expeditions.

Haldane's greatest contribution to the knowledge of human respiration came from testing carbon dioxide in his own lungs on top of Ben Nevis and in deep mines. It was the revolutionary fact that normal breathing depends exclusively on the carbon dioxide pressure in the respiratory center. In 1905 he and Dr. J. G. Priestley reported the discovery in a famous paper. Haldane was contemptuous of the "accidental" discovery, which is announced without caring particularly what is done with it. He threw himself into practical applications. He investigated tunnel workers and, like Bert, came to divers, then "an obscure sect," as G. C. C. Damant, one of Haldane's associates, termed his profession. Haldane found that divers were suffering from the effects of poor theory and dangerous techniques. He proposed to the Admiralty that a commission be formed to study diving. In 1906 the Lords Admiralty promulgated a committee of Haldane and three line captains, with Dr. A. E. Boycott, of the Lister Institute, as medical deputy. They needed several divers to work with them. Haldane did not want publicity-seeking "human guinea pigs," but experienced divers with brains, courage and patience. He found them on H.M.S. *Excellent,* the gunnery and diving school of the Navy. The first was Lieutenant Guybon C. C. Damant, a wiry red-haired Isle of Wight man, twenty-five years old. At that time there were no diving ratings in the Navy; since Elizabethan days diving had been the job of gunners. Damant says: "Unlike most of my class of budding gunnery lieutenants, I found going under water to be a delightful experience and infinitely preferred it to the study of ballistics and field gun drill." The second diver was Petty Officer Andrew Yule Catto, Damant's fatherly instructor in diving. Damant described him as "modest, shrewd and tactful. Haldane, a brother Scot, took to him at once, and in all the underwater experimental work, relied on Catto's practical knowledge to ensure that accidents, outside of physiological ones, did not occur. I knew him for years before I learned that he was the brother of Lord Catto, head of a famous mercantile house and afterwards Governor of the Bank of England."

Haldane's little band started where Paul Bert left off twenty-eight years before. They had also the observations of Professor Leonard Hill, another valuable contributor to the physiology of pressure. Hill had suddenly decompressed frogs from twenty atmospheres, equal to the pressure of over six hundred feet in the sea. In the microscope he watched the decompressed frog's semitransparent web. The blood flowed normally in the capillaries for an instant, "then small, dark bubbles, first one, then another, then numbers, scurried through the vessels and drove the corpuscles before them," he said. "In a moment or two the vessels became entirely occupied by columns of air bubbles and the circulation was at an end." Hill rapidly placed the frog under the original pressure. The bubbles of nitrogen disappeared, going back into solution in the blood, and the frog was alive and unhurt. Bert had first compared the action with champagne. Corked champagne under pressure drives its bubbles of carbon dioxide into solution. When the cork is drawn, the wine leaps to atmospheric pressure and the bubbles foam out of solution.

The human champagne bottle held no humor for Haldane, Boycott, Damant and Catto. The team wanted to turn Bert's work into systematic knowledge. They sought records of helmet dives beyond the one hundred-foot Navy limit of the time. They relied only on naval reports, in which the depth had been sounded and where the diver had brought proof from the floor. The deepest dive was by a team of Greek and Swedish divers off Patras, Greece, in 1904. These men had inspected the hull of the sunken destroyer *Chamois* at 190 feet in ten-minute submersions. It was twice the standard depth range, a promise for the Haldane team, if they could find how to do it safely.

At the Lister Institute they compressed goats to pressure equal to two hundred feet. A fat old billy named "Pa" seemed nearly immune to bends, while young skinny "little Billy" was quickly paralyzed. Everybody had thought lean young men were best fitted for diving. Pa's virtuosity reminded them of the master diver, Alexander Lambert, famous for his ale adiposity and descents in time and depth ranges that had crippled other men. Dr. H. M. Vernon, of Oxford, showed them that nitrogen is six times as soluble in fat as in the blood. Fat men took longer to saturate. The trouble was that when Falstaff got good and saturated, he took that much more time to decompress. Lambert's epic dives on the *Alphonso XII* had ended with partial paralysis below the waist. (Sir Robert Davis, who knew the John L. Sullivan of the brine, told me, "He also had difficulty retaining his urine.") Toward these researches before the actual diving began, Professor Haldane had an air of aloofness and disinterest, letting the others compress the goats. It seemed quite unlike the usual Haldane enthusiasm. His diving aides discovered why; Haldane knew exactly what was going to happen. Damant says, "By pure reason he knew what the result would be. His experiments were more like demonstrations to satisfy others." Haldane had thought it out. Paul Bert showed that divers did not suffer bends when drawn quickly from thirty-three feet to the surface. Haldane said, "Therefore I can haul a man from six atmospheres to three." The trick was to halve the pressure. From greater depths, he would halve the pressure by several stages. The diver would be hung for periods at each stage to pass off nitrogen. This was the discovery of underwater stage decompression, the safeguard of all divers since.

When diving began, Haldane was all keenness again. He fumed when he saw the Navy's leaking hand pumps which puffed insufficient, oily, hot air to the man below. Looking back fifty years, Captain Damant told me, "Present-day divers have no notion of how tough one had to be to struggle along at, say, fifteen or twenty fathoms, in pre-Haldane days. Accounts by mountaineers of their experiences at high altitudes, panting for breath, forced to rest absolutely quietly for a half minute between each step, give an idea of the respiratory distress. In English waters it is hard to suspend effort for a moment with the tide tearing at one's body and the pump, if it was one of the badly leaking ones of 1906, often failing to keep the suit inflated and pressure off the chest." The Haldane team produced a working pump.

Although they had the craft to systematize compressed-air diving to the absolute physical limit of three hundred feet, the Admiralty had asked for data on dives to only two hundred feet. To double the working range seemed to My Lords a worthy aspiration, since two gunners had already died of paralysis after dangling their boots a little more than two hundred feet down. Indeed, Professor Haldane seemed a bit radical in agreeing to two hundred, but practical considerations were pressing. The newfangled submarine boats were swamping and falling on the floor in this range. Ever in the minds of admirals, diving had been a servant of ships, whether the gunners were sent to scrape barnacles under Admiral Sir Francis Drake, or, in later days, to salvage sunken submarines.

When the team went to sea for real dives, Damant had never been lower than 110 feet. He and Catto had been compressed in a water tank at Lister Institute to 180 feet, but a sea dive was different; murky, cold and alone the helmet man goes down on his swaying pipe and lines, caught and swept and whirled in tide and current, a risky spider swinging on a skein which will never become a web. The air blows hot into the helmet; he minds his suit to keep internal pressure in the tightening vise of water, and thinks of the character traits of those above who tend his life. One does not escape in a moment, as in the pressure pot, where the attendant outside turns the wheel and the air whistles off to normal. The sea encompasseth him about. In the sea, experimental data is hard to gather objectively from a sweating man in copper hood and rubber raiment. The helmet diver's tired and slow ascent home is even more dangerous. He must make his given stages and rest weary frigid minutes, perhaps with a leaking suit and water creeping toward his neck. Always he must keep tactile sense in his numbed and wrinkled finger tips, to valve air so he does not balloon and soar, ever-expanding, past his safety stages.

The experimental dives were made from H.M.S. *Spanker* off the Isle of Bute. On the first descent Catto, the more experienced diver, reached 138 feet. His pupil Lieutenant Damant went to the same depth. The second day they both went to 150 feet. The *Spanker* steamed through the Kyles of Bute to the entrance of Loch Ridden, where on the third day the pair went to 162 feet. They then dived to 174 feet. Catto tried for 180 feet. He took his scientific equipment, a glass vial in which the diver collected his ex-halations so Haldane could analyze the gaseous content. Catto held the vial in his hand. It was connected by a rubber tube to a special tap on the hel-met, through which he valved off air. Although they set depth records one after another, the team did not publicize them. They were excited by the information on man in pressure.

Mr. Catto's 180-foot dive was further complicated by the fact that he was expected to perform exertion tests on the bottom. They consisted of hauling like a sexton on a rope, carried up through a block, from which hung a heavy weight. Haldane spared them nothing that would produce data. By now the divers had joined his pursuit of knowledge, which they were to carry on after him.

Mr. Catto went down a ladder over the side of the gunboat. There was no such thing as a diving tender in any navy at that time. The freeboard of the *Spanker* was eight feet. The diver had to descend and climb with forty pounds of breast and back weights, two twenty-pound boots, helmet and gear, an all-up burden of 155 pounds in air. (Among the recommenda-tions of the 1906 Committee were hoists for divers.) The impedimenta outweighed Catto or Damant.

Mr. Catto dropped to 180 feet and began pealing his silent bell rope. His life line became fouled in the tangle from the *Spanker*. They could not raise him. He continued to haul the weight, imbued with scientific devo-tion. The depth was the limit to which the rebuilt hand pump could fur-nish proper air to a resting man. Catto's New Year's Eve concert went on, with the bellringer panting heavy and heavier. Up on top they pumped desperately to cope with his exertions, and tried to disentangle his lines and haul him in. Catto kept on, nearing unconsciousness from carbon dioxide poisoning. He was on the bottom at the unprecedented depth for twenty-nine minutes before Damant cleared his safety line and hauled him in. Catto seemed a hospital case, but he was back to dive the next day.

The *Spanker* sailed into deeper water in Loch Striven. Damant elected to try the deepest dive attempted to that time, to 210 feet, where the pressure was over a hundred pounds per square inch. This was doubling the navy range with two fathoms to spare. Staggering under his weights but care-fully holding the fragile test vial, Damant went down the ladder, felt the blessed relief of weight as the water closed around him and rapidly sank.

On the bottom, 35 fathoms down, he took an air sample from his helmet and signaled on the rope to be hauled up. He not only had to mind his suit pressure, but take care that the flask did not explode in lighter pressure. At 110 feet he stopped for decompression and let some air from the sampling tube. Damant surfaced without harm from the extraordinary feat. It was to be eight years before a diver went further.

Throughout these experiments, Damant was improving the diving gear. He substituted a leaden belt for breast and back weights. It helped to prevent the suit from ballooning, but was hard to keep in place. Then he thought of lacing the suit firmly at the back of the legs to prevent ballooning. His leg laces are still used. The final ballooning experiment turned into sports day. Professor Haldane asked for volunteers to make a shallow dive with him; forward stepped two ship's officers and his son, thirteen-year-old Jack Haldane. In the pressure chamber he taught them how to clear their Eustachian tubes when wedging into pressure, and the professor and pupils went to thirty-five feet on their first dives. For young Jack, it was an unforgettable experience. A third of a century later, as Professor J. B. S. Haldane, he was to take up his father's researches and help the combat divers and underwater chariot crews of the Second Great War. Haldane of Cloan did not live to see that war. He died in 1936, after returning from Iran and Iraq, where he had been studying heat stroke among oil field crews. Professor Haldane's report was published for sixpence in 1907. There was no further excuse for navies and salvage contractors to endanger divers through ignorance of decompression. They were not quick to learn. At the time U.S. Navy diving was in a more backward shape than the pre-Haldane Royal Navy. Diving was limited by regulations to sixty feet. There had been a diving school since 1882 at the Newport, Rhode Island, Torpedo Station, which was begun by a retired chief gunner's mate named Jacob Anderson. Anderson trained twenty volunteer gunners at a time in a two-week course. Practically the only job the Navy gave them was diving for practice torpedoes in the firing range off Newport. Visibility was almost zero and the divers had to combat a one-knot current. Often the torpedoes buried themselves in the bottom and had to be washed out by a powerful water hose. The divers tramped around in narrowing circles to locate torpedoes. One man met a strange fate in the range. The tide carried his lines over a torpedo sticking up from the sand. The contact started the propeller, which wound up the diver's lines, hauling him into the blades where he was hacked to death.

It was all very nice and regulation for the Navy to confine diving to sixty feet, except that the torpedo range was 130 feet deep in places. Anderson recovered torpedoes for a bonus which paid high for the first hour of search, then progressively lower as the hunt went on. Later, another former gunner's mate, the famous Tom Eadie, took over the range diving. He and a fellow civilian diver recovered three hundred torpedoes a year, until the Navy at last took up the chore with enlisted divers in 1920. Anderson and Eadie customarily exceeded the regulation depth to earn their living. In his thousands of dives, one of which earned the Congressional Medal of Honor, Eadie had only one attack of bends.

That is how it went until 1912, when a bold fellow, Chief Gunner George D. Stillson, decided U.S. Navy methods were a disgrace. He knew about the five-year-old Haldane report and how his colleagues in Britain were diving by the safety tables three times as deep as Americans. Gunner Stillson wrote a general report on the situation, in which he stated mildly that "existing methods of diving are inefficient and the apparatus in great need of improvement." He requested assignment to some area where he could experiment. Stillson handed the manifesto to his commanding officer. The CO endorsed it to the division commander, who endorsed it to Atlantic Fleet commander-in-chief, who endorsed it to the Bureau of Navigation, which endorsed it to the Torpedo Station and the Bureau of Ordinance, which in turn endorsed it to the Bureau of Construction and Repair. It took ten weeks for the longest parlay any underling ever pulled off. And it took only a year more for Stillson to be assigned the special duty he'd requested.

Gunner Stillson, exhilarated at recovering his own bottle paper from the bureaucratic sea, planned a 220-foot diving tank at the New York Navy Yard. (The biggest one in existence today, at New London, Connecticut, is not nearly that high.) Instead, he had to use a pressure pot at A. Schrader's Sons, Brooklyn, principal contractors for Navy diving gear. Stillson's experimental team consisted of four chief gunner's mates and an enthusiastic officer, Surgeon G. R. W. French, who had studied at the Royal Navy Diving School and was a diver himself. Stillson and French figured divers could safely go beyond 200 feet. Haldane and Damant had, of course, known this but had been instructed by the Admiralty to find the laws for a 200-foot range. Stillson's gunners went under pressure of 256 feet in the Schrader pot. In 1914, from the destroyer, U.S.S. *Walke,* they reached a new record of 274 feet in the open sea.

Having quadrupled the permissible Navy maximum, Stillson wrote up his report, recommending that the Navy name an Inspector of Diving, organize a proper diving school, publish a manual and name a board to continue research. Stillson's second paper also got results. He was named Inspector of Diving to start a school at Newport. Even before the new doctrines spread, Stillson's work paid off. In 1915 the submarine U.S.S. *F-4* sank in Hawaii to the fearsome depth of 304 feet. Navy diver Frank Crilley reached her on a dive rarely matched again by a helmet man breathing compressed air. Frédéric Dumas went a few feet further in a compressed-air lung in 1947, also on a working dive, but this was the limit of compressed-air diving. It was like the sound barrier in the air—the propeller-driven plane reached it, but when it dived beyond, the plane disintegrated. The work of Bert, Haldane, Damant and Stillson was completed. Now it was up to science to find new breathing mixtures if men were to go deeper.

Several sciences were blindly converging on the problem, and the breakthrough of the deadly fifty-fathom line came from a couple of astronomers and the inventor of the cream separator. Jules Janssen, the nineteenth-century French astronomer, looked at an eclipse of the sun through a spectroscope and saw in the sodium yellow bands, now known to astronomers as D-1 and D-2, a brilliant refracting ring never before noted. He reported the unknown phenomena around the time that an amateur stargazer, Joseph Norman Lockyer, a clerk in the British War Office, started looking at sunspots in 1866. This autodidact was to receive a knighthood and a chair of astronomy for his brilliant researches. His spectroscope picked up Janssen's sparkling sun ring. Lockyer thought it might indicate hydrogen and began laboratory work to see if hydrogen could produce the mysterious band, which he dubbed D-3. He tried forward and backward and upside down, but could not create D-3. He concluded that it was an element not present on earth and he named it *helium,* after the Greek word for the sun.

It was a new element all right, but Sir William Ramsay soon discovered that helium was here among us. He boiled radioactive minerals in sulphuric acid and got the Janssen-Lockyer effect. While cooking his rocks, Ramsay also discovered neon, krypton and xenon. Helium was a sort of scientific realization of alchemy, an element formed from the disintegration of radium and other radioactives. Sir James Jeans thought maybe the whole of outer space five hundred miles up was helium. Helium was odorless, tasteless and invisible, and the lightest gas next to hydrogen. However, hydrogen was explosive and helium was not. In 1900, helium cost $2,500 a cubic foot. Then it was discovered in incredible quantities in natural gas wells in Texas. Today a million cubic feet of helium is wasted into the air every day in U.S. natural gas production. Four Western U.S. wells are the only natural helium deposits yet exploited.

The cream separator man who gave the magic sun gas to divers was Professor Elihu Thomson, an electrician and all-out inventor of Massachusetts. Among his seven hundred patents were electric welding, the centrifugal cream separator and street arc lights. He founded the Thomson-Houston Company in 1883, which was merged with Thomas A. Edison's company in 1892 and called General Electric. Thomson-Houston remains a leading electronics firm in Britain and France, however. At the G.E. experimental laboratory in Lynn, Massachusetts, Professor Thomson looked into helium. It was not harmful to animals; it was inert chemically and only one-seventh the density of nitrogen, and it was the least soluble of gases. All of these seemed desirable characteristics for a diving gas. In 1919, Thomson dropped a note to the U.S. Bureau of Mines, suggesting that helium be used in place of nitrogen in the breathing supply of deep-sea divers. He thought they could go fifty per cent deeper on helium. He did not write to the Navy because he thought that the problem was that of marketing helium, the proper business of the Bureau of Mines. Among the queer foster parents of diving progress, this was the champion combination: stargazers, a chemist, an electrician, and a mining bureau.

The Bureau joined with the Navy and a mine safety appliance company. Deep-sea diving experiments began in Pittsburgh, Pennsylvania, five hundred miles from the sea, in 1925. Physiologists tested helium-oxygen on animals, which remained frisky and unhurt in extreme tank pressures. When these animals were decompressed, it was found that they could be brought back to normal atmospheric pressure, without injury, in one-sixth of the time required for compressed-air "locking-out." Then human subjects went under pressure, breathing 80 per cent helium and 20 per cent oxygen. They came out as happy as the dogs in one-fourth the usual decompression time. They had remained clearheaded in depths where compressed air stole a man's reason. The divers said helium took no effort to breathe. It made them feel very cold and also it changed their voices into high-pitched nasal whines. A team of physiologists explained that a man pumped light helium past the vocal chords much faster than nitrogen and it did not resound as heavily in the sounding cavities around the larynx. However, helium dissolved more quickly than air in the blood and tissues, which obliged divers to take more decompression time for shorter dives. On prolonged dives less "locking-out" was required than on air dives.

A keen young U.S. Navy doctor named A. R. Behnke started work on helium diving with a colleague, Dr. O. D. Yarbrough. At the Navy Experimental Diving Unit in Washington in 1937, they built up tank pressure on a helium diver clad in a flexible helmet suit. He was compressed to an equal of five hundred feet, far beyond the depth any man could survive breathing compressed air. The diver did not know his simulated depth, which was controlled outside the tank. The doctors heard him squeaking lucidly on the phone, with no evidence of discomfort or irrationality. They said, "How deep are you?" The diver piped, "It feels like a hundred feet." (They broke the news to him later.) On the "way up," or as the pressure was reduced, Lieutenant Behnke stopped the diver at three hundred feet and changed his breathing mixture from helium-oxygen to compressed air. The gentle *castrato* voice changed to a frantic baritone, "Haul me up! I'm dizzy . . . Don't know what I'm doing. Pull me up!"

On board ship on a bitter December day in 1937 on Lake Michigan, a slender young engineer named Max Gene Nohl got into an odd diving suit of his own contrivance. It was a self-contained dress with baggy rubber coverall, boots like Eskimo mukluks and a turret helmet with windows running all around, like the top of a lighthouse. Strapped to his back were two gas cylinders. The scene had the air of another furious dreamer testing a cockeyed diving suit and perhaps killing himself. This effort, however, was cool, competent and scientific, the product of years of laboratory experiments at the Marquette University School of Medicine on the effects of various gases breathed by divers. Nohl's experiments with Dr. Edgar End had shown that the multiplied nitrogen in the air breathed at great depth caused "diver's blackout," or what was later called nitrogen narcosis and rapture of the depths. Following the lead of Navy physiologists, End and Nohl had substituted helium for nitrogen in the breathing mixture. It had shown marvelous results in the lab; but what would it be like in actual depth? That was the question Nohl went down to answer. Swung over the side on a heavy cable, Nohl disappeared into the depths. He reached a new record of 420 feet and came up clearheaded for his hours of decompression. Here was the proof of helium foreseen by Professor Thomson when he said divers could probably go 50 per cent deeper with the sun-gas. In 1946, diver Jack Browne, of Milwaukee, Wisconsin, made a simulated dive breathing helium-oxygen in a tank. He reached a pressure of 550 feet.

The feat called for an actual dive to this zone. Few diving experimenters outside the United States had been able to get helium. Congress barred foreign exportation to deny Hitler the possibility of air raids by zeppelins carrying the noninflammable gas. Airships were passé in World War II, but the regulation remains. Overseas diving experimenters can get helium if they have the signed approval of the Secretary of the Interior, the Secretary of Defense and the President of the United States. In 1948 the Royal Navy had some Lend-Lease helium still on hand, which inspired Captain W. O. Shelford, then Royal Navy Diving Superintendent, to organize a series of dives to see how far divers could go in the event of deeper submarine boat sinkings.

Captain Shelford was about to leave command of the *Reclaim*, the diving tender. He said, "My secret ambition, aside from what we might learn by controlled experiments, was to send a signal to the Admiralty, 'This day so-and-so has broken the world's diving record from H.M.S. *Reclaim*.'" Shelford had already been through harrowing experiences with helium. British divers did not like the U.S. helium helmet. The heavy injector made the helmet topheavy and they did not have the U.S. "Shell-Natron" flakes of caustic soda, used to purify the oxygen. They had to use soda lime. Different schools of diving get set in their ways and fixed to familiar equipment. Shelford had a bad time with a helium-oxygen dive by a veteran mine recovery man. Lowered to 320 feet, this man began screaming. There was only one compressor panel for mixing the diver's gases, so that no other diver could reach him there beyond the fatal barrier of air. Shelford ordered him hauled quickly to 130 feet, the first emergency decompression stage, and lowered a submerged decompression chamber with an attendant. This device, called the "S.D.C." is a diving bell, invented by Sir Robert H. Davis. It is open at the bottom, with a ladder for the diver to climb into the dry and take his decompression stages with an attendant who wears no diving dress. As the S.D.C. went down to the screaming man, a stand-by compressed-air diver was dropped rapidly. He found the distressed man hanging limply on the shot rope, trying to unscrew his front glass. The helium man roared, "Get me out!" and clawed frantically at the faceplate. The stand-by man wrestled him to the ladder of the submerged chamber and phoned to the attendant above, "Stop him from taking off his glass!" The tender came down the ladder thigh-deep in the water and kicked at the crazed man's hands with his sea boots. "It was a pretty nasty scrap," said Shelford. "It was pitch black in the loch and we could hear the uproar on their phones. We raised like mad, got the chamber on deck and sort of shook the three of them out in a tangle. We shoved the helium man in a recompression chamber and sent the stand-by back down on a shot rope to decompress. We stuck the S.D.C. attendant in another chamber. Had the whole lot cooking. I checked the oxygen-helium rig and couldn't find anything wrong.

"The chap came around all right in hospital. A doctor said he had acute claustrophobia. This sounded wrong to me, after the man's brave record. Then something happened in the ward to make me think. One of our officers called on the diver. The diver said, 'What happened to you, sir?' The officer had broken his arm ten days before and the diver had seen him wearing a sling. We already know that when a man has oxygen poisoning he loses memory of recent events." It was oxygen, not helium, that had made him crazy. Shelford spent months experimenting with the oxygen-helium mixture, and found formulas differing from the standard U.S. Navy instructions. His men continued to blame helium. They called it "Yankee gas" and "Stuka juice."

This was the unpromising atmosphere aboard the *Reclaim* when Captain Shelford sailed her to Loch Fyne to try the deepest dives ever made in flexible dress. The record helium dive still belonged to Gene Nohl—420 feet in Lake Michigan ten years before. Due to the different weights of salt and fresh water, Nohl's depth-pressure equalled 410 feet in the sea. The canny Shelford selected a mooring with fifty fathoms under the keel, so close to the loch bank that he could moor the *Reclaim's* stern on a tree and throw out a gangplank leading to a handy public house. Shelford sent eighteen divers down to progressively greater depths, letting men drop out if they liked, checking them medically and watching for nervousness and subjective reactions. He erected a "diving thermometer" which cartooned former depth records and their own increasing marks. Freddie Field, the ship's engineering officer, was the goat of the thermometer. He had submerged four feet to repair a valve on the side. The Olympic Games were then on in London, so when a diver came up with a new mark, the former holder handed him an "Olympic torch" and the champion had to hold it up and run around the deck in his diving boots. They passed into the helium range without incident, and morale increased in the holiday atmosphere Shelford had induced to lighten a very serious affair.

They passed three hundred feet and the divers were so eager they knelt to touch their helmets on the floor to record a few more feet. As they faced 360 feet there was some apprehension—that was beyond the level where a good man had been hauled up screaming and trying to tear off his visor. It was the turning point for the men, although Shelford was completely confident he had overcome the oxygen-poisoning factor. Shelford decided an officer should lead the way. Torpedo Gunner William Barrington volunteered. "Bill did a fine thing," said Shelford. "I completely forgot that the night before we'd held our ship's dance ashore and Barrington had stayed up with me till 4 A.M. I thought him very brave to do it on a hangover."

At 450 feet they passed the official U.S. Navy helium diving record of 440 feet. There were two *Reclaim* divers left, Petty Officer William Soper, of Devonport, and a stocky, shy, red-faced petty officer from the Midlands named Wilfred Bollard. Shelford said, "Bollard was just about the last man I would have figured. When he joined us the year before, he overran his air and nearly passed out on shallow dives. I used to say, 'Who sent this bloody Bollard to the ship?' But he'd come round very smartly, and had dived consistently very well throughout the trip. He had not yet qualified as a deep diver, however. But there you were; two good men had reached 450 feet. The trial stages were over and we could now try for the depth I calculated we could go. The last helium in England was running out. There was just enough left for one man beyond 500 feet if we were to hold back the last of it for an emergency stand-by diver. I called a divers' meeting and explained it. I said it was between Bollard and Soper. I held out one long and one short match; long man would dive. Bollard, the junior diver of the two, drew the long match."

The *Reclaim* moved over a flat bottom 540 feet deep. Bollard unemotionally went about his preparations. It was only thirty-six hours since he had been to a record 450 feet. Shelford stood at the mixing panel, to alter Bollard's breathing mixture at various depths. The loudspeaker inter-com system kept him in constant communication with the diver. Bollard went down the ladder and pushed off. He sank in the loch. Soper was suited up, ready to go to his aid in case of trouble. The tenders let Bollard down very rapidly, at a hundred feet a minute, to shorten his descent and gain time on the bottom and in the long slow decompression stages coming up. Shelford fed him straight compressed air to 200 feet, where he turned on the helium-oxygen. In six minutes Bollard was on the loch bed. "How do you feel?" Shelford asked. The man nineteen atmospheres down, breathing enough volume for two baseball teams, answered in a clear falsetto, "Fine. I could do a couple of hundred feet more." Bollard stayed on the bottom for five minutes. If he had been breathing compressed air he would have died during that five minutes. Instead he was clearheaded, able to move freely. He could have passed a reeving line through the eye of a sunken submarine.

The submerged decompression chamber and attendant were waiting at 160 feet for his initial decompression. It would take hours. Bollard arrived at the bell, climbed the ladder and sat down. The tender unbolted his helmet and gave him oxygen. The S.D.C. was very tight quarters in which the two men had to remain upright. Shelford decided to heave the S.D.C. before the time was up and rush Bollard into the deck recompression chamber. Bollard took only a moment between the S.D.C. and the big caisson. Shelford looked in the window at Bollard stretched out on a cot. "How do you feel?" he phoned. "I have a bit of pain in my elbow, sir," said Bollard. In a minute the air pressure had removed the pain. They bolted a mug of steaming tea in the food lock of the chamber. Bollard unlocked the inner door and grinned at them as he gulped the brew. He was to be decompressed for eight-and-a-half hours.

Captain Shelford sent his famous signal to the Admiralty: "This day Petty Officer Diver First Class W. Bollard has broken the world's diving record from H.M.S. *Reclaim,* attaining a depth of 540 feet in Loch Fyne." The festive crew got ready for the last mile of the Olympics while Bollard was sleeping in the chamber. "But who was going to pass the torch to Bollard?" said Shelford. "Then I remembered we had aboard one of those Neufeldt and Kuhnke articulated armored suits designed for 500 feet maximum. We broke it out and stuck a burning torch in the claw and hung a sign on it, OUT-OF-DATE. We unlocked Bollard. He came out and made some unprintable remarks. Then he went over and took the torch and ran around the deck. We had lots of fun on that show." Shelford put in for decorations for Bollard, Soper and Mr. Barrington, the dauntless hangover diver. Only Barrington received a medal.

Haldane of Cloan's son was built of the same briarwood. Professor J. B. S. Haldane, another towering rugged intellectual, followed his father's interests in diving physiology and industrial diseases, and added quite a few of his own. He worked on the genetics of mosquitoes, men and fruit flies; developed statistical methods for biology; thumped for decent bomb shelters in blitzed London, and wrote popular science pieces.

When the submarine H.M.S. *Thetis* sank in 1939, several members of the Amalgamated Engineering Union, employed by the constructor, were lost with the crew. The Union asked Professor Haldane how to make submarine trials safer for its members. That began his great courageous experiments in the safety of man under water. As the Second World War came, Haldane joined Royal Navy experimentalists. Haldane said: "My main job was to tackle the physiological dangers to which divers and men trying to escape from submarines were exposed. Most of our 'dry' work was done in Siebe, Gorman's Chamber No. 3, a steel cylinder like a boiler eight feet long and four feet in diameter. Three people can sit in it, but one can't begin to stand up. At one end a steel door opens inwards and has a rubber flange, so that there is a good air pressure inside. One communicated by a code of taps, by shouting or by holding messages to the window." The other experimental tank was wet, ten feet high and six feet wide, in which the experimentalist was under water and compressed to the conditions of great depth. Haldane of Cloan had called it "The Chamber of Horrors." His son's group called it "The Pot."

In the Pot, you longed for the wide open sea. "It was a queer experience," said Professor Haldane, "to wait under water in this rather dark tank, knowing that one might lose consciousness at any moment, and perhaps wake up with a broken back, conceivably not wake up at all, and to look out through the very small window at butterflies, bicycles and other familiar things." They studied pressure changes on the eardrum. Explained Haldane: "The drum is a thin membrane across a bony passage which goes from the outside to one's throat, and incidentally was a gill slit when our ancestors were fish. The passage to the throat, called the Eustachian tube, is normally shut. Most people can open it by holding the nose and blowing vigorously. When the air pressure is raised, there is some pain in the ears, which one relieves by blowing this way, so as to equalize the pressure." A mask diver can pinch off his nostrils through the rubber flange, but Haldane's Royal Navy charioteers wore full faceplates and could not reach their noses. "Occasionally," said Haldane, "an inexpert charioteer hurt his ear and one or two may have burst their drums. This makes one deaf for a month or so, but the drum generally heals up, and if a hole remains in it, although one is somewhat deaf, one can blow tobacco smoke out of the ear in question, which is a social accomplishment."

Haldane made scores of dives in the Pot. One time he "dived in the dry" two hundred feet in ninety seconds, a pressure change equal to that of a jet pilot diving at fifteen hundred miles an hour. He was not affected on the compression, but on the way up at the same speed one of his teeth exploded. It was a filled tooth in which air pocketed under the filling could not leak out fast enough and, expanding, blew the tooth apart.

"In 1940 the view was current in the Navy that it took a long time to learn to stand rapid decompression," Haldane reported. "I rather think the qualified divers encouraged this superstition. When I told certain officers that I did not share it, they said that no doubt trained biologists could learn quickly, but ordinary people could not. So I applied to the Communist Party for four tough guys of genuine working class origin with no experience in diving or compressed air work. We got every one of them up to a pressure of ten atmospheres (three hundred feet) in five minutes of the first attempt. I think one of them lost consciousness, but none asked it be stopped."

Queer things happened in the thick air. A man tried to fan himself with a newspaper and it tore to pieces. Haldane fanned him with cardboard, which he had to force through the air. The air current did not reach the man for some seconds. Insects could not fly in the heavy air. The human voice changed. Haldane said: "Englishmen sound as if they were trying, not very successfully, to imitate an American accent." They were affected by nitrogen narcosis, or rapture of the deep. "Nonsensical words seemed to me very important," said the Professor. Haldane took into the chamber Dr. Juan Negrin, the former Spanish prime minister. Negrin had "a curious velvety sensation on the lips." They tried multiplying two four-digit sums. Haldane reported: "One distinguished Fellow of the Royal Society put down two figures in five minutes, one of which was wrong, and said he thought it was a bloody silly test." However, "The moment we switched over from air to helium-oxygen or hydrogen-air, we felt more normal within a few seconds, and were capable of doing arithmetic within one or two minutes."

They breathed pure oxygen under pressure to see how it affected divers. Haldane's wife, girl assistants and professional friends volunteered for these perilous tests. They had oxygen convulsions, which were like epileptic fits. "The muscular contractions," said Haldane, "were violent enough to break a bone." Mrs. Haldane "dived" ninety feet on oxygen seventeen times. Once she lasted eighty-eight minutes, another time she had a convulsion in thirteen minutes. The Professor had two fits, one crushing some vertebrae. They found that people convulsed under oxygen at quite different depths and individuals showed wide variations in convulsion time at the same depth. They tested underwater combat men, who were to use their findings in action. One of them was a former professional boxer. He convulsed and blacked out. He awoke on a cot with a man wiping him with a towel. His first words were, "What hit me?" A wit replied, "Oxygen Pete." After that Haldane found chalked in the pot, "Oxygen Pete sits here," and when there were several fits, people would say, "Oxygen Pete's in form today." Haldane said: "I suppose a number of gods and devils started their mythological lives in some such way in the past. Fortunately Oxygen Pete arrived on the scene too late to be incorporated into a religion."

During work on bends, the Professor got a bubble of nitrogen in his lower spinal cord. "For several days," he said, "I had a burning pain in the skin of my buttocks. This gradually died down to a tickle, combined with loss of ordinary sensation. Both of these are still there after six years." Haldane was concerned with the safety of mine demolition divers who might be caught under water during an enemy air raid. With a few minutes between the alert and the underwater explosions, they would have time to get out of the water, but not to decompress. The middle-aged professor and his wife tested on themselves various mixtures of air and oxygen to reduce the risk of nitrogen embolism and at the same time not invite oxygen convulsions. When they found the formula, the pair decompressed themselves in two minutes from depths where Navy tables called for forty-seven minutes of underwater stage waits. After that the underwater demolition men had a breathing supply permitting them to work deep and get out fast.

The Haldane group worked on submarine escape problems and even those of a theoretical submarine sunk in Arctic waters. Haldane and his colleague, Dr. E. M. Case, went into the pressure chamber and got into bath tubs full of water and ice blocks to see how long they could last. They were compressed and a pump poured in carbon dioxide, the noxious gas that is the main problem of trapped submariners. Haldane could endure the polar bath for twenty minutes, before shivering became uncontrollable. He found that cold only slightly lowered a man's resistance to carbon dioxide.

When Captain Shelford's team, with which Haldane worked, tested the first British underwater chariot, two Navy volunteers made the first runs under oxygen. Haldane said, "Captain, why didn't you give the machine to my assistant, Helen Spurway? She's insusceptible!"

The Royal Navy Physiological Laboratory reverted to peacetime strength with a hard-working team under Dr. H. J. Taylor. I went down to Alverstoke, Hampshire, near Portsmouth, to visit them in their villa laboratory in a middle-class street. It reminded me of the emergency military offices in England during the war, passages mouseholed through

Victorian pantry and parlor, labyrinths of backstairs scuffed with GI boots and maid's cubicles serving senior officers. The Portsmouth area was heavily bombed and the laboratory was low on the priority for rebuilding. Huge compression tanks and pots were squeezed in a little garden, beside the pens for experimental animals. Dr. Taylor is a tall incisive man, a connoisseur of Chinese porcelain. He said that one of the main concerns of the laboratory was free escape from sunken submarines, that is, men emerging from submarines without breathing apparatus. The Royal Navy is gradually abandoning the classic Davis oxygen lung, which has been the escape kit since the First World War.

Free escape was an actuality, invented by trapped men as far back as 1851 when Wilhelm Bauer broke out from a wrecked submarine sixty feet down. It took navy doctrine about a hundred years to catch up. The success of the naked method was conclusively demonstrated by a survey taken in 1945 by Captain Shelford and Dr. Taylor. They interviewed escapees from eighty wartime submarine sinkings, including Germans, and found that the greatest number got to the surface without apparatus. These findings impressed the Ruck-Keene Committee, set up by the Admiralty after the war. The Committee visited the United States and found its transatlantic naval colleagues equally interested in free escape. Indeed the U.S. Navy was first to put it into official practice in 1946.

Free escape consists of flooding a submarine with sea water until the air it contains is compressed to the degree of the water outside, at which point single hatches or double-hatch airlocks are opened to let men into the sea. The man going out contains in his lungs the necessary counter-pressure to armor himself. On the way up, he must whistle off his air pressure through pursed lips so that the air will not swell in his lungs and explode them.

The U.S. Navy sent its men up slowly in the tower tank at New London, Connecticut, at a rate of two feet per second. "We differed," said Dr. Taylor, smiling. "It places too much reliance on the men to go up slowly. We could not expect a man to hold his breath and flotation for seventy-five seconds, especially in the rapid expansion of his air near the surface. And it is not possible to rise that slowly from beyond 150 feet." Dr. Taylor planned to release naked men three hundred feet down and send them up at four to five feet a second.

One of his colleagues, Dr. Horace Wright, proved that it could be done in 1948. He went into a wet pot without breathing gear and was rapidly compressed to a depth of three hundred feet. The air was let off in seventy-five seconds. For an experimental jet pilot in a vertical dive, this would be a pressure change of nearly three times the speed of sound, or something like thirty-five miles a minute. Dr. Wright came out of the pot okay. Since then the staff of the Alverstoke lab have made many tank dives to three hundred feet without helium. Dr. Taylor introduced me to those who'd done it, the deep-sea divers of the garden on Aspadistra Row.

Two bashful young men came into the room, a long dark one named H. V. Hempleman and a short rosy one named Cyril Rashbass. I asked Dr. Rashbass how he came by such a fine name for a diving experimenter. "It's Hebrew," he said. He had been forty times or so at pressures of three hundred feet. I asked, "Did you feel exhilarated?" He grinned and said, "I'm not that kind of person." Dr. Hempleman, who had been crossing and uncrossing his shanks, gained *amour-propre* when he saw the talk was on physiology and not about perils and adventures. He said: "We are trying to improve Haldane's 1906 diving tables. Haldane believed tissues picked up nitrogen at different rates. I thought the fibrous joint tissues always got bends first, and they took a long time to saturate and were cleared much later. By diffusion of nitrogen, I believe. We started coming up fast, but I failed to calculate the stage stops. The math got beyond me. Cyril took over with a more accurate theory of diffusion and succeeded. He found a new method of stage decompression."

While it was too early to be sure of the new figures they had struck for decompression times, the team said: "Stage waits will be less for dives of shorter duration, even down to 240 feet. Practical diving will be shortened. For instance, take a thirty-minute dive to 180 feet. Haldane says one should decompress for an hour; the U.S. Navy says eighty-three minutes. We say forty-two minutes and the stage levels will also be changed. It is more striking on a fifteen-minute dive to 180 feet. Haldane calls for thirty-five minutes of stage decompression; your navy thirty-two minutes. We believe it can be done in nine minutes. On the other hand we find that longer dives need more decompression than the present tables ask for."

On the banks of the muddy Anacostia River in Washington, D.C., there is an old compound called the Naval Gun Factory. Just about everything except guns are manufactured in the Naval Gun Factory. The Navy makes its divers there, and it is the location of the Experimental Diving Unit. Here Behnke and Yarbrough evolved the helium tables, and here today basic research goes on with arcane gadgets with such names as the Scuba (Self-Contained Underwater Breathing Apparatus); the Helium Hat, a grotesque helmet with many valves and a copper snood; the Beast, an underwater bicycle; the Trapeze, a device for swimming hard and not getting anywhere; and the Igloo, a steel pressure dome with a parlor in the upper part and a swimming pool below.

Recently I went to the Gun Factory and met the experimentalists,

Lieutenant Commander J. V. Dwyer, a fair-haired engineering officer; tall, slab-handed Lieutenant Kenneth Ploof, who began helium diving in 1939 on the sunken submarine *Squalus*; and Surgeon-Lieutenant Edward H. Lanphier, a dark-complexioned physiologist, who marveled at his luck in drawing such a fascinating tour of duty. While helmet-diving trainees plumped into the river outside, Ploof and Lanphier described their work. Dwyer excused himself to attend a lecture. He had a running nose. I said, "I guess you won't be diving with that cold." He said, "It's hay fever. I'm going down as soon as possible. Diving is wonderful for hay fever. The compressed air is not pollenated." Lieutenant Ploof said their tank and open-water experiments were made with seventeen divers, including themselves. "We make a point of officers going on the harder dives," said Dr. Lanphier. "The regular divers are extraordinary people. There is a difference between them and other fellows. You are impressed with their rough-and-readiness and their quality as men." Ploof said, "We like to recruit the divers from artificers, shipwrights and people with mechanical trades, because so much underwater work calls for that kind of skill. But we'll take 'em from any classification, if they stand up as diving material."

Lanphier said, "Our A-1 activity now is working out nitrogen-oxygen mixtures. We are trying to get the oxygen content high and the nitrogen low to reduce decompression times. It is very tricky, because oxygen tolerances vary with depth and time and they differ for individuals. At one time we had the cockeyed idea that we could stabilize individual differences by telling the divers they had to cut out smoking and drinking. We would put them on uniform diets and tell them when they could have intercourse, things like that. I didn't know divers as well as I do now. We never put the program into effect. It wouldn't mean anything. You might be able to prove that a certain group of Trappist monks made ideal experimental subjects, but not divers." Henry Siebe, an early historian of diving, put it, "Divers do not constitute shining lights in teetotal societies."

Lanphier and Ploof showed me the Helium Hat. The principal difference between it and a compressed-air helmet was a streamlined copper chamber across the back of the neck. A Venturi tube drew off the helium-oxygen in the diver's helmet and passed it through caustic soda to repurify the oxygen. The fresh mixture then went back into the helmet on the other side. Lieutenant Ploof opened the faceplate and said, "Feel the chin button in here." I touched the button and it clicked easily. He said, "That is an emergency feature. If your pressure gets too high in the helmet you nudge that with your chin and it exhausts into the water. But we found it wasn't enough security. A man had to die to put this on the helmet."

He unscrewed a double nonreturn valve on the crown of the Helium Hat. "When the pressure gets too high inside, this valve automatically passes off the pressure. Water cannot get in through it."

He continued, "It came about when we had a diver down to 495 feet. He phoned that he felt uncomfortable. Soon it was apparent he was in distress. We brought him to 400 feet. He became silent and we knew he had passed out. What we didn't know was that his head fell over to the right against the chin button and held it open. His helmet pressure drained off. When it became less than the outside pressure, water entered the valve. The Venturi picked up the water and blew it through the caustic soda. A sludge of caustic soda poured back into the helmet, burning his face and he took it in his lungs. The diver was burned inside and out. I went in the recompression chamber with him and bathed him with boric acid. His face burns were not serious in my opinion, but his lungs were badly burned. We put him in an oxygen tent and speeded up the respiration to get oxygen in his system, but it was useless. Something that is always with you in diving—progress too damned often depends on men dying to reveal new problems."

Lieutenant Lanphier led me through a hatch into a tall tank. There was a circular hole in the deck looking down on a wet tank, where divers are compressed to simulate ocean depths. At the moment the tank was dry. A vertical metal frame hung below. "That's the Trapeze," he said. "A diver goes in with swim fins and a breathing set and takes hold of the Trapeze. We tie a line to his waist and run it up through a pulley. There is a heavy weight on the other end of the line. The diver then swims as hard as he can, going no place, while we tap off samples of respiration gases into measuring instruments on the outside." There was a bench full of meters and indexed machines, flasks and tubes. The Beast, a stationary bicycle, was in another pressure chamber. Lanphier said, "It's actually a hydraulic ergometer. Measures energy output."

We entered the Igloo. Lanphier explained, "When we have a case of bends on Table 4—that requires a thirty-eight-hour decompression—we fix up the Igloo like a parlor for the doctor and the corpsman. They look after the patient and occasionally go for a swim in the tank below. The last time we had a Table 4 case, Commander Moffitt K. Holler was with the patient the whole way. When the man suffered his distress at one hundred feet, Holler went down to help him decompress, came up with him and went into the tank with him for nearly two days. So we like it to be comfortable in here."

The Experimental Diving Unit joins some experiments at the University of Pennsylvania laboratory of Dr. Christian Lambertsen, an athletic expert in oxygen breathing. Dr. Lambertsen invented the oxygen lung used by U.S. Navy underwater swimmers during the war, and served with clandestine underwater units of the Office of Strategic Services. His latest lung, the Flatus, can be used with pure oxygen or nitrogen-oxygen mixtures.

Because of the Navy system of automatically posting officers to new jobs after several years, continuity in diving research is sometimes interrupted. Not every physician assigned to the E.D.U. will have Dr. Lanphier's gusto for pressure physiology. He wishes there were a team of doctors. "When you know everything there is to know about diving," he said, "you find out that you know hardly anything. The unknown is enormous in this field. I wish more civilian doctors would take an interest in it. For a couple of years we have been training four medical students in their summer holidays and they have been swell. The first group assigned by the Navy included two Negroes studying to be dentists. It is not likely that they can go on with diving work, but they were very effective while they were here.

"I'm taking a month's vacation in Europe this fall," he continued, "I'm going to try to visit the G.E.R.S. at Toulon and the Royal Navy Physiological Lab. When I listed all the diving centers and people I want to see, there wasn't much time left for sightseeing. In London I had to decide whether I wanted to see St. Paul's or Sir Robert Davis. I think it'll be Sir Robert, if he'll see me."

A slender twenty-eight-year-old Swedish engineer named Arne Zetterstrom attempted during World War II to tame explosive hydrogen and breathe it in great pressure. He took up J. B. S. Haldane's lead that hydrogen would not explode when mixed with one-twenty-fifth part of oxygen. Zetterstrom worked four years at the Royal Institute of Technology at Stockholm on how a man breathing such a starvation ration of oxygen could live through the top hundred feet of water. Once at four atmospheres, the fourfold oxygen would sustain life, and hydrogen promised to take men deeper than helium. The diffident, blue-eyed searcher was "a fascinating young man and an ingenious constructor," said Commodore Herbert Westermark, R.S.N., the naval surgeon who worked with him. "He never hesitated in staking his own security in pursuing his task."

In 1944 Zetterstrom discovered how to proceed across the superficial zone. His tenders pumped him pure compressed air as he sank to a hundred feet. There he stopped his descent to switch to hydrogen-oxygen. "This cannot be done by a mere changeover," said Zetterstrom, "since at the juncture where air and hydrogen combine, the mixture becomes an explosive. But if the air is removed by replacement of a mixture of 4 per cent oxygen and 96 per cent nitrogen, the risk of explosion is completely eliminated." Zetterstrom then turned on his hydrogen-oxygen and proceeded on down. He dived to 363 feet. Sound traveled faster in hydrogen than in helium; Zetterstrom's telephone reports from this depth were so high and nasal that people on deck could not understand him. He fitted a telegraph key for the next dive.

He sailed out upon the Baltic August 7, 1945, the day after the atomic bomb was dropped on Hiroshima. He intended to dive far deeper than any man in a flexible dress had ever gone to show that divers could aid crews of submarines lost in previously undaunted depths. I have not been able to find information on Zetterstrom's tender. Lieutenant Ploof thinks the arrangement may have consisted of a vessel laying head to current with one deep bow anchor. Zetterstrom stood on a wooden diving platform, holding on to its stays, and was lowered from a boom at the stern. To keep him reasonably vertical in the current, a retaining line was carried from his stage to a windlass in the bow. The young experimenter went down through the water. He was stopped at a hundred feet, where he ventilated his suit and helmet thoroughly with nitrogen-oxygen, then opened his hydrogen-oxygen valve and signaled to be lowered away. Down went Zetterstrom into the black Baltic Sea, tapping regular messages that he was all right. He reached 528 feet, which was then 88 feet further than a diver in soft dress had ever gone on helium. Zetterstrom used his own stage decompression tables for the return from this prodigious depth. No Navy tables existed for his problem.

He reached his first stage and waited it out, reassuring his comrades that all went well. At the 165-foot stage, his winchmen stopped him for another decompression period, but the people at the bow continued to haul the retaining line. Stupidly and strenuously they heaved Zetterstrom past 100 feet. He had no time to make his gas changeover. He was hoisted into the thin layers gasping on the faint supply of oxygen. He passed out. When they got him aboard, Zetterstrom died. The medical report said he perished from "acute lack of oxygen and caisson disease of a violent character." Zetterstrom's tragedy was in no way due to hydrogen or his changeover technique, but to "an unpardonable mistake" by the man in charge of the retaining line. No one has continued his hydrogen-diving experiments.

Zetterstrom's brief experiment, however, led to long, daring thoughts of the possibility that man may one day breathe water. Zetterstrom lived on a gaseous mixture of hydrogen and oxygen, and water is almost entirely hydrogen and oxygen. Perhaps a device could be surgically introduced in the body to permit man to inspire water and complete the cycle of his story; risen from the sea, he returns to the old home.

Drowning is less dangerous than breathing the noxious gases that can build up in breathing sets. Dr. R. E. Davies, the Oxford biochemist who leads the British Cave Diving Group, gave the following advice to oxygen divers if they had exhausted their bottles: *"Let your last act be to flood your lungs; by that you preserve some chance of being revived later."*

4

Treasure or Trash

A SLOW-WITTED, egotistical ship's carpenter named William Phips, of Bristol, Maine, one of twenty-six children by the same Puritan father and mother, was the man who turned the age-old dream of sunken treasure into reality. In 1687 he took $1,500,000 in gold and silver from a sunken Spanish galleon in the Bahamas. Ever since then undersea gold has been the bait of promoters and confidence men, the delight of writers, the torture of investors and occasional work for divers.

There is no record of when the Spanish ship went down, but the rumor of her loss was widely spread by 1680. Phips, who had learned to read and write at the age of forty-two, used his new knack to get up a treasure-hunting prospectus and went to England in 1684 to look for money. He was learning the truth of the old Viking saying: "A man must have much silver before he can go in search of gold." Phips found a ready ear under the curly wig of the second Duke of Albemarle, son of General George Monck, who had abandoned Cromwell's army and restored the Stuarts. Monck had been given a dukedom but no fortune, and his son was greedy for gold. His Grace took the carpenter to the King. Charles II was impressed with the big-talking Phips and loaned him the frigate *Algier Rose*.

When Phips got to the Bahamas he couldn't find the wreck. He saw some people grubbing in an old hulk at Grand Bahama Island, but it did not look like a treasure galleon to him. Actually, it contained a small silver lode, which was being salvaged by another American privateer named Captain Thomas Paine, who was ready to defend his claim with an eight-gun frigate, the *Pearl*. The dull Captain Phips sailed back to London. King Charles was dead but His Grace of Albemarle was still eager. A tanned sailor named John Smith turned up from the Indies, his earrings bouncing as he told them his tale. He had looked down on a galleon wedged upright on a reef between Cuba and Turk's Island, Bahamas. He swore he saw the glister of gold and silver through the turquoise sea.

Albemarle was dead broke but he raised £800 among his cronies and sent Phips in two little ships, the *James and Mary* and the *Henry,* with John Smith aboard as pilot. The Duke loaded the ships with goods to sell the Spaniards. Smith took Phips out in a big Indian canoe which could negotiate the dangerous coral heads, and found the wreck in three days. They sent naked Bahaman divers into the shallow hulk, while they built a crude diving bell. (Salvage bells had been used a century before Phips.) In three months three Indian divers and sailors in the bell lifted tons of bullion and coin. Phips sailed into the Thames in September, 1687, with his loot, and England was stricken with gold fever. Salvage expeditions sold shares in a hundred illusionary treasures. One of the promotions was a diver in an armored suit, who gave demonstrations in the Thames, while prospects were wined and dined in a pavilion at the water's edge. Investors lost many times the amount Phips had received.

The Duke became a rich man. Phips' share was only $75,000, but he was knighted and sent home as High Sheriff of New England. John Smith, who had found the treasure, got nothing. He petitioned the Crown for a fair share and was heard in Privy Council. Albemarle was forced to pay him a small amount. Sir William Phips became Royal Governor of New England and misgoverned dully and energetically. He was recalled to London to explain, and died there of malignant fever in 1695.

One of the most persistent treasure legends is the "Tobermory Galleon," a wreck in a little harbor of the Isle of Mull which has embroiled Scotsmen in feuds and follies for fifteen generations. She is supposed to be the *Duque de Florencia,* a Portuguese ship of the Spanish Armada, one that was driven in a storm in 1588 all the way around John O'Groats into the Western Isles. Her captain, Dom Pereira, found haven in Tobermory Harbor and arrogantly demanded food of the villagers. He was lucky to get back aboard with his ears still attached, for the Scots were falling on other distressed armada crews and slaughtering them to a man. But Tobermory was busy with a war of its own, between the Macleans of Duart and the MacDonalds of Ardnamurchan and saved the Portugee for later. The MacDonalds told Dom Pereira to mind his manners and come back with some gold. Lachlan Mhor, chief of the Macleans, was shrewder. He gave the Portuguese meal, mutton and water, and suggested that Pereira lend him the four hundred soldiers he had aboard. With these troops, Lachlan Mhor crushed the MacDonalds.

The chief held on to his balance of power. The *Florencia* remained at anchor as chill autumn came. The shivering southerners were willing to risk Drake's fleet again, rather than the Scottish winter. Pereira asked his leave of Lachlan Mhor. The Scot took three Portuguese officers as hostages and began talking about his need for gold. The seething Pereira returned to his ship, weighed anchor and started out of the harbor with one of the Macleans, David Glas, aboard. According to Tobermory lore, Glas fired the powder magazine. The galleon heaved up in two parts and sank. Only two men survived. And with the *Duque de Florencia* there sank a treasure of $10 million in gold.

It is a very nice tale, much believed. Its principal shortcoming is the fact that several scholars checked the Spanish naval archives and found that the *Duque de Florencia* carried no gold and returned to Spain after the defeat of the Armada. There is an old ship, or ships, in Tobermory Harbor, however. Five bronze cannons, iron cannon balls, water jars and a few ancient coins have been found in the harbor during many campaigns. The ship may be the *San Juan Baptista,* which also left no record of a gold horde.

The real merit of undersea gold is that it develops salvage techniques and gives employment to divers. The Tobermory wreck has also provided a traditional challenge for the dukes of Argyll: each heir must grapple for the family wreck. The House owns it in their right as hereditary Admirals of Scotland. They fought the Sassenach for it, and won. In the seventeenth century a diver found three cannons and the second Duke visited the wreck in a bell in 1730 and found another cannon and some coins. At that, up spoke the Duke of York, Admiral of England *and* Scotland. He waved his patent as custodian of all wrecks on the part of the Crown. There was a passionate legal contest over the moldering hulk. Sir Walter Scott upheld Argyll and visited Tobermory to obtain local color. "Divers were actually at work on her," he wrote Robert Surtees. "The fishers showed me the place where she lay, and said there had been a good deal of treasure and some brass cannon got out of the wreck." The Duke of Argyll won out over the Duke of York by showing that ships that sank in Scotland before the Act of Union between England and Scotland in 1707 belonged to Argyll, while later wrecks belonged to York.

In 1902 another cannon, swords and fifty coins were retrieved. By 1922 there had been fifty salvage expeditions at Tobermory, and the total value of all recoveries in three centuries was about $1,000.

In 1954, the eleventh Duke, fifty-three-year-old Ian Douglas Campbell, began again with a reconnaissance team led by Commander L. P. K. Crabbe, the wartime underwater warrior. The following year Underwater Surveys, Ltd., of London, arrived with an ex-tank landing craft. After an echo-sound survey of the harbor, which averages fifty feet deep, a conspicuous mound was selected only 150 yards from the town quay. The new men adopted the archeological method of trenching across the site, with a big grab operated from a thirty-three-ton automobile crane moving in the open well of the LCT. The grab dumped spoil on deck where it was washed out, or "slurried," with high pressure sea water hoses to uncover any items of interest. When the gumbo had been examined a snow-plow tractor pushed it out over the bow tank-ramp.

In July, craneman James McDonald (apparently the Macleans did not get *all* the MacDonalds in 1588) was lifting a ton of mud from a twelve-foot trench. "Go slow!" came cries from the deck. In the grab was a seven-foot section of ship's timber encased in lead. From the slurry came a cannonball, broken wood and more lead plate. Diver Stephen Fox went down and felt ship structure in the trench. The salvors believed they had struck the top gun gallery of the old ship. The method was changed. Divers swam down to outline the wreck with buoys, after which they would dredge a trench around the sides. By this time the anticipated treasure, bullishly inflated by a corroded cannonball, had grown to a "£30 million crock of gold in doubloons, ducats, roubles and moidores," according to a London newspaper. At current prices that would be about two long tons of gold. It must be quite a good-sized crock. It will take James MacDonald two trips to fish it up.

Another shimmering hope of gold in dark waters lies in northwest Spain among the famous "Galleons of Vigo Bay." In November, 1955, a British company called Ventures, Ltd., secured a concession from the Spanish government, the thirteenth recorded salvage effort on the wrecks. The tale of the ships goes back to 1702, during the War of Spanish Succession, a confused and treacherous brawl over the throne of the dead Austrian king of Spain, Charles II. For three years Spanish treasure convoys from South America and the Indies had not dared bring the annual tribute of gold, silver, pearls and gems, or valuable cargoes of cochineal, indigo, ambergris, mahogany, tobacco, balsa, sarsaparilla, sassafras, tamarind, cocoa, ginger, sugar and vanilla. Philip V, the Bourbon pretender, crushed the Spanish people with taxes, the soldiers were unpaid, and the life of the country almost depended on the loot of South America. Don Manuel de Velasco decided to bring the treasure ships from the Plate in 1702. He crossed the Atlantic in twenty great galleons and rendezvoused at sea with an escort of twenty-three French warships under le Comte de Château-Renault, who was to defend the treasure from the Anglo-Dutch fleet then blockading Cadiz. The French suggested Velasco come in to Brest, but he was afraid his cargo would get lost in France. The French and Spanish ships sheltered in Vigo Bay in northwest Spain, a refuge since it was the Roman *Vicus Spacorum*. The Spanish ships went deep into the inner San

Simeon Bay, cut trees from the wooded slopes and laid a log boom across the bay mouth. The French ships guarded the boom, while the irresolute Spanish decided what to do. They did not unload the treasures and start them overland because no instructions had been received from Madrid. The coast buzzed with gossip of the riches in Vigo Bay and the English and Dutch decided to go after them. A month passed before an official arrived from Madrid. He was sitting aboard Velasco's flagship, gloating over the wealth belowdecks when Admiral Sir George Rooke crashed the boom at night with a gold-lusting, screeching horde of *ingleses* and *holandéses*. The French ships engaged at close quarters and for thirty hours men fought hand-to-hand with cutlasses, pistols and rifles, and fired flaming asphalt and red-hot cannon balls at each other. The Spanish decided it was time to get their stuff ashore. Most of the galleons were in flame as little boats tried to discharge the treasure. A small vessel named the *San Pedro* was ferrying a shipment ashore, when it was sunk in shallow water by a cannon shot. Local fishermen came out with huge rocks and dumped them on the wreck as the battle raged to keep the raiders from fishing up the treasure. They even threw in the pedestal of a statue of the Virgin. In the shambles, English sailors dived into the water and boarded flaming galleons to grab gold. Many of them died in the fires. The British flagship went down. The English captured four galleons afloat and the Dutch five. Six French ships were taken, while Count de Château-Renault withdrew with the remnant of his force. In all twenty-four ships sank in the flaming riot for gold. The twenty-fifth victim was the biggest galleon, which was sent away as a prize in the charge of Sir Cloudesley Shovell, an admiral unlucky as his name was wonderful. He rammed the galleon on an island in the bay mouth and lost her in 110 feet of water. Five years later, Sir Cloudesley's lapses as a navigator led to the destruction of four great ships, two thousand men and himself, when he led them into the Scilly Islands.

Before the Battle of Vigo Bay ended, English sailors began diving for the wrecks, under gunfire from the shore. When the victors withdrew they had about £5 million in treasure. A French expedition secured a salvage concession twenty-five years later and recovered one valueless small boat. Another attempt failed in 1748. In 1825 an English salvor named Captain Dickson arrived in the brig *Enterprise* and worked the wrecks with a diving bell. He definitely recovered silver and sailed away suddenly at night, with what finds no one knew. A decade later a Spanish attempt came to nothing. In 1858 the Spanish government gave a ten-year salvage concession to David Langlands. He had no success in the wrecks, but he knew the one sure-fire way to make a fortune from sunken gold—by selling the concession. He sold it twice.

The first buyer was Saint-Simon Sicard, a Parisian who got up a considerable subscription in France and went after Spanish finance. In Madrid he met another Frenchman, a young banker named Hippolyte Magen, who has left a classic report on the fantastic events that ensued, *Les Galions de Vigo,* a rare little book which forms one of the main curiosities of the undersea library of Frédéric Dumas. *The Galleons of Vigo* is a charming tale of horror, written in precise bankerese, and should be required reading for anyone interested in treasure salvage. I hope it is known to Ventures, Ltd., who are trying the hulks almost a hundred years after Magen.

Magen first thoroughly checked Sicard's tale in the Spanish archives and found a mass of evidence that showed there was treasure in San Simeon Bay. He agreed to direct the operations. During the inevitable delays of organizing the expedition, the Spanish government, which was in a new turmoil, issued a secret decree invalidating Langlands' rights and therefore Magen's. Magen found that all the documents concerning Vigo had been removed from the archives. The Spanish monarchy was overthrown shortly afterward and the republican government restored the concession and renewed it for ten years. On that cue, Langlands sold it to a redoubtable salvor named Colonel Gowen, who had lifted the sunken Russian fleet at Sevastopol. The French society was knocked out of the picture. However, they had raised a good amount of capital and Colonel Gowen agreed to combine with them. Then Gowen started selling very successfully in London, which overweighed the French contribution. Sicard and Magen felt "paralyzed." While the Colonel reconnoitered Vigo Bay in a diving bell, the French regained control of the galleons and Magen bustled around raising divers and equipment.

He was going to use the *aérophore* diving gear, invented by Denayrouze and Rouquayrol, which had just proved itself in the Greek sponge fishery, and he wanted Auguste Denayrouze as his salvage superintendent. Denayrouze was still engaged in the Aegean, but he put Magen on to six skilled young French divers and a clever engineer named Ernest Bazin, of Angers. Magen hired the basement of a salt warehouse overlooking San Simeon Bay as his headquarters and diving began in terrible weather in January, 1870. An aged fisherman who had worked for Dickson's expedition in 1825 pointed out five wreck locations. Bazin sent two divers in succession and Magen made sure that their descriptions were objective by putting the helmet on the second man before the first diver had removed his. The second man could not hear what the first one said. They confirmed ten wrecks in twelve days. Bazin's gadgets began to arrive, including an underwater electric lantern, which weighed nine hundred pounds, and a two-man observation chamber. The Vigo customs house delayed everything for days; the weather often drove the salvors off the Bay, and the Spanish government stationed an official observer on the salvage barge. The people in the fishing villages knew the names of each wreck, which comforted Magen until he discovered they simply called a ship by any name that struck them. Early in the salvage Bazin's men lifted an iron cannon from a galleon which must have been completely surprised in the gold raid. The tampion was still in the muzzle. They unplugged it; air whizzed out, and the inside looked as though "freshly cleaned the previous night." They found a fused mass of two hundred cannon balls, and a decanter, a boarding hatchet, a bag of Brazil nuts, a dagger handle, a silver bowl, human bones and a long carved pipe case with an Indian woman standing on the back of a naked kneeling man.

The Spanish gathered around these relics with avid interest. "Everybody's imagination was working overtime," said Magen. "Cases of indigo turned into silver vases and lumps of iron into silver ingots." The customs pests came around, continually asking Magen where he had put "the case of gold." They forced him to send all finds ashore under Spanish protection. Magen wrote to Paris, "I am charged with the safety of these things by the Spanish government and the company, and they will not let me near the customs house." He wailed, "Everything will be stolen."

The expeditionary artist, Durand-Brager, descended in the chamber and painted a vast shallow wreck the locals called the *Madera*. The electric lantern beams "on these contorted masses in brown and reddish oxide colors are really marvelous," wrote Magen. Storms drove them off this wreck. The natives said it was the worst winter in memory. The inhabitants of resorts always flatter tourists this way. The salvors worked on a more sheltered hulk, denominated *La Ligura*. The divers broke into her and found themselves in the sick bay, grabbing basins, pills and rotten rolls of bandage. They blew her apart and recovered a compass, a metal cup and a high heel of a dandy of the time of Louis XIV. No treasure came up. The company was going broke. Magen discovered the worst money drain of a salvage operation was the time the whole force stood by, waiting on the weather. They moved to the wreck called the *Tambor*, thirty-eight feet down. In good weather they dived through the night with the big lantern. She yielded hawse pipes, blocks, spoons and pots.

They moved over the *Santa Cruz* and found a huge iron anchor catted on her side amidships. Their little steamer could not haul this anchor. The *Almirante*, fifty-two feet down, yielded fifteen cases of indigo, which turned into gold in the soaring imaginations of the locals, while the salvors were going broke. They found Château-Renault's ship, thirty-two feet down, and the *Espicho* at a depth of fifty feet. A quarrel arose between engineer Bazin and the director over which wreck they should stay with and work extensively. Bazin won because they had a good stake-out on the *Almirante* and it was easier not to move the moorings. They got nothing but indigo, cochineal and lumps of fused metal, which they tossed back in the water in disgust.

Magen was lunching one day in the fetid salt house (where his cordovan boots turned green with mold) when he spied Bazin coming ashore in a boat, waving a handkerchief and holding something in his hand. The director ran to the beach. Bazin came ashore, kissed him, and shouted, "This is it!" He held a loaf of grayish metal, which one of the divers had broken in half. Inside it was sparkling pure silver. They got 130 pounds of it in fast order, which the excited Spanish marched off to the storehouse. Bazin rushed to Paris to report to the company.

Madrid sent three more inspectors and they asked "millions of questions." Four separate parties in Madrid politicked to grab the Vigo concession. The divers dug a crater in the wreck, among landslides and heavy dangers. Three of them were paralyzed by severe bends in the arms. Rumors went round that they had been eaten by conger eels. Soon there was only one diver able to work, and all the money was gone. Magen went to Paris to raise some more.

The silver yield worked magic and more shares were sold. Bazin drew up plans for wonderful new salvage gadgets, but Magen insisted the new funds be spent on operations only, going on with the equipment they had. Bazin resigned. Magen engaged four more divers and sent them to Spain. He wired the expedition to stop the killing work on the *Almirante* and shift to a more accessible wreck, the *San Pedro,* the little vessel that the fishermen had covered with stones during the battle. A pyramid of rocks covered the ruin, almost cemented together by fossil concretions in 168 years.

Magen also sent them a chemist from Paris. This party grabbed one of the gray lumps of metal they had been chunking back in the water. Analysis showed it was pure mercury-silver covered with oxidization. A pound of it contained 450 grams of silver. The Spanish Government sent a coast guard ship to hang around and referee the division of treasure. This was scrupulously done, but what little payment was made to the salvors was soon swallowed in the work.

Auguste Denayrouze arrived in Paris and agreed to take over the operation. As he was about to leave for Spain, the Franco-Prussian war broke out. Denayrouze immediately joined the engineers, saying to Magen, "Don't worry, it will only be a week or so until we whip the Germans, and then we'll get on with the job." Magen stayed in Paris to wait for him. Denayrouze fell ill with pneumonia and was carried off to his birthplace, unable to whip Germans or raise galleons. Two days before the

Prussians surrounded Paris Magen received his last letter from Spain. The divers were on strike. They had not been paid for a month. Work was at a standstill. Magen wanted to rush through the closing gap of Germans, but he was restrained by his doctor. He was weak with fever after the months in the salt house. The ring closed. Unable to function, Magen resigned from the directorship.

The company hired a Paris engineer named Étienne, who said he would guarantee to get through to Vigo and take charge. "I'll cross the German lines in a balloon," said this cool individual. He hired a gas bag named *Le Galilée,* and a ready sailor as his crew. On November 4, 1870, at 2 P.M. he left the Gare d'Orleans, like a commercial traveler going out to the provinces. The balloon contained five hundred pounds of ballast, nine hundred pounds of letters from besieged Parisians and official dispatches giving the results of the October thirty-first elections. The sailor took a spyglass and maps on which to enter the German positions.

Le Galilée ascended slowly and was taken in an northeastern breeze at one thousand three hundred feet. As she sailed over the German redoubts, the enemy fired several shots into the gas bag. Fortunately it was compartmented. Étienne and the *matelot* dumped out ballast and went up to nearly a mile. Toward evening they descended in the Beauce plain, which seemed devoid of Prussians, but a farm wife warned Étienne the enemy was about. He chucked out more weight and sailed off. He came down five miles from Chartres. Villagers helped him deflate the conspicuous balloon. Two German hussars rode up. The people formed around the two balloonists. The German officer barked, "If you interfere, we will burn your village." The peasants walked away, growling, as the aeronauts were arrested. From the dusk came shouts of *"Aux armes!"* The villagers were coming back with clubs and rocks to rescue the balloonists. The German officer said to Étienne, "If they throw one stone, I'll shoot you." Étienne said, "I'll speak to them." He walked over to the villagers and slipped them the government dispatch box and whispered "Take it to the government at Tours."

The German officer fired four shots into the air and a troop of hussars rode up and took the captives to Versailles. The German commandant questioned Étienne on conditions in Paris. Étienne said Paris was heavily armed and had vast stocks of food. Actually, they would be eating rats before long in Paris. The commandant said, "You are a spy," and held up the sailor's maps. The Germans confiscated the funds he was taking to the salvage job. The captives were taken outside, where soldiers drew their fingers across their throats and yelled, "Kaput!" They were marched with a column of soldier-prisoners toward Cologne. The guards fed the military prisoners, but gave Étienne no food. Near Château-Thierry, the guard of canal lock fell in step beside him. This person named Martin said, "Any messages you want to send to Paris, monsieur?" Étienne said, "How in the devil can you get word to Paris?" Martin replied, "Put letters in a bottle, and throw them into the Marne and they float into Paris." The engineer gave a message about his situation. Martin said, "Really, monsieur, with this spy business, the schlocks will shoot you. Why don't you try to escape?" Étienne shrugged and looked at the guards. Martin disappeared, running ahead of the plodding column. In Château-Thierry, Étienne and his shipmate were surprised to be billeted separately from the others in a room in the *Mairie*. Martin had arranged it with the mayor. That night, Martin turned up and said, "Follow me." He led them downstairs, where the Prussian sentry was asleep. "The one with the spike on his *chapeau* has been tasting our excellent wines," Martin said. "I put in some strong stuff, too." Once more on the road to Vigo, the engineer was given peasant clothes and passed from person to person on an underground railway through German-held territory. He got to Spain at last and found the operation completely shut down and the divers dispersed. Étienne's epic struggle to reach the galleons came to nothing.

Two years later Ernest Bazin was back on the job with new money. He located five more wrecks and concentrated on dredging behind the *Almirante*. No treasure came up, but Bazin's funds went down. On November 22, 1872, the workers quit. There was no more money. There wasn't even enough to ship the salvage equipment to France and sell it. They left the gear there and went away.

One arthritic winter morning recently, I walked down Haymarket to Pall Mall to meet the man who salvaged twenty-five million dollars in gold from a sunken ship. He had written me from his cottage on the Isle of Wight, "I am coming up to London tomorrow for a meeting of the Physiological Society and shall be stopping at the United Service Club.—G. C. C. Damant." I checked my figurative umbrella with the bemedaled commissionaire in the marble lobby of the Club and asked for Captain Damant. He appeared in the grayed light—a trim man with faded red hair, halted a trifle by seventy-four years, many dark depths of ocean and the English clime. He looked a good deal like U.S. Supreme Court Justice William O. Douglas, given a couple more mountains.

Captain Damant ushered me to a corner of a big lounge and ordered tea. I was aware of a beetling oil portrait hanging overhead of a former member, an admiral in knee britches, sashes and starbursts of several orders, and saw behind his white stockinged calves a burning city. The brass legend on the frame said he was Rear Admiral Sir George Cockburn and the city he'd burnt was Washington, D.C. I did not feel that Captain Damant had deliberately selected such a rendezvous with an American, but it introduced a cautionary note, which his first remarks bore out. "I don't like personal publicity," he said firmly. "Practically everything I know is in Sir Robert's book, and, if you are interested in diving physiology, look up Professor Haldane in the *Journal of Hygiene* for 1906." I said, "I read them. I got a lot out of them. But they are by great experts and the public can't follow all of it. My idea is—" Captain Damant said, "It wasn't like this in the old Navy. No publicity, no nicknames. We hadn't a journalist in sight the seven years on the *Laurentic*."

I gathered that Captain Damant had met quite a few journalists in his time. Indeed I found out later that he'd had a letter from "a lady writing on sunken treasures," and was freshly irritated with my trade. She suggested that Captain Damant write his chronicle "with as much detail as possible" which she would put into her own words. "Look here," he said, "there's no use writing about what we did. It's over and done with. Why don't you write about these new chaps, the frogmen, all lashed up with teevee sets?"

Having burned a bit of Washington, Captain Damant drank some tea and amiably discussed diving. I put away my notebook. It was difficult to keep on the Damant epic, because he quizzed me about Cousteau's salvage of the Greek argosy off Marseille. "Those eighteen-inch bronze treenails, imbedded in charred oak dowels," he would say, "how do they account for them?" while I tried to ask him, "Who introduced the idea of percentage bonuses for the divers on the *Laurentic*?"

I was able to gather his story from that talk, the record, and amusing letters he wrote on a typewriter "with a conical roller that makes radiating lines like radio coming out of an antenna," as he described it. "I began diving as a gunnery lieutenant in 1904," he said. "I'd gone to the *Excellent*, the principal gunnery school. Diving came within the province of the gunnery lieutenant at sea, and we were given fourteen days' diving instruction, just enough to know what we could expect from divers and the necessary precautions for safeguarding them. Few of the young officers took any interest in the subject. We did not appreciate that war would bring submarine disasters, sunken treasure ships, emergency repairs or mine clearance to increase the importance of the craft. All that naval divers expected to be used for was clearing an inlet valve or a fouled propeller, scraping barnacles off a ship's bottom or searching for something lost overboard.

"I made a dive under the instruction of Warrant Officer Andrew Catto. He was a first-class officer and an experienced practical diver. I found going under water to be a delightful experience and infinitely preferred Catto's fatherly instruction to the study of ballastics and field gun drill. I loved it. Diving amused me. In those days, we knew that pressure was dangerous; divers wore under their dress a wickerwork frame to keep the fabric expanded. We called it the crinoline. We wore red tassel caps. They were comfortable, but if one slipped off your head it was a damn nuisance. The tassel might get in the outlet valve. One time in Liverpool there was an inquest on a diver who drowned on a dock job. They asked a chap from the docks 'What first led you to suspect the diver was in difficulty?' He replied, 'When I saw his red cap floating, I guessed something was wrong.' " Captain Damant chuckled.

One of his first salvage jobs was in 1907, on Torpedo Boat 99, sunk in 150 feet of water four miles off Torquay in the English Channel. Damant was in command of a torpedo gunboat, H.M.S. *Spanker,* with six divers. The boat was ill-fitted for salvage diving. Walter Trapnell, a shipwright diver, was on the bottom in a stiff tide, when the current swept his life line away and snagged it on the wreck. His air pipe was carried in the opposite direction and fouled the propeller. Trapnell's best friend, Sydney Leverett, dived to his aid, but discovered that his air pipe was too short to reach the distressed man. Leverett signaled to be pulled out. Young Lieutenant Damant had no extra pipe and no boat to send ashore for more. And a man was pinned below in nearly six atmospheres of pressure. Trapnell had already been down an hour.

There were two hand pumps aboard, one for each diver. The Lieutenant acted. He had the tenders strip rubber pipe out of the idle pump and splice it on Leverett's air hose. They tapped both diver's hoses into one pump and Leverett dropped into the water. The men on deck pumped furiously to supply them both. Leverett reached Trapnell, who reached out his bare hand and squeezed his friend's. The rescue diver struggled for hours in the darkness and cold current to free Trapnell. When they hauled them up, Trapnell had been down for five and a half hours. He was barely conscious. He had lost his hearing and rambled incoherently. In a few hours he was dead.

Damant retired from the Navy at the end of his statutory hitch in 1911. He worked with Professor J. S. Haldane on mine rescue apparatus and on diving physiological experiments with his great friend, Dr. A. E. Boycott. The war hastened him back into the Navy. "I fought two wars on the re-tired list," he said. (In World War II he was salvage officer in the Mediterranean and Suez Canal.) "In 1914 submarines began sinking, especially enemy submarines." A U-boat sank off Dover and Damant was sent with two divers to have a look at it. "We had none of your diving ships," he said. "We went out in a rowboat." Damant dived to the shallow wreck. It was only twelve feet down to the conning tower. He found twelve mines still in the wet tubes. This type of German mine layer carried its mines outside in silos exposed to the water. He tried to open the conning

tower hatch. "I couldn't get it open," he said. "I decided to try a very
little gelignite to jar the hatch open. Took about seven hundred yards of
circuit wire on a reel made of handspikes, a very temporary rig. Set the
gelignite, fastened the priming wire and got back in the rowboat. The
idea was to row to the end of the wire and set the charge off, due to the
possibility that the mines would go up too. About a hundred yards off the
charge went off prematurely and the mines went, too. We were not
hurt, but there was a huge wave coming off the explosion. I could swim,
but the two divers were in their heavy boots and would drown. The wave
arrived, but our little boat rode over the crest without spilling. Bit of
luck, that. There wasn't enough left of the U-boat to learn anything."

Soon after that a U-boat deposited a mine off Malin Head, Donegal,
which made one of the luckiest contacts of the war—the White Star
liner *Laurentic*. She was bound from Liverpool to Halifax without passengers. After the explosion the big ship sank quickly in the bitter January
Atlantic, and 354 of the crew drowned or died of exposure in the boats.
It was a heavy score for a dumb mine, but the shipbuilding struggle
would make it up and more men would come forth to sail the ships. It was
only a passing incident to Damant, rushing here and there on salvages
and demolition.

It was not, however, a light matter in Whitehall. Damant was called
to London, where several admirals received him in a solemn atmosphere.
The Director of Naval Ordnance impressed on him the high secrecy
of the facts they were about to tell him. The enemy did not know his
mine had taken the *Laurentic,* and more certainly did not know what
had been sunk in her. Very few persons in England knew and Lieutenant
Commander Damant was about to become one of this select group. The
Laurentic carried in her second class baggage room £5 million in gold
bars. They had been dispatched to Canada by the government to pay for
war materials. The loss was a blow to the national economy. The admirals
asked Damant if he thought recovery practicable. He said yes. They said,
therefore, would he kindly go get the gold? He was to have all the men
and equipment he wanted *"if they were available."* "I walked on air,"
Captain Damant told me, "I knew just what I wanted and where to find
old diving allies. It was quite a change for a dug-out lieutenant commander gunner to be responsible to the Admiralty only."

It was an unprecedented thing to face. The wreck lay 120 feet down
in the cold open Atlantic, in surging tides and currents. The position was
swept by northers and westerly gales of the ocean and behind it was
Lough Swilly which piled high with water in a storm and unpiled in
high waves. The man who loved diving set about the job. There was still
no proper diving tender in the Navy. The best Damant could find was a

little mooring lighter, the *Volunteer*. It had no crew quarters. He rapidly made for Malin Head six weeks after the sinking. A reconnaissance diver found the *Laurentic* lying heeled sixty degrees to port. It was impossible for the heavy-footed man to walk either on her deck or high side. It was an unusual position. Most merchant wrecks land upright, given a level floor, which was the case here. The ship was intact, however, and the drop to the high starboard rail was only sixty-two feet. Moreover there was a cargo port on the high side on the same deck as the gold room. A dangling man could make this big entrance without fouling his lines on davits or top hamper. They blew the steel hatch off the cargo port and prepared to enter. But they had to step aside for a weird jailbreak from Davy Jones' locker—buoyant casks and cases, which rumbled out in a stream and soared to the surface.

The divers went in with crowbars and unpacked more debris in the passageways, including sacks of flour, most of whose contents were dry and loose, protected by the outer casing of wet flour. They blasted an iron gate which barred the corridor to the gold room, and Diver E. C. Miller phoned up to Damant, "I've got to the strong room, sir." He faced a steel door, behind which were 250 tons of gold bricks. Miller felt the door hinges and lock in total darkness, inserted his chisel and banged the steel door loose. He lumbered into the strong room, kicking wooden cases of gold, each six inches high and a foot square. Lifting one was almost beyond him. It weighed 140 pounds in air and about 85 pounds in water. Miller pushed and crawled one of the cases out to the port and slung it. He suffered an attack of bends for his overexertion, but was cured in the decompression chamber. They took £32,000 in the first two weeks' work, before a nor'wester drove them to shelter in the Lough. They were jubilant; at this rate the "impossible" job would be cleaned up in ten weeks.

Damant kept his eye on the sea, and noted that a lot of fresh wreckage was piling up on the beach. He took a walk around the lough with the rescued boatswain of the *Laurentic*. The debris was widespread. Damant came to a litter of rubber floor tiles. "Where do those red and white tiles come from?" he asked the survivor. "Second-class smoking room, sir." Damant said, "Oh, where is that?" The bosun said, "Amidships. Three decks down." Damant knew the wreck was working to pieces.

Soberly they returned to the wreck and found their big mooring buoys carried away. They staked out on new ones and lowered a man to the open port. Damant watched the pressure gauge on the compressor, which gave an estimate of depth. The needle did not stop at 62 feet. The diver took more air and kept going as the needle climbed. It stopped at 103 feet. The diver came up and reported that the *Laurentic* had collapsed. The steel decks had fallen into each other, so that the passageway to the gold hoard was now about 18 inches high and blocked with tangled girders and plate. The high rail of the ship was 103 feet down. Damant suited up and dived. He landed on the starboard rail, and started along it "like a cat on a ridge of a roof," he said. He clung to the rail when rollers surged at him and moved along the rail between them. The heavy blocks on the lifeboat falls, extended sixty feet when the boats left the ship, swung at his head in the dark water. He made his way into the cargo port and started crawling head down in the shrunken passageway. Soon he came to an impasse. He had to push himself backwards out of the tunnel, minding his air pipe and life line. The tunnel was full of torn steel.

There seemed two alternatives: to enlarge the collapsed passage with a series of light guncotton explosions and shore it up with pit props; or to blast through the five steel decks on top of the gold room, lifting out tons of steel to reach the treasury. Both would be long, hard jobs. The ten-week loot took on the dimensions of months. Fortunately for their morale, no one could guess that it would take seven years.

Damant chose to tunnel. As the divers burrowed, their explosions killed fish in a thousand-foot sphere. The divers slipped and fell on dead fish. Damant noticed that one species, the dogfish shark, was not affected by the explosions. Sharks snatched fish near men trying to lay precise guncotton charges; and seized floating bodies before the foam of the explosion had subsided. There were other explosions, too. Mine-laying U-boats continued to seed mines in the water round, and British sweepers harvested them, sometimes detonating mines in their drag wires. The divers were shaken up and one stunned by an explosion two miles away. They continued foot by foot, week by week, sapping their way to the gold. Then a diver reached the gold room. It was 120 feet down, the depth of the floor itself. On the phone Damant heard an excited voice announce, "The gold's not here, sir! It's gone. The deck is full of holes." Damant thought, "Evidently the gold had slid away to port and downwards, dropping through decks and bulkheads as they tore asunder during the collapse of the ship." He pondered this cruel defeat of all their grand exertions.

The gold bricks were scattered deep in the debris. "It was now clear that the entry port route was too dangerous and must be abandoned," Damant said. "There were five decks above the divers, supported by nothing in particular, and settlement was still going on, as was evidenced by loud noises and tremors which occasionally disturbed the men as, in darkness far inside the wreck, they struggled to squeeze themselves onward through narrow chinks."

He decided to blast down, deck by deck to the gold, lifting out everything to make a wide shaft. They toppled the mainmast and cleared the tangled rigging and began. A diver slung a heavy wire cable over the loose corner of a plate and the ship's winch heaved it up so the man could crawl underneath and place and wire his charge. One afternoon diver Blachford was under a plate hauled in tension. He was phoning instructions, when a shackle on the hauling cable parted. The plate snapped down on his back pinioning him with a bag of guncotton in his hand.

On deck they saw the cable whip out of the water. Damant listened intently to the phone and heard a calm voice, "Give me all the air you can, sir." Blachford thought he could relieve the weight on his back by turning his suit into an air cushion. Damant opened the valve further. "That's right, give me more yet," said the diver, "and get another diver down here as soon as possible." Diver Clear, who was half undressed, hastily got back in his suit. The tenders bolted his helmet and handed him the bight of a new cable. Damant saw on the pressure gauge that Blachford's dress was inflated past the bursting point. Damant figured that it might have already exploded, and the trapped man was trying to pile up pressure in his helmet to keep from drowning. It was "a dilemma, not to be solved by question and answer," said Damant. "The roar of the air already passing through his helmet all but drowned his voice on the telephone, and evidently he could hear nothing of ours." He throttled the air a bit to hear what Blachford was saying. The voice said slowly and deliberately, "Give me more air." Damant decided, "Balancing the risks, it seemed wiser not to do so."

Diver Clear was by now sinking rapidly with his hand around Blachford's air pipe as a guide. He landed and bent the cable around the plate. He phoned, "Heave away, three feet." The plate creaked and rose, revealing Blachford swollen like the Michelin man. His suit had not exploded. He valved off air and crawled out. On the surface Damant said, "I was afraid your dress would burst." Blachford said, "You know, sir, I never thought of *that*. I was afraid I'd break my back."

After nine months' toil the team was called away for urgent work on sunken submarines. They had recovered £800,000 in gold by then. Damant tried to scrounge a better salvage vessel and came upon H.M.S. *Racer,* a teak-built barque on which he had served as a cadet in 1895. She had been laid up in the knacker's yard, until Sir Frederick Young, the bustling salvage chief, exhumed a half dozen of her type, gutted them and installed beat-up destroyer engines. Damant was very wary about his choice of Young's salvage fleet, because some of them had port engines out of twin-screw torpedo gunboats, and these propellers turned the wrong way. (Later, another of Sir Frederick's conversions broke up on the rocks near the Lough Swilly. Damant's people boarded the sinking hulk and hove out her priceless pumps.)

Damant found the *Laurentic* little changed in 1919, but the gold mine soon petered out. Apparently the lode had burst out in two piles and the largest part was somewhere else. The shaft had been driven down through the well deck, or depressed main deck which was overhung by the public rooms of the liner. These had not collapsed, but as the excavation deepened the saloons threatened to fall in on the divers. "So long as gold was coming to hand I was very reluctant, however, to break off work for the purpose of dealing with these superstructures," said Damant. When they started to work the next spring, 1920, they found the top deck had been swept into the hole. The crater was sealed off with steel and plank decking, and underneath it was a compacted mass of rubbish, hundreds of smashed saloon chairs, mattresses, carpets, bedsprings, bathtubs, tiles and paneling. Waterlogged debris of furniture was washing to and fro, and it settled into a fresh excavation overnight. The mess was almost like cement, for now the sea was sweeping sand and pebbles into the shattered *Laurentic*.

They went to work to clear the crater. Damant tried a powerful twelve-inch suction pipe, but it clogged on mattresses and rugs. The only way left was the most primitive one of pulling the junk out by hand. The divers became ragpickers. They went down with rubbish sacks around their necks and fire hoses to loosen the mess. In the dark swirling water, they delved for gold with their bare hands. They could not feel a gold bar through gloves. They wore their fingernails to stumps and their fingertips raw. The extra exertion brought queer cases of bends. A man who had screwed a series of shacklepins knew he would have bends in his forearm.

One day Miller was in the decompression chamber when Commander Damant began to see double, an hour after a dive. His sight grew worse and a severe headache came. He waited outside the chamber for Miller to finish decompression. The diver looked out the port and saw his chief in distress. Miller still had forty minutes to go on his cure, but he blew off his pressure, opened the door and admitted Damant. Compressed air whistled them into depth pressure and Damant's eyes cleared. Miller's bends reappeared, owing to his gallant interruption. He was in pain in the chamber for six and a half hours, with Damant staying inside to aid him. At 1:30 A.M. with a new dawn of diving coming up, the chief diver begged Damant to blow off pressure so the master could get some sleep. Miller's seizure lasted far into the next day.

At the end of four years' work they had only a fraction of the gold. The war was long since over and England's life did not depend on blind men grinding their fingertips off in the black icy water. But they carried on.

The salvage began as duty. The man who brought up the largest single haul—$225,000—had been given fifty cigarettes. Damant accrued a morale problem with men risking their lives in years of painful work to bring up gold for somebody else. The government decided to give the divers one-eighth of a cent bonus on each dollar recovered. It produced lust for gold among the gropers. Treasure hunter Light was one day working headdown between steeply slanted plates with his life line and air pipe tied off out of harm's way on a projection forty feet off. He saw a gold bar sticking out of the sand below him. He stretched far down to grab it. The air in his suit rushed to the legs and ballooned him. He soared out feet first and came to a stop forty feet up on the end of his tether, grotesquely inflated. His sleeves stood straight out from his shoulders so stiffly that he could not move his arms to valve air. This might have seemed slightly droll, since his relief man was almost due, except that water in his suit drained off into his helmet and rose over his scalp, promising to drown him. Light phoned Damant about the situation. Damant grabbed another phone and called Blachford, who was decompressing thirty feet down. Blachford slid down Light's lines to where they were tied off and severed them. Light rocketed feet first to the surface, was fished out and clamped in the recompression chamber. Blachford returned to thirty feet and resumed stage decompression.

The salvage of the *Laurentic* was completed in 1924, after five thousand dives in seven years. The ragpickers recovered all but 25 of the 3,211 gold bricks, at a salvage cost of less than 3 per cent. Their commander brought them through without the loss of a man or serious injury. The divers received decorations and Damant was made captain and retired for a second time.

I asked Captain Damant if he had taken any souvenirs from the *Laurentic*. He replied, "I found a groat of the time of Edward First. Part of someone's private coin collection, I suppose. I was allowed to keep it." He remarked, "Today I would do this business of gold salvage differently. You should leave it down there as long as you can. It gets more valuable. Then get it up and send it to America." He grinned. "I'm not talking about ancient treasure wrecks. The only gold worth going after is in a newly sunk ship, when the government shows you the bill of lading and where the strong room is. Vigo, Navarino and what do they call that one in the west of Scotland, the Tobermory galleon? How does anyone know there is any treasure there?"

The man who brought up £5 million in gold did not believe in treasure under the sea.

During the *Laurentic* work, speculation revived of treasure in the torpedoed *Lusitania*. Simon Lake, the Captain Nemo of the time, talked about it, and he could always drum up a front-page story. The loudest clamor of gold came from Benjamin Franklin Leavitt, a big, personable diver born in Toledo, Ohio, who claimed as his home town any place he happened to be promoting the Leavitt Lusitania Salvage Company, Inc. At the time his home town was Traverse City, Michigan, he appeared in a semiarmored diving dress, resembling an earlier Australian outfit, and splashed into Lake Michigan, breathing oxygen. Leavitt claimed he reached 361 feet, which was recognized as a world's record. A man in pressure-proof armor could survive such a depth but Leavitt's suit had flexible arms and legs, which would require him to keep up internal pressure. Only by breathing helium could he have lived through that depth. Helium was not used on dives until much later. On oxygen he would have most definitely come up dead. Benjamin Franklin Leavitt did not come dead. He had "proved" that his suit could reach the *Lusitania,* which was sunk around 300 feet down. The Lusitania Salvage Company mailed brochures from its Philadelphia home office: "We will salvage the *Lusitania.* She has in her strong room $5 million in gold. There is estimated to be $1 million in cash and jewelry in the purser's safe. This is a moderate estimate, in view of the fact that many millionaires were among the passengers. Mme. Antoine Depage had a hundred thousand in gold. Alfred Gwynne Vanderbilt gave $75,000 to the purser." Theatrical magnate Charles Frohman and Elbert Hubbard, the rich author, were also aboard. Leavitt couldn't stop. "It will be easy to salvage her with our suit," he said. "There is also a $5 million cargo in copper, brass and tin. It is estimated that the returns will be twenty to one. Join us and your name will go down in history as one who helped salvage the *Lusitania.*"

Certain considerations were not mentioned in the prospectus. The *Lusitania* was eastbound when torpedoed, and there wasn't any strongroom gold going in that direction in 1915. The purser's safe, Leavitt's second pitch, might have reminded some remembering readers of the horrible story of the purser's safe in the *Empress of Ireland,* which sank in a St. Lawrence River collision in 1914. Surviving passengers and relatives of the drowned laid claim on the Canadian Pacific Steamship Line for a million dollars in valuables entrusted to the purser. The company brought up the safe with some difficulty. It was opened in the presence of the claimants. It contained 5 per cent of the value claimed.

Leavitt exhibited his suit in the window of Namm's Department Store in Brooklyn (during the period when his home town was Brooklyn) and when he was admitting to nativity in Manhattan, the *New York Times* reported that Leavitt "talked yesterday about what can be accomplished in recovering the shimmering treasures of gold and silver and precious stones with which old ocean's floor is carpeted." He said he knew of twelve wrecks containing a grand total of $127 million. Leavitt was trying to float a million shares of $5 stock certificates in the *Lusitania* venture. He had once actually salvaged 350 tons of copper ore from a Civil War wreck, the *Pewaubic,* in Lake Michigan, and used to bug out reporters' eyes with his desk souvenirs, which included a girl's square-toed shoe from the *Pewaubic.* He would hand this to a visitor and say sadly, "After we'd had it here awhile, a piece of her foot fell out of it." Leavitt showed parts of eight armored dresses in a loft machine shop. He gave prospective investors scenic tours of this *Lusitania* salvage factory.

He made so much noise that jealousy entered the breasts of Old World colleagues, notably Count Charles Landi, who was manager of the Aye-Ready Salvage and Towing Company of London. The Count topped Leavitt. He said he had a diving suit that would go to five hundred feet and that he was going to bring up the *Lusitania* intact. "I expect to have her afloat in the Atlantic for the traffic rush next spring," he announced. Lest folks did not believe him, the Count cited the time he raised H.M.S. *King Alfred,* "fourteen thousand tons," from Belfast Lough and found a phonograph with a record of *Rule Britannia,* half played when the torpedo struck. The Count said he then played the rest of the record. (I checked the Admiralty on this. It found documents on Count Landi, which showed that he skillfully *towed* the *Alfred* [four thousand tons] and several torpedoed ships, but had never dived for any as far as the Admiralty's records went.)

The *Lusitania* cause interested the London bureau of the *Christian Science Monitor.* It sent a reporter to check the facts. The Cunard Steamship Company, owners of the *Lusitania,* stated, "What do we want with the *Lusitania?* We got the insurance money." The reporter went to the Admiralty, which had no trace of the underwriter. A British shipping magnate told him, "If anyone is fool enough to risk his money on salvage, he would come in for his share of course. These stories of salvaging the *Lusitania* are all the bunk. There is no bullion aboard. All the gold was going to America in those days, not coming from it. There is nothing worth salvaging."

The brouhaha reached Germany. The *Lusitania* had been an American excuse for intervening in the Great War, and the Germans had a counter-alibi, which was now revived: that the *Lusitania* torpedoing was justified because she was alleged to carry two submarine boats, munitions and torpedoes. The National People's Party in the Reichstag demanded to have delegates present when the *Lusitania* was raised.

Leavitt's venture was marinating in wonderful publicity, but he could not make it cook. He had acquired an old wooden schooner to salvage the 32,000-ton *Lusitania.* She was called the *Blakeley.* Instead of salary, her skipper, Charles S. Rickards, was offered $10,000 in treasure stock, which the *Lusitania* would repay twentyfold, according to Leavitt's delirious

propaganda. By this time, late summer of 1922, the company had sold
$95,000 worth of the *Lusitania's* treasure, and was willing to settle for
$30,000 more. The *Blakeley* was moored in the Delaware River in Phila-
delphia and Leavitt was giving diving exhibitions to raise meal money. He
was nearing the first of October, the day his old prospectuses promised
the big pay-off for those who wanted their names to go down in history. It
must have been a relief for Leavitt to sink a few feet in the river and think.
He announced that investors needed more time to appreciate the *Lusitania*
opportunity. In the meanwhile he would pick up some easy treasure wrecks
in the Mediterranean to keep in tone, or maybe go after "the Jap ship
Yosaka Maru with $12,500,000 in gold," or the "S.S. *Geelong* with
$6,000,000 in jewels belonging to the Maharajah of some country." Cap-
tain Rickards put an end to it. He refused to take any more treasure certificates. Fourteen years later an early echo-sound tape picked up the silhouette of the *Lusitania* stark upright on the floor. The receptacle of plots and
dreams still stands there. The odds are good that she will remain undisturbed.

The cruelest gold bricks were the cargo of the *Egypt,* rammed in fog off
Brest in 1921. She went down with ninety-four souls and $6 million in
gold. Lloyd's of London paid off on the gold, which had been insured at
less than 1 per cent. The firm had, in effect, purchased two tons of gold in
a strongroom fifty fathoms down at an unknown location in the turbid
stormy waters of the Bay of Biscay. It was beyond the range of divers and
locked under three steel decks amidships. Many people started to figure
how to recover the gold for Lloyd's. Contrary to treasure yarns, sunken
cargo remains private property, and a salvor receives only a percentage of
what he brings up.

A parade of victims of undersea fiction came to Lloyd's with impractical
schemes. A serious engineer, C. P. Sandberg, reduced the problem to its
essence, a matter of men versus pressure. The working limit for compressed
air divers was 200 feet; the *Egypt* was believed to be at 300 feet; therefore
Sandberg needed pressure-proof diving armor. He signed a "save and pay"
contract of 37½ per cent of what he could recover; otherwise he got nothing. A U.S. Navy officer told him of diving armor manufactured by Neufeldt & Kuhnke in Germany, a bulbous monster with articulated legs and
arms with mechanical claws. The gear would withstand pressure to 700
feet. Sandberg found his salvager in Italy, a barrel-shaped engineer named
Giovanni Quaglia, head of Sorima Salvage Company of Genoa. Commendatore Quaglia tested the armor on an operation in the Bay of Rapallo.
He sent divers down 318 feet into the wrecked U.S. steamship *Washington,*
the deepest individual descents made to that date. He devised big electromagnets to lift metal from the wreck. The Neufeldt & Kuhnke bottles were

too stiff in that pressure for a man to move his limbs, so Quaglia simplified them to rigid cans with viewing ports and mechanical claws. The divers lifted seven thousand tons of copper ingots and railway steel from the *Washington*. Whole axle-and-wheel assemblies came up clustered to the magnets. Quaglia made a profit on the job and ran a second rehearsal for the *Egypt* off the French coast. It paid off in eight hundred tons of zinc, copper and steel billets. Then, in 1928, he sailed his tenders with a superb diving team around to the Bay of Biscay.

The *Egypt* had not been located. When Quaglia arrived, two Norwegian ships and a French trawler had dragged two luckless seasons for the gold ship. He hired the skipper of the Brestois steamer *Seine,* who had rammed the *Egypt,* and on that party's guess of where he had been seven years before in thick fog, Quaglia laid out a search area with a mile-wide lane of buoys, which his tenders, the *Artiglio* and the *Rostro,* swept with a cable stretched between them. When the strip gave no indication of a wreck, they made a parallel buoy lane and swept it. Thus began what none of them dreamed was to be years of struggle and disaster.

The Bay of Biscay was too rough for sea stations from October to May and squalls came without warning in summer. During storms Quaglia ran his ships to shelter behind Belle-Ile between Lorient and Saint- Nazaire, and kept his men profitably occupied on a Belgian wreck, the *Elizabethville,* 240 feet down. She was said to have a box of diamonds in her captain's safe. They got the safe up in a scissor grab and found it empty, but they did get eight tons of Congo bull elephant ivory. They went back to the ceaseless sweep for the *Egypt* as the stock market crashed, street fights and hunger marches came on land, and even as the nations renounced the gold standard. Many times the drag caught obstructions on the floor and Quaglia bottled men and lowered them away to see what was there. Always they found the cable fouled on rocks. He tightened the cable to catch only the top hamper of a big ship.

Mussolini made a Fascist romance out of their work; the divers of Sorima were well publicized. The *Times* of London had a staff reporter, David Scott, on the *Artiglio*. In the evenings the divers sang *"Giovanezza,"* the Fascist hymn. It was all about youth and springtime and strength. They were good workmen and Italians like to sing to one another. At the end of August, 1930, when the autumnal storms were due, the dragline caught something firm at the far sidelines of the plot, three miles from the spot picked by the captain of the *Seine.*

The veteran diver Alberto Bargellini let himself into the neck of the steel bottle, tested his oxygen system and phone and was lowered away. The winchman stopped the can halfway into the water so he could flood the ballast compartments. The cable ran out evenly. The chamber reached

318 feet, the greatest depth they had ever been. Bargellini phoned to send him on. He reported no bottom at 350 feet, none at 375, and he passed 400 feet without sighting land. At 414 feet he said, "I see bottom. Very slowly, please." The winchman touched the can gently in the ooze 426 feet down, far deeper than any diver had ever gone. The voice from the sea said, "Raise me a bit so I can see around." The winchman sucked the can from the floor and Bargellini had the sensation of a man in a cocktail shaker. An object dangled in the depths turns, sways in currents and bobs with the roll of the ship. It is also jerked up and down by the stretch and contraction of the cable. Bargellini tap-danced on the vibrating floor, and tried to see through his encircling portholes as the chamber cavorted. He saw the side of a big ship, standing upright, and asked the tender to move him slowly along the side. He looked up through his tiny ports and made out a line of davits leaning against the faint daylight that filtered to seventy fathoms. He phoned to the ship, "The davits are swung out. This ship has launched boats. I'm sure it's the *Egypt*!" To be certain of her, Quaglia went for the captain's safe on the bridge deck. They had to remove a three-ton derrick to breach the captain's quarters. The bottled men hung down there, phoning precise directions to the men lowering explosives, and with patient, oft-failing movements of their mechanical claws, they battened the charges in the right spot to uproot the derrick. In this work, which lasted months, the observers anchored themselves to the floor to stabilize the chamber. Imprisoned in the dark water they played pin-the-tail-on-the-donkey for the winchmen above. In this wise they got the safe. It was opened by the British consul in Brest. He found Foreign Office dispatches that had been sent on the *Egypt* and a mocking bit of metal, a key labeled, "Bullion Room." Quaglia had located the *Egypt* after nearly three years, and she was not fifty, but seventy fathoms down.

He sent the divers to blast through the promenade deck, the upper deck and the main deck to the bullion room. After each blast they lifted wreckage on the magnets. This process was most tedious. It took ten minutes to lower the chamber, ten minutes to hang it right, and perhaps a half hour to lower the dynamite into the mechanical claws and batten it to the right spot on the wreck. Then came twenty minutes to haul the diver out, explode the dynamite and lower him back. After that came the big electromagnet, which had to be placed just so. And there were always the winds and waves to stop work for days.

Quaglia found a sheltered wreck to work during storms, the U.S. munitions ship, the *Florence H.*, torpedoed in 1917 in Quiberon Bay behind Belle-Ile. She was only fifty feet down and the French authorities wanted her demolished as a menace to navigation. Quaglia took no chances that some of the *Florence H.'s* explosive cargo was still active after thirteen years in the sea. They fixed many charges on the wreck to detonate whatever munitions were left. The *Artiglio* moved at least three miles off the wreck to fire the charges. Chief diver Albert Gianni went down to fix the last charge to flatten the sternquarters. He came up to the tender and she moved a thousand feet away to give a good margin of safety to the light dismantling explosion. Gianni held the detonator wires in either hand and slowly brought them together. There was a colossal explosion of T.N.T. that had remained alive in the wreck. The *Artiglio* was blown to pieces. Gianni and the famous divers Aristide Francheschi and Albert Bargellini and eleven others were killed.

Commendatore Quaglia lost his diving team and his tender. He went back to Genoa, fitted out the *Artiglio II,* trained more divers and returned to the *Egypt* the next year. They breached the top deck that summer and blasted a crater through two more decks. Late one evening, when the wind was raw with the imminence of autumn gales, a diver looked through the blasted door of the strongroom and phoned a babble of gold. The storm came and drove them off for six months. When they went out the next spring, 1932, the first observer found the forty-foot crater completely filled with debris. It took a month with the grabs to clear the hole. In June the grab swung out of the sea and over the deck and the jaws were tripped. The spoil thudded heavily. There were two gold bars in it.

Sorima had been four years on the job and there were to be three more years of fishing for gold before the six million dollars was up. It was the deepest salvage victory, profitable to Lloyd's, Sandberg and Sorima, if not to Gianni, Francheschi and Bargellini.

A rugged band of Australians dived even deeper for sunken gold than the Italians. In 1940 the mail liner *Niagara* sank thirty miles out of Whangaroa, New Zealand, in 438 feet of water. She carried another lot of that tangible government gold—the kind with waybills. Captains J. P. Williams, of Melbourne, and James Herd, of Brisbane, were sent to get it. The lading was ten tons of gold bricks, about $12 million. The *Niagara* was the victim of another lucky German mine. The Nazi raider *Orion,* the only German vessel in the Pacific, had mined the Auckland Roadstead.

Diver J. C. Johnstone went down in an observation chamber to check probables which had been located by echo-sound and dragging. On the second dive in the can, he found nothing on the floor and phoned to be raised. On the way up, he heard something scraping on the chamber, and saw that it was a strange weed-covered cable. Before he reached the surface the scraping stopped. He was puzzled. It was not a line from his tender, the *Claymore.* When his ship weighed anchor Johnstone found out what the strange cable was. The ship's anchor cable came up fouled to a big German mine.

The mine bobbed very close to the *Claymore*. Captain Williams lowered the mine away from his hull, transferred the anchor cable to a buoy, and left the mine too deep to harm a ship. He went in to report the affair to the Navy. He came back the next day with a minesweeper. Johnstone put on a helmet suit to deal with the nasty object. Because the *Claymore* carried his pump, she had to moor right over the mine. Because of the danger of blowing up, all her people were removed to the sweeper, except Captain Williams and four diver's attendants. Johnstone went into the water with a thin wire leading to the minesweeper. He had to fasten this to the mine, after he'd freed it of underwater entanglements, so the sweeper could tow it away. Johnstone tenderly shackled the sweep wire to the mine. Then he saw that the mine's cable had been sawing away on the *Claymore's* newly laid anchor cable. The holdfast of the deadly bomb was nearly broken. Then it parted. Johnstone's air pipe and life line were caught on the horned detonators and he was carried to the surface atop a live mine. It came up under the ship's bottom, with Johnstone and his helmet as a cushion. The diver maintained this valuable position, keeping the detonators away from the hull.

Captain Williams sent word to the minesweeper to haul gently on the sweep wire. Johnstone bumped along the *Claymore's* wooden bottom, shielding the mine with his body, and untangling his lines for a personal resignation from this affair when and if he got the mine safely off. It took a long time. Then the light sweep wire broke and Johnstone bailed out. The mine came up free ten feet off the *Claymore's* bows. Johnstone was hauled aboard. The *Claymore* got her anchor up as expeditiously as possible and moved off for the minesweeper to destroy the *Orion's* nasty spawn with a machine gun.

It took nine weeks more before Johnstone finally looked from his chamber upon a ventilator lying on the floor beside the bulk of the *Niagara*, 438 feet down. The wreck was lying on her side at a seventy-degree angle, which meant that they would have to blast diagonally through the side and be very careful not to use too much explosive and collapse the wreck. The first charge went well. A wounded shark and parts of deckhouse came up in the blast. The next explosion punctured the fuel tanks and a thick blanket of oil on the surface ruined visibility for days. They blasted on in, lifting torn plates with a big grab, and singing "The Lambeth Walk." The men below in the chamber could hear the song over the phone. When they got to the gold vault the grab started to pay off rich. In seven weeks it lifted all but 6 per cent of the gold, not a bad rate of interest to pay on a dirty mine.

5

The Intelligent Whale

M ANY were the seers of the submarine boat:
Roger Bacon in the thirteenth century; Leonardo
da Vinci, who said he would never divulge his plan because of the evil uses
men would make of an undersea vessel; and Mother Shipton, who sang
three hundred years ago:

> Under Water men shall walk,
> Shall ride, shall sleep, shall talk.

In 1505 the Swedish Christian historian, Olaf Magnus, visited the cathedral at Asloe where he saw displayed two amazing spoils of a recent foray
of King Haakon to Greenland. They were sealskin submarines, each ac-
commodating three pirates of Gruneland, or, in another rendering, locals
who wanted to equalize their dealings with European traders. The underwater kayaks crept up on visiting ships and bored holes in their bottoms,
which improved the bargaining position of the islanders. Whether a blockade was expressed economically through superior trading advantage or by
open military show, the submarine idea often occurred to the weaker de-
fending power. In the mid-seventeenth century a French traveler found Cos-
sacks attacking warships of the Sublime Porte in cowhide submersibles
carrying up to forty rowers, who breathed through reeds as they closed on
the Turkish ships. It was the same situation which produced the crude undersea galleys of the Confederacy in the American War of Rebellion two
hundred years later.

A Hollander, Cornelis van Drebbel, built a working submarine around
1620, which made Mother Shipton a *post factum* prophetess. The two best-
informed historians of antique submarine vehicles, Lieutenant de Vaisseau

Maurice Delpeuch and G. L. Pesce, regard Drebbel as the first real sub-mariner. He was an intellectual, who was jailed on the Continent for his ideas. He went to England and became tutor to the children of King James I. He made friends with Robert Boyle, the great physicist, and Bishop John Wilkins, who was so bold as to issue *A Discourse Tending to Prove That 'Tis Probable Our Earth Is One of The Planets,* a fine instance of the scientist announcing the obvious with a weather eye out for ignorance.

Drebbel's submersible galley for twelve rowers had a breathing tube to the surface through which air was forced down by a bellows. The boat went down to twelve feet in the Thames and became a famous novelty of Ja-cobean times. He plied the craft between Greenwich and Westminster for at least ten years, as a scientific demonstration and joy ride. Once King James risked the crown on a voyage beneath the sewery river. The crew and passengers were sustained for hours (the rowers could make about four miles per hour downstream and half that returning) by a mysterious chem-ical which revived the air inside. Drebbel called it "quinta-essentia," the quintessence of air. Neither he nor Boyle knew, according to later science, that oxygen is one-fifth of the atmosphere; that waited for analysis four generations in the future.

A generation after Drebbel's death, his son-in-law came to Secretary of the Admiralty, Samuel Pepys, trying to sell for £10,000 "Cornelius Dreb-bel's secret of sinking or destroying ships in a moment." He would not tell Pepys what it was. He said that was for the King's ear alone. Pepys was afraid the thing would be dangerous to carry in navy ships, but the caller insisted it would not be. Perhaps the son-in-law was peddling the old submarine. Memories are short for novelties.

In *Mathematical Magick,* 1648, Bishop Wilkins saw that submarines would be secure in bad weather and from pirates, could attack surface vessels without detection, supply blockaded ports and conduct scientific exploration of the deep.

An early undersea craft was built by John Day, a dockyard laborer at Yarmouth. "He was a man very illiterate and indigent in circumstances," said N. D. Falck, M.D., who knew him. "His temper was gloomy, reserved and peevish, his disposition penurious; he was remarkably obstinate in his opinion and jealous of his fame." So the lonely embattled inventor looks to those outside his dream. "But withal," the doctor added charitably, "he was allowed to be penetrating in his observations, acute in his remarks, faithful to his patron, and unshaken in his resolutions." Around 1772 John Day built an enclosed tub in which he descended 30 feet into a pool at Norwich. Thereupon he set out to make a proper underwater boat. He found a backer in London who gave him £340 to buy and convert a fifty-ton sloop, the *Maria.* Day painted her red and announced that he was going down to 300 feet for 24 hours. In 1774, the *Maria* was towed out into the pool of Plymouth where the water was 130 feet deep. The gloomy, obstinate man entered the submarine with a watch, a candle, biscuits and water, and was sealed in. Dr. Falck said, "She was sunk at two o'clock in the afternoon of the 20th of June, and Mr. Day descended with her into perpetual night!" There were some air bursts on the surface, but John Day and the red *Maria* never came up. Dr. Falck gave as his opinion that Day froze to death. One can imagine Day's penetrating observation had he heard that one: "By God, sir, I was bloody well drowned!"

A Connecticut Yankee named David Bushnell built the first craft to make an undersea attack in war, the *Turtle*, of the American Revolution. Bushnell was a Yale University graduate of 1775. That incubator of scholars and divines permitted the student to spend four years pursuing his own course in submarines and infernal engines designed to confound the British. Governor Jonathan Trumbull, of Connecticut, sent Bushnell to General George Washington. Washington told Thomas Jefferson that Bushnell was "a man of great mechanical powers, fertile in invention and master of execution. He came to me in 1776, recommended by Governor Trumbull and other respectable characters, who were converts to his plans. Although I wanted faith myself I furnished him with money and other aids to carry his plans into execution."

Up the Hudson at Peekskill, Bushnell built of barrel staves and iron a submersible he called the *Turtle*. He likened it to two turtle shells clamped together, with the neck openings forming a hatch for the conning tower. A single operator sat inside with his head at the level of the conning tower windows. This individual had plenty of duties. The vessel moved by a spiral screw in front which was hand-turned. (Maurice Delpeuch regarded Bushnell as the first to apply screw propulsion.) When her ballast tanks were flooded to submerge, the pilot sent the *Turtle* down by another vertical helical hand-turned propeller. He also tended the rudder in the rear. The vessel had two short air tubes to the surface, one intake and one exhaust. Although the *Turtle* could dive under water to evade lookouts or make contact with hulls, she had to hold the pilot's eyes above water on the run to target. The craft was fitted with a compass and pressure gauge with phosphorescent dials. The armament consisted of a case of 130 pounds of gunpowder faired into the stern. The mine could be detached by the pilot. It was made fast to a line carried forward to an upright screw. The pilot was to warp his craft under a vessel and turn the screw firmly into the ship's bottom. He was then to release it and the mine, which was detonated by clockwork a half hour later, affording the submarine time to get away.

The *Turtle* was a magnificent conception when seen against the techniques and materials of Bushnell's time. The Archimedean screw was much less efficient than the later blade propeller, but it was the actual revolutionary transition from oars to windmill propellers soon to be found by Robert Fulton and later engineered by John Ericsson. One energetic man could actually propel and dive Bushnell's baby submarine, the inventor's brother Ezra.

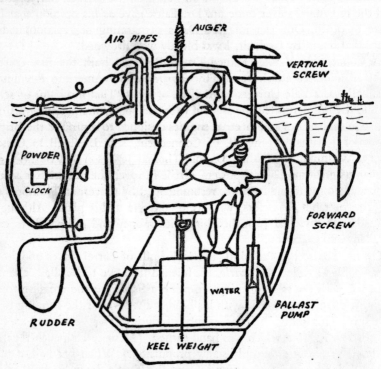

Hypothetical diagram of David Bushnell's *Turtle,* 1776.

However much he lacked faith in the *Turtle,* Washington was willing to try anything. He had no navy. England had a big one, which was conspicuously showing the flag in New York Bay. The Revolutionary War was about to begin when good summer fighting weather came in 1776. The unopposed British fleet could supply and ferry troops, interdict Washington's communications and throttle the New York economy. Washington had marched his guerrilla army from New England to a Long Island front, and his antagonist, General Sir William Howe, had brought ten thousand professional troops by sea to Staten Island. Howe arrived two days before the signature of the Declaration of Independence in Philadelphia on the Fourth of July, which was not known in New York until the tenth. On the

A free diver, the first real space man, enters the "Cathedral of Notre Dame," a divers' haunt near Cannes. →

Henri Broussard

Frédéric Dumas and Jacques-Yves Cousteau at Planier lighthouse, 1943, during filming of *Épaves.* Dumas wears the first Aqualung, Cousteau carries 35 mm. *ciné-camera.* ↓

ousteau

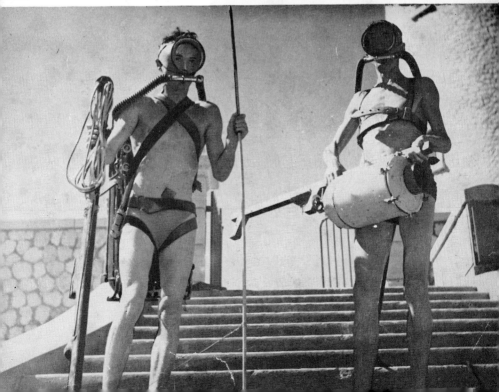

Malay diver lassoes a sea turtle. Transparent tortoise shell was used in early diving masks.

Indian Ocean pearl shell divers have used this technique for perhaps 7,000 years.

Sixteenth-century coral divers in the Mediterranean. Note the goggles.

Jean Stradanus, from the Frédéric Dumas collecti

In the billycock hat is the great diver, Alexander Lambert, at the Chelsea Naval Exhibition of 1891 with (left) diver Edward Jones; J. W. "Ginger" Bateman (in diving suit); and in bathing suit, the Greek sponge diver "Professor" Newman.

Siebe, Gorman

Escape from a sunken submarine with the Davi oxygen lung. The window-blind gadget was pulled out to retard soaring speed. ↓

August Denayrouze's fully independent compressed air lung, 1875. Diver carries electric lantern.

François Vilarem

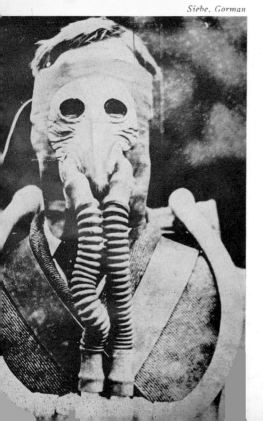

Augustus Siebe's original open helmet, 1819, made way for his historic closed-helmet suit.

←

Henry Fleuss' first independent oxygen diving lung, 1878. Ancestor of submarine escape lungs, combat swimmers' gear, firemen's respirators, aviators' masks.

National Maritime Museum, Greenwich

An early unsuccessful attempt to raise the 108-gun *Royal George* at Spithead, 1783.

The first modern salvage job, H.M.S. *Royal George*, Spithead, 1839–42. Army sappers were the divers. They invented salvage techniques and taught the navy to dive.

Mariners' Museum, Newport News

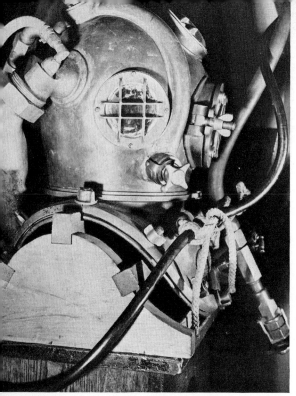

← The Helium Hat, as worn by W fred Bollard, R.N., to 540 feet, t greatest depth reached in a flexib suit.

U.S.N. Experimental Diving Unit

Fatigue experiment on an underwat trapeze. Diver swims against fram top, pulling a weighted line, whi his exhalations are analyzed from t breathing bag on his back. ↓

U.S.N. Experimental Divin

physiologist, John Scott Hal-
who found the stage-decom-
ion tables that made deep
g safe.

In the pressure pot, an experimenter, left, nears the point of oxygen convulsion, observed by a medical officer.

n diver on his way down for the gold of the
Egypt at 428 feet. Bay of Biscay, 1930.

The suit that was going to salvage the *Lusitania*. Benjamin Leavitt's semi-armor, 1922.

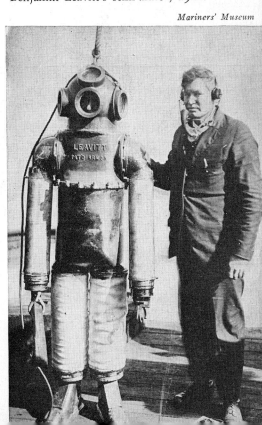

Part of the silver bullion recovered from a depth of 90 feet in the wreck of the S.S. *Oceana*, English Channel, 1912.

The Draeger submarine sled, built in Germany, 1912.

Electric Boat

n P. Holland, the Irish school-
her who designed the first sub-
rines of the U.S. and British
ies.

Mariners' Museum

Simon Lake's first submarine, *Argonaut Jr.,* 1894.
The wheeled wooden contraption actually worked.

Simon Lake's wheeled *Argonaut,* 1897, a successful bottom crawler, from whose airlock
ladies picked clams from the floor of Long Island Sound.

Mariners' Museum

The Abbé Raoul, Vicar-General of Carthage, built this sponge-picking submarine in 1908. It dived to 330 feet, but never replaced Greek divers.

Simon Lake's submarine "for peace and profit," the *Explorer,* which rolled along the floor on wheels, with grab operated from inside.

1901: Bridgeport, Connecticut—the shell of Simon Lake's submarine *Protector* is hauled to the town dump to be completed.

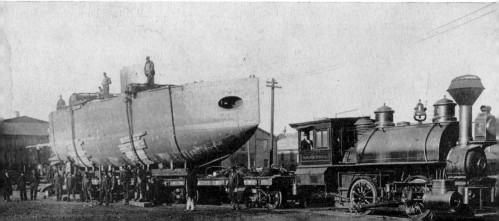

1856: The undersea band concert for the coronation of Czar Alexander II in Wilhelm Bauer's submarine *Sea-Devil* at Cronstadt.

The U.S. atomic submarine *Nautilus*, 1955. Previous *Nautiluses* were Fulton's, 1800; Verne's, 1869; Ash and Campbell's, 1885; and Wilkins and Lake's, 1930.

Here comes H.M.S. *E-11* from the historic raid in the Golden Horn, 1915.

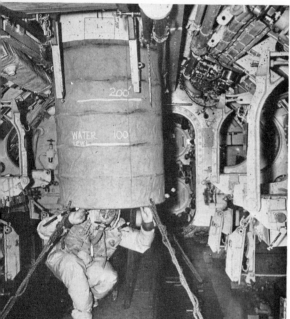

←

Beginning a simulated escape from sunken British submarine, the crewman enters "the twill trunk," which guides him past obstructions. In a real escape the submarine is flooded to the chalk marks on the trunk. Escaper wears an immersion suit, in which he might survive polar waters for 2 hours.

One of the Confederate *David* submarines. *David IV* sank U.S.S. *Housatonic,* first submarine victim in history of warfare, 1864.

↓

Alexandre Ivanoff

Louis Boutan photographs a helmet diver, 1898.

Auguste Boutan

's riposte to jokes about his
vater photos: three bathers stand-
ist deep, 1898.

Twelve feet down, Louis Boutan held this pose for seconds to demonstrate his undersea
"snapshot" technique, 1898.

Auguste Boutan

"Then the bearers approached; the bo
in a tissue of white byssus was lower
into the damp grave"—*Twenty Thousa
Leagues Under the Sea.* Williamson's u
dersea version, 1915.

←

Williamson's *Photosphere,* from whi
the first undersea movies were taken
1914.

Williamson's undersea movies, made
years ago, were framed in the circu
window of his Photoscope.

←

In the first undersea movie (1914)
Bahaman diver grasps a shark's fin
slices the belly open.

George Eastman House

he Peau's 1906 photo of a Maya
eating a fish: Le Havre—13 feet
—half-second exposure by arc light.

→

itri Rebikoff and his "movie torpedo"
e off to film a sunken ship.

Georges Barnier

Captain Fathom and his crew in Weekee Wachi Springs. Television serials take to the water.

New Vista Productions

California diving geologist measur
dip in rocky floor with an instru
embodying a compass, clinometer,
writing pad.

Geologist of Capricorn Expedition hovers over
a giant coral 125 feet down in Alexa Bank,
Pacific Ocean.

Love and death of squids in La Jolla canyon. The male's tentacles squeeze eggs from the
female. The mother attaches the egg cases to the floor, the parents die, and predators dive
into the dying squids.

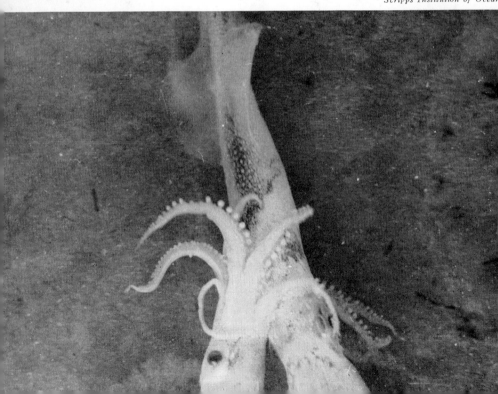

twelfth, Sir William's brother, Admiral of the Blue Lord Richard Howe, paraded through the Narrows under a thousand squaresails of ships of the line and 150 transports new from England. Admiral Howe brought in his sixty-four-gun flagship, H.M.S. *Eagle,* an order to fish or cut bait. If the rebels wanted a war, he was to aid his brother in providing same. If the Americans were intimidated, the Howe brothers were to insure peace with their powerful advantage. Washington saw an opportunity to annoy the British whales with a needlefish. Bushnell's device risked £100 sterling and one resolute man. It was the classic doctrine of military submarines, which were the resort of a weak or defensive naval power until Royal Navy boats crashed the nets in the Dardanelles and intervened gaily on the offense in World War I.

David Bushnell resolved to blow up H.M.S. *Eagle.* On the eve of the attack, Ezra Bushnell, the trained pilot of the little submarine, fell ill. David Bushnell asked General Samuel H. Parsons of the American army for volunteers to learn the *Turtle.* The general told him to make his own appeal as this was not in his line of oratory. Bushnell spoke to the troops. He could not reveal the nature of the task in an area seething with spies, but he managed to raise three volunteers, two unknown and a sergeant from Lyme, Connecticut, named Ezra Lee. Bushnell trained them in Gravesend Bay, hard by the enemy fleet, a peril forced on him because no pilot could be expected to crank the little shell more than a mile and the *Turtle* could not be towed on a target run with a vulnerable surface vessel. Sergeant Lee was the best pupil and was given command of the world's first military submarine. At the end of August, the Howe brothers uncapped a combined assault on New York, ferrying twenty thousand troops from Staten Island to Gravesend Beach, Long Island. The *Turtle* happened to be right in the path of embarkation.

Bushnell's team pulled off an acrobatic escape, hauling the boat out of the bay onto a big wagon and dragging her overland to Whitestone ahead of marching redcoats. Into Long Island Sound went the midget boat and was hauled to New Rochelle. General Howe pressed speedily upon Flatbush, threw Washington's army into Columbia Heights and squared off for a siege. Washington sneaked his men away to Manhattan in the dead of night, whereupon Admiral Howe moved his fleet to the north of Governor's Island, standing firmly between the two armies. The unexpected fleet move worked in Bushnell's favor. From New Rochelle he could tow the *Turtle* through Hell Gate and let her drift down the East River into the British anchorage.

The submarine was tied to three canoes on a calm fine evening, when the run began at Hell Gate. The canoes glided past river rocks and Blackwell's Island, between the silent farms of Manhattan and the Newtown marshes,

and came in sight of the tall British poles in the anchorage on Dimond
Reef in the river mouth. The canoeists could see the white cannon wales,
bank on bank, bright with brass muzzles, waiting for Sergeant Lee and
the submersible. He stepped from the bow of a canoe into the *Turtle's*
hatch and closed it. The canoes cast loose and paddled for New York. Lee
flooded his tanks, brought the tiny conning tower almost into the water, and
strained his eyes through the flawed glass ports and wavelets washing green
over them.

There was a strong ebb tide running. The *Turtle* had been set adrift in
the current designed to take her to Howe's flagship, but all the way Lee had
to exert himself on the tiller and propeller to correct for the errant tide. The
noise of his machinery was loud in the sea, and he heard the ship's bells
ringing the clock in the anchorage. In his two-and-one-half-hour struggle
with the tide, he heard many bells, saw the ship's lanterns lighting up
through his fogged ports and labored his way in lowering darkness. He got
in under the *Eagle's* counter, in the feeble glow of lamps from the carved
windows of the Captain's quarters. He heard sailors walking about and
blaspheming peaceably. He had not been spied. The tide was slacking and
the moon rising.

Sergeant Lee lashed his tiller and reached up for the crank of the diving
propeller; he slaughed it round and round and kept on turning the forward
screw to get down under the flagship. H.M.S. *Eagle* drew over ten feet, a
deep dive for the *Turtle*. Under the stern, Lee let his conning tower press
up against the hull. The assault had been well timed. He arrived in dead
slack water so that the *Turtle* held firm. He periscoped the screw against
the hull and threw all his strength into driving it deep. He did not feel the
bite of oak, however. He heard a dull clang and his craft wobbled. H.M.S.
Eagle was heavily sheathed in new copper to discourage shipworms, and
the biggest one was Ezra Lee. He bounced off repeatedly, trying to penetrate
the metal, knocking loud in the amplifying dark water, blows that seemed
certainly audible in the ship. Still no alarm was raised. He risked betraying
himself by noise, but he could not pierce the sheathing. After hours at it,
he thought perhaps there was an unprotected area forward. He cranked
and bumped toward the bow, looking everywhere for a gap in the copper
plates. He lost his trim and the *Turtle* slid off toward the surface. The
Turtle broke water and Sergeant Lee saw that he was off to the east of an
anchored ship, silhouetted against the first glow of dawn. He dived immediately.

He was now fair game, with day coming on ablaze, crews turning out
for their chores, gigs and bumboats stirring in the water. New York Harbor
was not then befouled with sewage and oil: the water was green and fairly
clear. His craft would be easily seen through a few feet of water. His best

tactic was immediate retreat to save himself and the *Turtle*. Lord Howe's flagship could be sunk another day, if he could keep his secret. Still submerged Lee moved off vigorously for the toe of Manhattan. His compass went wrong and he was forced to surface to get his bearings. He came up directly under the British-held redoubts on Governor's Island. A soldier spotted him and yelled. Inquisitive Britons and Hessians ran to the seawall to see what manner of thing there was in the water. They launched a boat and started rowing toward him. It was too much for their imaginations to realize that the *Turtle* was a hostile vessel, but Lee saw them quickly approaching to discover that fact. He was a stubborn man. He did not care to surrender. He reached behind and pulled the lever which freed the gunpowder mine. The clockwork started to rattle, and he loosed the screw over his head, figuring the mine might amuse the pursuers long enough for him to get away, and might explode among them. The British boat was within two hundred feet, when its crew saw the strange underwater craft divide into two parts. The rowers yelled, "Look out! It's a Yankee trick!" and rowed swiftly back to Governor's Island to let their officers figure out what to do. Sergeant Lee turned his crank with scared strength and arrived off the American works at the Battery. He gave recognition signals and was aided ashore. As he staggered out and sat on the grass, the mine went off with a brilliant report and a great waterspout. No one was near it.

General Washington soon had to run again to avoid encirclement. He pulled back up Manhattan Island to Harlem and dug in. The *Turtle* was dragged along in the North River. The Admiral of the Blue, still unaware of what had caused the explosion, posted some ships at the mouth of the North River to cut off American communications. Ezra Lee thereupon drifted down to attack a frigate. He found a lovely wooden hull unprotected by copper and was beginning to drill when an alarm was sounded. Lee heard yells and pounding feet. He was forced to dive and retreat, without sticking his mine. He made a third attempt in the river, but was sighted on his drift to target and cannonaded by a small ship. He submerged and the cannon balls bounced harmlessly on the water, spent themselves and sank slowly to the river bed.

By this time David Bushnell was discouraged and ill. He abandoned the submarine and turned to his infernal engines. The *Turtle* was dismantled and remained a secret to the Royal Navy. **Parts of it are still in existence,** but no drawings have been found. Sergeant Lee survived the war and was rewarded with a job in the customs and excise in Middletown, Connecticut. Bushnell, in 1777, journeyed down the Thames in New London, Connecticut, in a whaleboat and cast a big contact mine adrift for H.M.S. *Cerberus*. It missed and was fished out by some nosy boatmen, who were blown up for their zeal. Bushnell continued mine harassment. At Christmastime,

1777, he launched a grand mine attack down the Delaware River on British shipping. He strewed the river with powder kegs, devised to explode on contact. While the mines were floating from Bordentown, New Jersey, the British unwittingly chose to change the ship anchorage. Bushnell was all too often frustrated like this, but his weapons had a certain psychological effect. As the power kegs drifted into Philadelphia, the garrison got the wind up and fired cannon and rifles at them, shouting defiance. Francis Hopkinson, the American poet, wrote a mocking ballad about it, "The Battle of the Kegs," to twit the redcoats.

After the war Bushnell designed more submarines. He went to France and was encouraged by Thomas Jefferson, then U.S. Minister in Paris. Jefferson had been busy in Philadelphia when the *Turtle* made her sorties. He wrote Washington at Mount Vernon, asking about the submarine. Washington replied: "I then thought and still think that it was an effort of genius, but that many things were necessary to be combined to expect much from the issue against an enemy who are always upon guard." Washington thought also that submarines would always be hindered by want of intrepid and skillful men to man them. In France, Bushnell was up against a swarm of inventive Yankee peddlers. Suddenly he threw in his hand and wiped out his past life. He went home and settled in Georgia, taking the name of Bush. He practiced medicine with success, and only after his death in 1826 was it discovered that Dr. Bush was David Bushnell of the *Turtle*.

The American Revolution erupted philosophers, artists, radicals and engineers on Europe. Like Tom Paine they owned anybody's revolution as their own, and France was having one. No less than four Yankee steamboat and submarine men went to France: Bushnell; James Rumsey, who had propelled a vessel by steam on the Potomac in 1785; John Fitch, who operated a scheduled passenger steamer on the Delaware in 1790; and a headstrong, brilliant Pennsylvanian named Robert Fulton, who was to eclipse his fellows at their game of steam and submarine. Fulton was thirty-three, a protégé of Benjamin Franklin. He had a full head of political steam, inventive genius and no patience at all. He took schemes for small canals, submarine boats and undersea mines as his tribute to the French Revolution, and did not mind if he was heavily paid for them.

Fulton was a poor Scotch-Irish farm boy from Conowingo Creek, near Philadelphia. He went to London and spent seven hungry years as an apprentice to the painter Benjamin West; decided he had no future in England, and went to France. In Paris he was befriended by the American poet, Joel Barlow, who had become a French citizen and was to die in Poland during Napoleon's retreat from Moscow. Bushnell, of the *Turtle*, was already in Paris, offering submarine boat plans to the French Directory. Fulton rushed into competition with a torpedo-shaped wooden shell, twenty-one feet long and six feet in diameter, called the *Nautilus*. She was the first submarine of that name in a long series of unusual boats to come, including Captain Nemo's cast-iron château and the first atomic submarine.

Fulton's boat was built at the Perrier yard at Rouen with the aid of his admirers, the mathematician Gaspard Monge and the Marquis Pierre Simon de Laplace, the great astronomer who explained the movement of the stars.

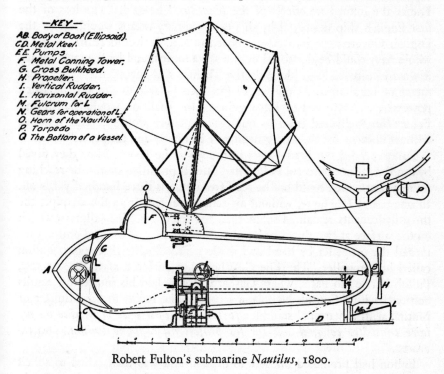

—KEY—
AB. Body of Boat (Ellipsoid).
CD. Metal Keel.
EE. Pumps.
F. Metal Conning Tower.
G. Cross Bulkhead.
H. Propeller.
I. Vertical Rudder.
L. Horizontal Rudder.
M. Fulcrum for L.
N. Gears for operation of L.
O. Horn of the Nautilus.
P. Torpedo.
Q The Bottom of a Vessel.

Robert Fulton's submarine *Nautilus*, 1800.

The *Nautilus* had a hollow cast-iron keel as water ballast tank, which Fulton hand-pumped to climb and flooded to sink. She had movable hydroplanes on the rudder to set the inclination of a dive and ascent. On the surface the *Nautilus* sailed awash, showing only her observation dome and a peculiar umbrella sail which folded flat on her deck when submerged. On a dive two sailors turned a four-bladed screw, itself a radical advance. Bushnell had used a spiral screw; Fulton altered it to the efficient windmill pattern for the first time. The *Nautilus'* weapon was a gunpowder mine, similar to Bushnell's. The mine was towed on a long line from the bow. The line ran through an eye in a spike sticking up from the conning tower.

When the submarine had driven the spike into a ship, she continued on, pulling the contact mine toward the hull and increasing her own distance from the explosion. Fulton and two bold sailors dived the *Nautilus* in the Seine at Rouen on July 29, 1800. They got down as deep as twenty-five feet on two dives in sharp currents.

Fulton's selling prospectus was a forensic letter, addressed to First Consul Napoleon Bonaparte on thirteen Vendémiaire, Year XI, of the Revolutionary calendar, or October 6, 1800. "Let us see first what would be for France the immediate effects of the *Nautilus*," he said. "The loss of the first English ship destroyed by this extraordinary means would throw the English Government into utter embarrassment. It would realize that the whole navy could be destroyed by the same means, and by the same means it would be possible to blockade the Thames and cut off the whole commerce of London. . . . How would Pitt then be able to support the allied powers? . . . Deprived of Pitt's guineas, the coalition would vanish and France thus delivered from its numerous enemies would be able to work without obstacle for the strengthening of its liberty and for peace."

Fulton carried out harder tests in the sea at Le Havre. Now they dived by candlelight; resourceful Fulton had fitted a primitive snort tube reaching up to a float which could not be seen from vessels three hundred yards off. In one test at Le Havre, without air renewal except from the air pipe, the three hydronauts remained submerged for six hours. The sailors rowed it on the surface at two-thirds of a mile per hour. In a submerged cruise, they turned the propeller by hand and made nearly double that speed. Fulton called his propeller "The Flier." When they surfaced after the big test, Fulton hurried to Paris, where Gaspard Monge laid his impressive results before the First Consul. Napoleon seconded the report to the Minister of Marine with a marginal scribble: *Je prie le Ministre de la Marine de me faire connaître ce qu'il sait sur les projets du captaine Fulton.*—BONAPARTE.

Fulton had promoted himself to captain and was then called to solicit Napoleon personally—a big day for the rapid man from Conowingo Creek. No record has been found of what was said at the audience, or how long Fulton bent Bonaparte's ear. They were both ambitious poor men; the Pennsylvanian wanted to escape from poverty, and the Corsican wanted to conquer the world. The *Nautilus* seemed useful to both aspirations. She might break the British Navy and hand Bonaparte a defenseless world. But Napoleon took it under consideration instead of grabbing the submarine. Fulton couldn't stand waiting; within a week he wrote a saucy letter to the Minister of Marine, threatening "to abandon the enterprise in France if I am not received in a more friendly and liberal manner." The minister promptly rejected the *Nautilus*. Perhaps he used something like the jinx sign which U.S. admirals stick on test reports of foreign inventions, "N.I.H."—*not invented here.*

Monge and Laplace picked up their moody friend, bade him not write to officials and got Napoleon to approve the *Nautilus* over his minister's veto. Fulton rebuilt her at Brest and dived with three men on July 3, 1801. He reported breathlessly to Paris: "On the third of thermidor I commenced my experiments by plunging to the depth of five then ten, then fifteen and so on to twenty-five feet but not to a greater depth than twenty-five feet as I did not concieve the Machine Sufficiently Strong to bear the pressure of a greater column of water. At this depth I remained one hour with my three companions and two candles burning without experiancing [I am giving Fulton's spelling.—J. D.] the least inconvenience. . . . Seeing that it would be a great improvement to despence with the candles I have constructed a Small window in the upper part of the Boat near the bow which is only one inch and a half diameter and of Glass 9 lines thick, with this prepared I descended on the 5th of thermidor to the depth of between 24 and 25 feet at which depth I had Suffecient light to count the minuets on the watch." Fulton had hoisted sail and "found her to Answer the helm and Act like a common dul Sailing boat." He traveled 1,300 feet under water, turned the submarine around when submerged and found his compass acting "the same as on the serface of the Water." He constructed a copper globe and filled it with air compressed to three atmospheres as an additional breathing supply for the crew.

Then he tested her attacking powers on a forty-foot sloop provided by the Brest Maritime Prefect and Admiral Villaret, the official observer. His "Bomb Submarine" contained twenty pounds of powder. Fulton trailed the bomb on a line behind the *Nautilus* and submerged 650 feet from the sloop. "Taking my direction so as to pass near the Sloop I struck her with the bomb on my Passage the explosion took place and the Sloop was torn into Atoms, in fact nothing was left by the buye and cable, And the concussion was so Great that a Column of Water Smoak and fibres of the Sloop was cast from 80 to 100 feet in Air." Confirmed by the witnesses, here was the shocking proof of the destructive power of a submarine, the first successful demonstration on record.

One can appreciate Admiral Villaret's feelings at seeing the submarine dive and a boat roar into the air in a fearful explosion. To the cannonball and squaresail mentality it was horrid. It was a menace to proper warmaking. The commissioners found Admiral Villaret's report hard to believe. Two months later they said Napoleon would like to personally inspect the plunging boat. Fulton replied that "She leaked Very much and being but an imperfect engine I did not think her further useful hence I took her to Pieces, Sold her Iron work lead and Cylenders and was necessi-

tated to break the great part of her movements In taking them to Pieces."
The *Nautilus* had disappeared! Fulton thought his demonstration had been
conclusive. He refused to submit drawings for fear somebody would steal
his idea. He demanded an "ample Independence," or a fat bag of louis
d'or before he handed over the design. Further appeals to Napoleon were
not answered. Fulton heard that Napoleon was calling him a swindler. His
republican sentiments were already outraged by Napoleon's dictatorial
course.

Encouraged by the new U.S. Minister to France, Robert R. Livingston,
Fulton built a steamboat which he operated on the Seine in 1803. Napoleon
was not interested in this either, although he was now at war with England
and steamers might have aided him against the British blockade. However,
there was a power very much interested in Fulton. A month after the war
began, the British Admiralty issued a secret circular to the commanders-in-
chief at Sheerness, Portsmouth, the Downs, Plymouth and the Sea. It
warned them of "a plan concerted by Mr. Fulton, an American resident
at Paris, under the influence of the First Consul of the French Republic,
for destroying the Maritime Force of this Country." It appears that British
intelligence knew all about the trials and the demonstration on the sloop,
and took them quite seriously, if Napoleon hadn't. Fulton had also described the submarine in general to his friend, Lord Stanhope, at a time
when the two countries were still at peace. The Earl had made an "alarmed"
speech in the House of Lords about it. Britain was not only alert to the
danger that Fulton boats secretly existed in the French Navy, but the Lords
Admiralty decided to see if the inventor himself could be brought to
Britain for insurance. A confidential gentleman went to Paris with £800 to
fetch Fulton. To be courted was a novel experience. The inventor sent a
letter by this "Mr. Smith" demanding £10,000 down and an English commission to examine his plans within three weeks. When the plans were
accepted, Fulton wanted £100,000 to train naval architects and operational
crews. It must have been a staggering moment when the confidential mes-
senger brought the letter to Whitehall. He said Fulton had gone to Amsterdam to await the reply and would sail from there for England.

Fulton fretted three months in Amsterdam without word and went back
to Paris. Several weeks later Mr. Smith reached Paris with a coded letter
from Lord Hawkesbury, the Foreign Secretary. My Lord said that Fulton
"must well know that it would be contrary to Established rules to grant
such sums, before your invention was authenticated," and such a sum
would also excite public attention. However, Fulton would be treated "with
the utmost liberality and Generosity" in England. The inventor took a
chance and decamped, arriving in London in April, 1804. He found Lord
Hawkesbury freshly out of office and Chancellor of the Exchequer William

Pitt the new Prime Minister in all but name. Pitt was a ferocious econ-
omizer. He would not listen to Fulton's windy arithmetic, or his evaluation
of his services as equal to that of one ship-of-the-line. Pitt said in effect,
Go build your machines; we'll give you the run of His Majesty's dockyards,
£7,000 for materials, £200 a month for yourself while you are working for
us, and half the value of each French ship you destroy. Fulton was delighted. Two hundred quid a month was a fortune to him; he did not see
that Pitt was pledging practically nothing, if the Navy did not choose to
build his engines or employ them against the French. Although Pitt was
genuinely interested in trying Fulton's military potential, he had already,
for a mere £800, attained his main objective, which was to steal this trou-
blesome man from France and get reassuring evidence that Napoleon had
no submarines. Their first interview was at breakfast in Pitt's country house
near Putney Common, with Sir Home Popham, Pitt's aide. Pitt listened
intently to Fulton's description of what the submarine would do. "When
Sir Home Popham went into an adjoining room," says Fulton's account of
the breakfast, "Mr. Pitt remarked that this is an extraordinary invention
which seemed to go to the destruction of all fleets; I replied that It was
invented With that View, And as I had no design to desceive him or the
government I did not hesitate to give it as my opinion that this invention
would lead to the total annihilation of the existing System of Marine War."
Fulton was not far wrong. Those who lived by the existing system did not
like it at all. Admiral Earl St. Vincent, one of Britain's sea dogs, roared,
"Pitt was the greatest fool that ever existed to encourage a mode of war
which they who commanded the seas did not want, and which, if successful, would deprive them of it."

Fulton and Pitt agreed the first attack would be on the French fleet at
Boulogne. Pitt decided to delay the building of a submarine while a commission pondered its awfulness according to the way the war went. If
things got bad enough, Pitt seemed prepared to force the terrible device
on his admirals. Fulton was immediately to build what he called "carcasses," which were gunpowder mines in copper cylinders that exploded
by contact or by a clockwork. These cost £14 with a contact striker and £22
with clock. He was punctually paid his £200 at the end of the first month.

Before long he had constructed enough carcasses to mount the attack on
Boulogne. Four small boats ventured near the French harbor and cast out
two bombs on the ends of a seventy-foot line. They were supposed to float
in on the tide and entangle ships. There were no explosions at Boulogne.
Fulton explained the failure in a lengthy critique which sounded like an
alibi. He began writing complaining letters to various ministers that the
dockyard was not co-operating. He charged that the government did not
intend to prosecute his method of attack. If he got no reply, which was

usual after several of his groaning billets-doux, he wrote a stronger letter
to a higher official. These almost abusive letters, from a friendless foreigner
to the ministers of the greatest power on earth, were met with silence; the
politicians felt that they simply had to put up with the cranky American.
He brought forth more schemes—one for filling the Channel with submerged contact mines, which was adopted in the Dover barrage 110 years
later.

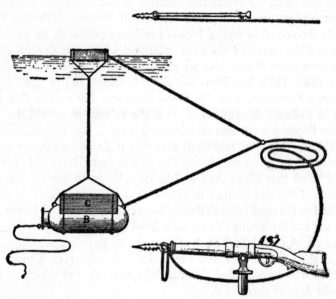

Robert Fulton's underwater harpoon gun for sticking mines on
ships' hulls, 1804.

In October, 1805, Mr. Pitt watched a demonstration of Fulton's carcasses
off Walmer Castle. Fulton set his mines adrift and blew the brig *Dorothea*
in two. She sank in twenty seconds. Fulton was ebullient; now certainly he
would have his way. Six days later a British admiral sank Robert Fulton.
Horatio Nelson destroyed the combined French and Spanish fleet at Cape
Trafalgar. No longer would Britain need undersea weapons, nor the difficult Mr. Fulton. He seems to have realized it. His copious letters changed
their theme to collecting money due him. He had received over £13,000 in
fees and the government had spent £11,000 on materials for the carcasses.
Fulton tried to collect the balance of a £40,000 reward which had been one
of the most ambiguous clauses in Mr. Pitt's contract. Fulton said he would go
back to America and make his undersea secrets public in a "good Philosophical work" and this would result in *all* navies being destroyed. He de-

manded an arbitration commission to settle his claim, as provided in the contract. Months wore out with no reply from Whitehall. Pitt returned from his invalid chair at Bath a few days before he died to find a huge angry letter from the American. At last the arbiters were named and heard him. Fulton won every debating point, but got no money. When Lord Grenville's government came to power, Fulton prepared another furious letter and went with it to Downing Street. He entered the Prime Minister's chamber and read the whole thing aloud to him. Grenville sat in silence throughout the performance and did not even say good-by.

Fulton sailed for home, frustrated, in October, 1806. Before he left, he deposited his letters and drawings of the submarine with the American consul to preserve the idea if he was lost on the voyage. The plans reveal a seagoing vessel thirty-five feet long, with a ten-foot beam and headroom of six feet. She had a good conventional sail plan with provision for quickly lowering canvas and masts to submerge. The vessel was to carry thirty mines, which could be anchored beneath the surface in enemy waters, a conception a century ahead of navy practice. The six-man crew turned a two-bladed screw, the most advanced yet designed and far ahead of actual screw propulsion. Fulton realized that the propeller would slow the boat under sail, so he hinged the shaft so the blades could be drawn up out of the water, an idea that waited two decades to be applied on early steamers. The conning tower had glass ports and there were two streamlined breathing masts, one for pumping in fresh air and the other to discharge vitiated air.

Back home Fulton wrote twice to President Thomas Jefferson to sell his submarine. Jefferson did not reply. Fulton turned to his merchant friend, Robert Livingston, and built his famous steamboat, the *Clermont*. For Fulton, his claim in history, the steamboat, was a retrogression in his ideas, his "mine of science" as he called it. At least seven practical steamboats preceded the *Clermont*. The historians who say justly that Fulton merely happened to be the steamboat designer who came along when the time was ripe, after others had pioneered, and succeeded by his powerful backing, would have found Fulton concurring. He thought steamboats were old hat. His passion was undersea boats; he sought in revolutionary France the climate for a proud over-leaping conception and had great hopes of the pragmatic English. But Paris and London were as conservative as Philadelphia.

At the end of his hard voyage, rich and renowned from his backward glance at the steamboat, Fulton returned to the submarine. He built in New York in 1815 a plunging ship, the *Mute*, which was eighty feet long with a twenty-two foot beam, and carried a crew of one hundred men. Fulton regarded them as horsepower; five men equaled one horse on the hand propeller. He died before she could be launched. The *Mute* passed away as junk from the navy arsenal.

Captain Johnson, a Hampshire man, who was one of the most popular smugglers in England at the beginning of the nineteenth century, perfected several methods for towing brandy and stuffs under water from France. Napoleon, who used the Channel smugglers as spies and buyers of English gold guineas at the black-market rate to finance his campaigns, was reputed to have asked Johnson to pilot a French sneak fleet to England. Johnson refused. The price must have been too low, in view of Johnson's subsequent changes of loyalty. The French jugged him. He escaped and joined the British revenue cutter, the *Fox,* turning in his smuggling cronies wholesale. It discouraged his admirers. Johnson took care not to leave the ship when in port.

At sea he was the scourge of what the historian of smuggling, Henry N. Shore, called the "Scientific Period." Johnson led several whacking battles against cognac ships and, at the attack on Walcheren, he swam to the forts, towing an infernal machine, and blew a pretty passage into the works. Striving to get ahead, Johnson, in 1820, sold some French plotters on a marvelous plan for springing Napoleon from St. Helena. He built a submarine boat a hundred feet long, with detachable masts so that sticks and canvas could be furled tight to the deck for submerging, not unlike Fulton's *Nautilus.* This craft was to liberate Napoleon from the far island and carry him to the United States. Johnson successfully demonstrated the boat and had his fee screwed up to £40,000 when Napoleon died of cancer.

Johnson's readily reversible allegiances were not exhausted. He tried to sell Napoleon's delivery boat to the Spanish to attack the French fleet at Cadiz. He submerged for ten hours in the Thames in a demonstration for the Spanish prospects, but lost the sale. So he got in touch with the French Ambassador to the Court of St. James, Monsieur de Polignac, and showed that worthy a boat shed in which lay five submarine boats, from twenty to sixty feet long, one built of iron. Johnson claimed his craft could resist three atmospheres of pressure, or a depth of sixty-six feet. He had a compressed-oxygen breathing supply in the boats. The French did not buy. We leave this talented rogue with regret; it is too bad that by the time Johnson had worked out his undersea craft there was no important war on, or he might have pushed undersea warfare a century ahead of time by selling his invention to both sides.

The idea of the submarine lay fallow until Germany ran into a powerful revolt by the Danes in 1848. Danish ships raided and blockaded the German coast. The helpless defenders were ready to try anything and a submarine plan came forward from a twenty-eight-year-old corporal in the Bavarian Light Horse artillery, a former woodturner from Dillingen named

Wilhelm Bauer. Corporal Bauer was the most intransigent of inventors, ragged, brilliant and unbeatable. Bauer built his first undersea boat at Kiel in 1849. The vessel was made of sheet iron roughly in the shape of a porpoise. Bauer actually studied porpoises to find the design. However, no shipwright had ever built a porpoise and during construction Bauer's boat was compromised. She came out with a porpoise's curves when seen from above, but the sides were flat and deeper than the width, giving the dimensions: length, twenty-five feet, beam, six and depth, nine. The four-bladed screw was turned by two men, spinning big helmlike wheels amidships. There were four square glass windows on the sides. The boat submerged by flooding ballast tanks and was inclined for a dive by sliding forward a large weight on a track in the bilge. It was not a very good system. Bauer called the boat the *Brandtaucher,* or the *Sea-Diver.*

She was the second submarine to attack in war. In December, 1850, Corporal Bauer took the *Sea-Diver* out of Kiel against the Danish blockaders. At the mere sight of her they broke and scattered. This stunning feat did not ease Bauer's way. There was a physics professor in Kiel named Karsten, who had conceived a heavy scorn for the unacademic inventor. Professor Karsten blasted Bauer's ideas in pseudoscientific papers. He called the submarine the *"Sea Devil"* and weakened military confidence in Bauer.

The besieged inventor sallied out again to attack the Danes with two sailors named Witt and Thomsen, in 1851. They submerged in the Kiel Roadstead, and the sliding weight clanked forward, forcing the bow down at a sharp angle. Bauer was navigating in shallow water as shown on the harbor charts, to give himself a margin of safety if the boat plunged too steeply. However, the charts did not show a sixty-foot pothole, which, by the worst luck, the *Sea-Diver* was passing over when she submerged. The submarine nosed into the vertical and went straight down. She crashed heavily into the floor and settled right side up. The crash and water pressure started collapsing the riveted sheet-iron hull. Most of her apparatus was buckled out of shape. The afterquarters were nearly stoved.

Bauer and his men frantically tried to blow the ballast tanks with compressed air, but the machinery was too badly damaged. Water squirted through the broken seams. Witt and Thomsen kept cool and did not add to Bauer's dilemma. The three moved around in the faint light of the windows and could hear excited voices in boats above them. Bauer saw that there was no hope of surfacing the vessel under her own buoyancy. He reviewed what he knew about pressure. He calculated that men could escape from a depth of sixty feet by going out the hatch with a lungful of air and soaring to the surface. But no hatch could be forced to open outward against nearly three atmospheres of pressure. The air pressure on the inside would have to be raised to equal that of the sea, but Bauer had no more compressed air to build up internal pressure.

There was one last trick. Bauer would make the encompassing sea raise his air pressure. He ordered the crew to open seacocks and systematically flood the submarine, until the water compressed their air to the right point. Then they could open the hatch and throw themselves into the sea. Witt and Thomsen were appalled. They cursed the idea. Bauer now had a near-mutiny on his bill of troubles. He pleaded with them, pointing out that it was their only chance for life. As he argued, the people above formed the idea of snagging the thirty-seven-ton submarine with their anchors to haul her up. Heavy anchors swung outside the ports, crashing the buckling hull and threatening to shatter his windows. There was no way to stop the would-be rescuers.

The inventor kept his wits in the pounding and panic. He talked on to his men. At last, after four hours in the wrecked boat, they agreed to submit to flooding. They swore if they got out alive they would dive again with Captain Bauer. They flooded up. Water slowly climbed up their legs, to their waists. The compression of the remaining air increased its carbon dioxide content, which had reached a critical point from their protracted exhalations, even before it was tripled by pressure. The pressure gauge had been broken in the crash. Bauer guessed when he had the correct air pressure. He ordered Thomsen to go out the hatch. They loosened the clamps and it felt easy. They swung the hatch open. Out went Thomsen, enveloped in a great bubble. Water cascaded in and air rushed out. Bauer shoved Witt out and skinned through himself as the hatch banged shut. They soared to the surface in blobs of air "like champagne corks," Bauer said. Mad cheers swept the rescue boats. It was the first submarine escape in history.

The *Sea-Diver* was salvaged in 1887 and put on exhibition in the court-yard of the Kiel Naval Academy. At the time she sank, however, the German Government, instead of honoring Bauer for his magnificent escape, decided Professor Karsten was right and refused money for another submarine. Bauer left for Austria. Through the intervention of a lady of the court, he got to Archduke Maxmilian, who named a technical commission to study Bauer's submarine plans. It reported favorably and Lloyd's Triestino shipyard was awarded 100,000 francs to build the boat. The Austrian finance minister, a great blockhead, cut off the appropriation.

Bauer decided he might sell a submarine in England, where concern was growing over the Crimea. In 1853 he exposed his plans to that enthusiast of inventions, Prince Albert. The Consort interested Lord Palmerston in Bauer's plan and introduced the inventor to his engineering cronies, Charles Fox, Isambard Kingdom Brunel and John Scott Russell, who had just laid down the *Great Eastern* steamship. These popular engineering radicals were exactly the types the buffeted corporal needed. Palmerston and Scott Russell took up a submarine design Bauer had entered for a British patent. It was a great improvement over the *Brandtaucher,* although Bauer persisted in the sliding weight principle that had plunged her to the bottom. He added air pipes reaching the surface. He called them "the hypnotic apparatus," to suggest that the boat could sleep secretly beneath the waves.

The submarine was larger than the *Sea-Diver,* of cleaner design, and was to be propelled by a piston engine using gas produced by saltpeter, sulphur, coal and ammonia.* The crew could reach their arms out of the boat through leather sleeves to fasten bombs under ships. Bauer wanted her to carry six five hundred-pound gunpowder mines. The wandering Bavarian thought Palmerston and Scott Russell were his partners, but they considered him a mere consultant. Scott Russell fancied himself a submarine designer. There was one too many geniuses in the consortium. Bauer was frozen out. He left England, protesting that his invention had been stolen. Scott Russell was safe. Bauer's patent designs were found with the notation, "This invention did not proceed to the Great Seal," meaning that it had been registered but not patented. The Crimean War broke out. Palmerston and Scott Russell hastily built a submarine incorporating very few of Bauer's ideas. It was no good.

Bauer offered his plans to the United States Government, which did not reply. He was by this time *persona non grata* in Germany, due to Karsten's campaign and the fact that he had offered his weapon to foreign governments. The restless engineer went to Russia to sell his undersea boat to England's enemy in the Crimean War. In St. Petersburg he found another prince with a gleam in his eye for submarines, the Grand Duke Constantine. Russian Admirals wished nothing to do with Bauer, but Constantine financed his third design, which Bauer sardonically christened *Le Diable-Marin,* or the *Sea-Devil,* Professor Karsten's epithet. Launched in 1855, she was porpoise-shaped, fifty-seven-feet long, carried a crew of thirteen and was built to withstand the pressure of 150 feet down. Air was purified in the submarine by an oxygen-regenerating system. The screw was turned by hand. There was an observation dome at the bow and an air lock through which a diver could exit, stick a bomb on a ship and return to the bottomed boat. The *Sea-Devil* existed fourteen years before Jules Verne pictured a windowed submarine with a diver's air lock.

Shortly after the *Sea-Devil* was launched, Bauer's royal patron was called away on a long trip. As soon as the Grand Duke left town, the knives were out for his protégé. In order to discourage Bauer, the admirals hauled the

* *Whew!*—AUTH.

submarine overland to the Naval Base at Kronstadt, taking eight months
for the short distance. Fortunately Bauer had found a devoted heart in
the Russian Navy, a young lieutenant named Fedorovitch, his second in
command. Fedorovitch even refused overtures by his superiors to steal
Bauer's ideas so the admirals could get rid of him. At last Bauer and
Fedorovitch were able to test the *Sea-Devil* at Kronstadt with a crew of
eleven. The extraordinary tests that ensued were practically clandestine as
far as the naval heirarchy was concerned. The former corporal of light
artillery and his devoted crew made 134 dives in the *Sea-Devil* from May
to October, 1856, the most intensive submarine tests of the century. They
dived the boat as deep as 150 feet, always on plan and to record data; they
made the first scientific observations of compass behavior under water; they
noted the effects on a group of men breathing air in a hermetically closed
space for hours at a time, and recorded the air pressure in the submarine
under many circumstances. Bauer even tried to take undersea photographs
through the windows.

During the first test, they stayed late at sea and returned after dark,
the sailors singing at the propeller wheels. Bauer stood on the bare rolling
deck like a man arriving on whaleback, and hailed the sentry on the outer
mole with the day's password. The guard dropped his gun and ran. They
passed each barrier to the Port Imperial, having fun panicking the sentries.
Bauer staged an underwater ceremony for the coronation of Czar Alexander
II. He took down four brass players of the fleet band. When the cannons
of Kronstadt boomed out a salute to the new czar, the musicians struck up
the Imperial Hymn. The four-hour subaquatic concert was heard by people
in boats above in a radius of six hundred feet.

After 133 dives, Bauer and Fedorovitch felt they were strong enough to
overpower the gold braid with a demonstration. Already in the south at
Sevastopol, Russian engineers were attacking British ships with underwater
mines electrically detonated from the shore. The demonstration was therefore to be the *Sea-Devil* passing undetected under a shallowly anchored
vessel at Kronstadt, to show that she could deposit one of her mines beneath a ship. On the submerged run everything went smoothly for the
Sea-Devil. She had the first professional submarine crew and they knew
their duties. All of a sudden, the *Sea-Devil* halted and yawed. The sailors
bent their backs to the propeller, but it was jammed. A high stand of
tenacious kelp had fouled the screw. Bauer ordered, "Blow the ballast
tanks!" Compressed air whistled into the tanks, expelling the water. *Le
Diable-Marin* stirred and the deck began to rise forward. The men held
on and leaned as the bow climbed. The seaweeds still anchored them by
the stern. Bauer and Fedorovitch climbed the incline and released the main
keel weights. The boat stirred and the bow went even higher, without

tearing loose from the clutching weeds. Fedorovitch reported the bow was out of water. Bauer ordered him to take all the men out by the bow hatch, and follow them. This would further lighten the craft and save their lives if she swamped. Bauer stayed behind to find a way out of the mocking situation. Water slapped through the forward hatch, which could only be closed from the inside. Bauer climbed to close the hatch. His weight sank the bow. Water cascaded into the *Sea-Devil*. He did the only thing possible and popped through to the surface. The *Sea-Devil* swamped and sank. Defeated by weeds, the wet inventor was picked up by smirking officers. Bauer had not been defeated by them, but by a reason he knew—there was yet no engine that would operate under water. Inventors are prisoners of technology.

Despite the inglorious outcome of his demonstration, Bauer had won a party in the Russian Navy to the submarine. He salvaged the *Sea-Devil* and was given an unique naval rank as Submarine Engineer, with a special uniform. He bounced back with a design for a bigger boat with a steam engine for the surface and a compressed-air motor for cruising under water. She was to carry twenty-four cannons. He began building in 1858, beset with criticisms and demands for alterations by the admirals. When they announced that the construction job was to be moved to Siberia, Bauer quit Russia. He turned up in Paris; France was the last great power he had not tried. He was interviewed by Napoleon III, who did not commission an undersea boat, but did give Bauer 150 francs as a present. The fight was over. The tormented spirit crept back to Munich, where he was afflicted by tuberculosis of the spine and lay seven years motionless before he died. Later the Munichers put a fine marble bust on his tomb and congratulated themselves that, "Posterity was more just to him than his contemporaries were." Bauer was more than a brilliant engineer. He had a deep sense of the sea and he saw that the submarine would also "carry peace in its interior." He said, "She is destined for a new progress; her equipment will serve for pearl fishing, for gold, for coral, telegraphy, underwater construction, and scientific discoveries in the depths of the sea."

Submarines turned up in strange places and times. In the squalling town of Chicago in 1851 a shoemaker named Lodner D. Phillips built two working submarines fifty feet long, which were propelled by hand cranks. Phillips once dived for ten hours in Lake Michigan, with his wife and two children, who looked out through a window in the bow. Phillips lost his life in a dive in Lake Erie, near Buffalo, a few years later. Another Chicagoan, George A. Baker, built a sidewheeler submarine in 1889. He used buckets in place of wheel blades. His craft was rejected in the naval submarine competition in 1892. Oliver Halstead sold a submarine to the U.S. Navy in the seventies called the *Intelligent Whale*. As diving ability went, the submarine was not as intelligent as a whale. It drowned thirty-nine men during trials. The hulk was preserved in the Brooklyn Navy Yard. Extracurricular interests shortened Halstead's career, and perhaps saved some sailors. He was shot and killed by his mistress' lover.

The American Civil War was a time of much experimentation in submersibles and underwater weapons. In Spain, Narciso Monturiol, of Barcelona, built an ingenious diving boat called *El Ictineo*. It had an oxygen-regenerating system, a cannon and a steam auger for drilling holes

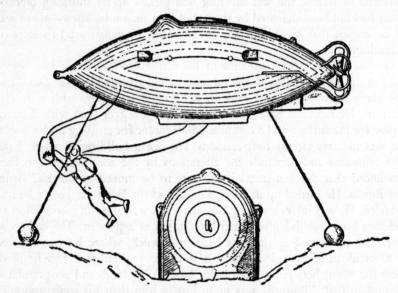

Oliver Halstead's *Intelligent Whale* (1872) drowned 39 men on tests.

in ship's bottoms. Monturiol dived her over fifty times and once stayed under for five hours. A Frenchman named Villeroi constructed a submarine for the U.S. Navy. She was 35 feet long, cigar-shaped and hand-propelled. Although the craft did dive, she was never used in battle. An Englishman named Winan built a 265-foot submarine, which was tried in the Thames in 1865. By 1869, the year *Twenty Thousand Leagues Under the Sea* was published, at least twenty-five authenticated crew-carrying submarines had been built and dived successfully.

France led the world in practical submarine building in the second half of the century. In 1863, Siméon Borgeois and Charles-Marie Brun built the *Plongeur*, a 435-ton craft 140 feet long, which ran on a compressed-air engine. She was the direct inspiration for Verne's *Nautilus* and the first practical naval submarine. The *Plongeur* dived to twenty feet and was a vital experiment that led to the advanced submarine, the *Gymnote,* launched at Toulon in 1886. She was planned by a brilliant naval architect, Charles-Henri Laurent Dupuy de Lôme, who may be called the first competent professional submarine designer. Dupuy de Lôme died during building and the work was finished by his peer and friend, Gustave Zédé. The *Gymnote* was a thirty-ton, streamlined boat fifty-six feet long. She ran on fifty-five horsepower electric motors at seven knots on the surface and five when dived. Her five-man crew had a periscope and electric lights. Gutave Zédé did not long outlive his friend. He was killed in 1891 in an explosion while working on torpedoes.

In the meantime an odd design partnership was at work in Britain, a Swedish engineer named Theodore Nordenfelt and the Reverend George William Garrett, who had built a little submarine in Liverpool in 1876. Nordenfelt looked like the Emperor Franz Josef and Garrett resembled the younger Bernard Shaw. Another piquant touch was that they were building a steam submarine for the Turkish Navy. She was a mammoth 110 feet long and displaced 160 tons. She carried two automobile torpedoes on her prow and two machine guns on deck. Turkish officers hung around the yard at Barrow-in-Furness, giving the Reverend Garrett a bad time during construction—another bunch of the naval "experts" that submarine builders had to put up with. Garrett had difficulty with his lateral stability, particularly when he fired a torpedo. When the torpedo's weight was suddenly removed, it changed the trim of the craft and she went down by the stern. Garrett would keep his conning tower hatch open to watch this operation. One time he had the gassy Turks aboard for a test salvo, when a big steamer came close by and rolled waves into the open hatch. The boat was swamping. Garrett fought the hatch shut and his works engineer, Mr. Lawrie, got the pumps going smartly. The submarine was tested in the Golden Horn and Bosphorus to the satisfaction of the Imperial Divan and the constructors were paid. Then she was laid up in the arsenal at Constantinople, and taken apart piece by piece by thieves and chandlers.

Nordenfelt built another whopping steam submarine at Barrow, 125 feet long, weighing 250 tons and with 500 horsepower, and sold her to the Russian government. She set out for Kronstadt, ran into a fog and was wrecked on the Danish coast. The obdurate Swede with the mutton chop whiskers designed another and offered the plans to the French and United States governments. Neither bought, but it did give the Americans the idea of holding the 1888 competition for submarine design which was won by John P. Holland.

John Philip Holland was a skinny, weak-sighted Irish pedagogue from County Clare, all his life poor and frail, but strong on ideas. With that and his musical lecturer's tongue this powerless man moved admirals and rich men. With the Frenchman, Gustave Zédé, the Swede Nordenfelt, the Russian Stephan Drzewiecki, and the American, Simon Lake, John P. Holland was the maker of the modern military submarine.

He designed a submarine boat while a boy teacher at the Christian Brothers School in Cork in 1859. When he was twenty he read of the battle of the U.S.S. *Monitor* and C.S.S. *Virginia* and understood that sea battles would from then forward be fought between armored steamships, and that his submarine might intervene in the new way of war. Holland dreamed of his boat sinking the British fleet. Submarine designers, from Fulton to Hitler's Professor Walter, have been inspired by the hulls of the Royal and merchant navies.

In 1872, when he was thirty, Holland emigrated to the United States and became a teacher in a parochial school in Paterson, New Jersey. One day a friend, looking through Holland's papers, came upon the 1859 submarine design. He urged Holland to submit it to the United States Government. Without looking at his boyish drawings Holland thought about submarines afresh and drew up new plans. He found they compared in detail with his forgotten scheme. Holland sent the drawings to the Navy. The Navy said, "However perfect in construction . . . it would be hard to find a man to work it." He found a backer who would go ahead on construction, without waiting.

In 1878 they built an undersea boat on the banks of the Passaic River at Paterson. At the launch, the submarine went nicely down the ways and kept on going down. Somebody had forgotten to close two plugs in the bottom. Holland fished up his submarine and began trials. His boat, known only as the *Holland No. 1*, differed from the Nordenfelt and French submarine boats. It dived on an incline by use of movable hydroplanes and it surfaced in the same slanting manner. The other practical boats were "sinkers"—they went down in a horizontal position. There were lively arguments over which was the better system. Today submarines submerge in a horizontal plane, or are supposed to.

Holland was an Irish patriot and the United States was full of them. The American branch of the Fenian Brotherhood had invaded Canada in 1865, and persisted with schemes for unhorsing the British Empire. Three leading Fenians were sighted aboard Holland's craft in the Passaic River, during trials in which the craft submerged to twelve feet for one hour. Holland's subcontractor had provided a worthless engine. The inventor decided, rather than fail on a Navy demonstration, he would scuttle his boat and build another. He sank his submarine under the Falls Bridge in the Passaic. She was raised forty-eight years later and is now in the Paterson Museum.

The Fenian Brotherhood enthused over the second boat which would down the British fleet. The Fenians announced a "skirmishing fund" for Ireland's cause, which was secretly a subscription for a new Holland boat. Two hundred thousand people gave money. Holland built a nineteen-ton submarine on the North River at the foot of Thirteenth Street, Man-

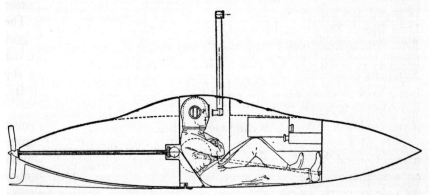

John P. Holland's one-man submarine, 1877. Note early periscope. Sunk under tow off Whitestone, Long Island, 1883. (The Submarine Library)

hattan. She was launched with what the Fenians thought extreme secrecy in 1881. The idlers of the city hung around the yard, but known newspapermen were strictly barred. The man from the New York *Sun*, who had been watching from a rooftop, wrote a fanciful feature in which he called the craft the *Fenian Ram*. The epithet stuck.

When Holland reckoned his vessel ready for a cruise, he cast off for Bay Ridge, Brooklyn, as a multitude hoorayed. Out in the stream, the inventor went topside to prepare for a dive and found a small Negro boy perched on the turret. Holland said, "Come below, boy. The boat is going under the water." The stowaway absolutely refused. Professor Holland delivered a short lecture on the theory of submarine navigation and its successful application in the instance of the *Fenian Ram*. He talked the kid into the dark interior. When they surfaced off Brooklyn, Holland opened the hatch and the boy shinnied past him to the dripping deck. The craft came up alongside two boys in a rowboat. When they saw a man in a bowler hat and a barefooted urchin emerge from the Bay, the rowers set an unofficial double sculls record to the beach.

Holland reached a depth of sixty feet in *Fenian Ram*. During the experiments the inventor had no salary. He was living with his cousin, John Scanlan, in Newark, and often didn't have the carfare to New York. In 1883, without notifying Holland, his financial partner and some Irish patriots absconded with *Fenian Ram* and a sixteen-foot one-man submarine Holland had designed, and towed them to New Haven. Holland said late in life that he never knew why they took his boats. Perhaps they were impatient with Holland's insistence on prolonged tests and modifications; perhaps it was larceny called patriotism. At any rate, the pirates swamped and lost the smaller sub in 110 feet of water off Whitestone, Long Island. They started hot-rodding around New Haven in the *Fenian Ram*, sinking imaginary British vessels and almost sinking real ones. The locals grew wroth with the putative Irish undersea fleet and had the boat declared a menace to navigation. The *Fenian Ram* was ordered drawn out into a barn on shore where she dived into obscurity until 1927, when she was taken to Westside Park in Paterson. There she is to be inspected today, if you can brush past the kids climbing over her.

Holland formed a new partnership with a promotorial artilleryman named General Zalinsky, who had schemes for putting huge deck mortars on a submarine. The notion arose from U.S.S. *Monitor,* which cruised with decks nearly awash, and from several low-board floating batteries which were built by the Federals in the Civil War. Holland and Zalinsky built a new submarine, the *Nautilus,* at Fort Hamilton in 1886. Setting up the launch, yard engineers underestimated the weight of the hull. The *Nautilus* was started down the slip and the timbers collapsed. The big boat kept on going, riping out plates on the pilings, and disappeared in the water, a total loss.

Back to the old drawing board went John P. Holland. Two years later he entered and won the first U.S. Navy competition for a submarine design, which he tendered through Cramp's Shipyard in Philadelphia. Cramp's forgot to enclose a deposit with the bid. Holland's boat was disqualified on the technicality. This was straightened out at the insistence of several young naval officers who had been unofficially watching Holland's experiments for several years and believed in his boat. In 1889, Congress made a new award for a Holland boat. While it was building came the new administration of President Benjamin Harrison, which diverted Holland's money to finish a cruiser. It seemed the end of the fight for an American undersea boat.

Holland continued to talk submarines in his persuasive brogue. He got no comfort from Washington, but, like Hyman Rickover after him, he inspired a group of young naval officers, who fought a partisan war for the idea. At last, in the fashion of so many historic decisions, somebody's brother-in-law got to a high-up friend and Holland was given $15,000, to build a steam submarine, the *Plunger*. It was 1895, a third of a century after he had designed a practical diving boat, and he was still working on the original principles.

The money had strings to it—gold braid and red tape. Although the Navy had no experience with submarines, a board was placed over Holland to see that the structural regulations were carried out, an instance of the official commission which Edward Everett Hale once defined as, "A board is long and narrow. It is made of wood." The wooden men insisted on unnatural alterations in the iron ship. Holland saw that the compromise boat would fail, so he started building a second submarine at Elizabeth, New Jersey, at the expense of his company. It was powered by a gasoline engine. He finished both vessels to specifications. The Navy craft was a failure. Holland's worked, but it pushed his company near to bankruptcy. Fresh capital was secured from Isaac Rice, who licensed the main patents of the *Plunger* and started a company called Electric Boat. Rice won Congressional appropriations for Holland's boat, and, in 1900, the U.S. Navy acquired its first submarine, the *Plunger*. Electric Boat Company has done well; in 1955 it launched the atomic *Nautilus*.

Holland's forty-year fight was over. In old age he made a bit of money from his patents and turned to designing airplanes. He wrote *How to Fly as a Bird*. He died in Newark five days after the outbreak of World War I. The old Fenian did not live to see submarines try the might of the Royal Navy, nor to see Holland boats fighting in that Navy.

In New Jersey in the 1880's a red-headed kid named Simon Lake read a wonderful book, *Twenty Thousand Leagues Under the Sea*, and his imagination leaped. From then on, he thought about little but submarines. He lived by the sea in the pious town of Atlantic Highlands, where he was soon building an undersea craft. At first, he could not realize his plans to build a gigantic boat, designated as the *Argonaut* in his drawings. She was to be an improvement on Verne's *Nautilus*. So he built the *Argonaut Junior*, a fourteen-foot, flatiron-shaped vessel made of two layers of yellow pine with waterproof canvas between them. The propeller was hand-turned, and the boat also had wheels to run along the floor. Lake got his compressed-air tank from a bankrupt soda fountain. His prettiest idea was an air lock in the bottom of the boat, through which the crew could duck out in bucket helmets, or simply sit on the edge of the hatch and dangle their feet in the water, fishing or reaching down for clams. The *Argonaut Junior* began trundling along the bottom in 1894. He took her to New York Bay in 1895. The city was enchanted. The gadget was as popular as

Cornelis Drebbel's seventeenth-century submarine had been in London. Lake was an inventor who never overlooked the uses of publicity.

He organized a company to build his big boat, a thirty-six-foot iron *Argonaut,* with seven-foot cast-iron wheels and a gasoline engine. She could not exceed periscope depth, because Lake had to keep air tubes out of the water to feed the engine and to exhaust carbon monoxide. The *Argonaut* and Holland's *Plunger* were launched from the same Baltimore yard in 1897. Several times Lake went down for ten hours. He took two dozen New York reporters under the Bay. Among them was Ada Patterson, star sob sister of the New York *American,* who had previously ventured into deeper pressure in East River bridge caissons. Lake's guests brought champagne. The teetotaling inventor found them a greasy cup for the underwater *vin d'honneur.* The reporters played happily in the air lock, raking up oysters and harbor jetsam. Editors loved the Simon Lake copy.

However, the Navy and scientists, whom Lake was trying to attract, paid no attention to the *Argonaut.* One time a fish stared through Lake's bow port for ten hours and the inventor remarked, "He had more interest in our submarine activities than many professors and admirals I knew." In 1899 Lake made some snapshots through the port, which were published in *McClure's Magazine.* He thought he was the first underwater photographer. Lake was snubbed and treated as a crackpot in Washington, where the Electric Boat Company owned official favor for its Holland submarines. Isaac Rice, president of Electric Boat, was a tough businessman. While Lake entertained reporters, Rice captured congressmen. Through one of his newspaper friends, the swashbuckling Karl Decker, who not merely reported stories but made them, Lake met the New York Junta of the Cuban Revolution. They liked the idea of buying the *Argonaut* and sneaking her to Cuba to creep into anchorages and mine Spanish warships. The deal was to be set when a naval expert of the Junta, a mysterious cloaked figure called The Admiral, approved of a trial. Decker brought the admiral to the submarine and the three went out to dive. When Lake turned on the whistling compressed air to blow his water ballast, the admiral began to keen. He simply came apart. Lake said, "He screeched like a parrot." They returned the admiral to the pier. Once ashore, he ran as fast as his legs would carry him, his cloak standing straight out behind. Lake never saw the Junta again.

As the United States went to war with Spain, the Navy mined Hampton Roads as a defense against attack. Lake decided on a demonstration to wake up the admirals. He secretly freighted the *Argonaut* to the Roads, slipped into the water and visited all the mines. He announced that he could have easily disarmed the mines, or even have stuck some on the ships. The Navy was not interested. Lake retreated to New York in the fall of 1898, navigating the *Argonaut* by sea, one of the first open ocean cruises of a submarine. He ran into a disastrous storm which sank hundreds of ships. The *Argonaut* came so near to sinking that Lake and his two-man crew rode topside with decks awash in winter winds that coated them with ice. When the submarine staggered into New York with all hands safe, the newspapers cheered. Simon Lake received his greatest accolade in a letter from Amiens, France, signed by Jules Verne.

To increase her seaworthiness, Lake cut the *Argonaut* in half and added a twenty-foot midsection. He found friends in Bridgeport, Connecticut, and moved his operations there. He invited thirty Bridgeport notables on an undersea picnic. They included the mayor, bankers and professional men, the flower of Bridgeport chivalry. He took the *Argonaut* down to the end of his air tube and opened the air lock. The guests delved for irides-cent jingle shells and picked clams for a big chowder. They sang and passed round the jug in fulfillment of their boyhood dreams of diving with Captain Nemo. People ashore grew nervous over their prolonged absence. City officials went out in a tug and rapped on the air tube. The chowder party was singing *"Down Went McGinty to the Bottom of the Sea"* and did not hear the knocks. The tug group returned, convinced that all were drowned, and swore each other to secrecy, until the ghastly revelation could be made from City Hall that Bridgeport had lost its leaders. They ordered a floating derrick from New York to lift the tomb. The whole town knew about it immediately and rushed to the water to see the derrick fish up the crazy inventor and the city's fallen pride. Then the air mast grew taller, the *Argonaut* swelled out of the water and chugged to Bridgeport, covered with waving figures.

Lake decided to build another submarine to sell to the Navy. With Bridgeport money, he constructed in the town dump, behind the gas works on the Peconic River, a sixty-five-foot submarine, the *Protector*. The Electric Boat Company claimed that Lake was using Holland patents. Isaac Rice put a libel on the Lake boat. Under Connecticut law it meant an automatic attachment of Lake's assets up to the extent of the claim. Rice named $1,500,000. Lake had $17 in the bank. He was legally forced to stop construction. A Bridgeport friend got the attachment halved and put up the bond. In trials at Newport, the *Protector* broke ice, dived under it and crashed back through the surface. The Navy took no note, although it was having difficulty with Holland boats. Lake tried to sell the boat to the U.S. Army, which was only too happy to occupy any vacuums the Navy left lying around. The Army actually committed itself for five boats

of the *Protector* class, to be used in harbor engineering, it said. Actually the
plan was to wrest undersea combat functions from the Navy. The Navy-
Rice lobby killed the appropriation in Congress.

"Only a faint glimmer of hope could be seen," Lake said. "The war
between Russia and Japan was under way." Three Japanese and the
Russian military attaché inspected the *Protector*. They had people shadowing Lake and each other, fishing for the submarine. Lake was called to an
intimate breakfast party in the New York mansion of a fantastic international schemer named Russell Flint, who arranged arms for anybody who
had a war going. The third breakfast guest was the Russian military
attaché. He bought the *Protector*. The next day Lake received the down
payment of $125,000 at J. P. Morgan's bank. The buyer required complete
secrecy in sending the submarine to Russia. He wanted to mystify the
Japanese and also forestall seizure of the boat as contraband by the U.S.
Government. The attaché did not tell his own agents, who continued to
play hide-and-seek with the footsore Japanese. Lake kept it a secret from
his own technician as well, while he figured out how to smuggle out an iron
whale.

He worked out a clever plan. In Norfolk, Virginia, he chartered S.S.
Fortuna, to carry a load of coal to Russia. In New York he hired a floating
derrick for an unspecified job off Sandy Hook. These two vessels were
timed to meet. Out of Bridgeport he took his technicians aboard the
Protector for a "routine sea trial." The three vessels made the rendezvous
and a providential, blinding rain curtained the derrick's lifting of the
Protector from the water to a special cradle fitted on the *Fortuna's* main
deck. Lake addressed his men. "We are going to Russia. Any one who
doesn't want to go, speak up." Fortunately, none withdrew. If any had,
Lake would have taken him along, anyway, to keep the secret.

In Bridgeport the Russian and Japanese beaks ran around wringing
their hands, as the press played up the *Protector* mystery. At sea the
Fortuna was accosted by a Russian destroyer which had spotted the submarine on her deck. The Russian ordered her to halt. The *Fortuna* kept
on going. The destroyer laid a warning shell across her bows. The freighter
hove to. A boarding party announced to Lake that the destroyer would
not permit him to carry the submarine to Japan. Lake laughed and said he
was headed for Russia. The destroyer officer announced, "You certainly
are. Under arrest. We confiscate the submarine." So Simon Lake and the
Protector came to Kronstadt. He and his men were to spend seven years in
Russia.

Lake was a stubborn, puritanical man with a drooping left eyelid. He had
destroyed the lid muscle while working on his periscope, and propped it

up with a monocle. He liked the Russians, but was shocked at their morals. He saw a "beautiful, well-educated young girl, trained dancer" offered for sale in the classified ads. One of the Kronstadt engineers tried to sell him his wife for seven dollars. Lake sent in a hurry for Mrs. Lake and the kids. They seemed to have spent their years in Russia with uplifted hands, gasping. The Russian sense of humor was likewise odd. One time Lake was carrying an admiral in a run with the decks awash and only eighteen inches of the open conning tower out of the water. Lake was up in the turret with his head sticking out the hatch. Suddenly the *Protector* went into a dive. He ducked and closed the hatch with an inch to spare, as the *Protector* went under. The admiral laughed so hard there were tears in his eyes. He had thrown the hydroplanes into diving position as a joke. The Czarist navy ordered five submarines, none of which saw service in the Japanese war. Lake moved to Berlin, where his designs were politely stolen. He licensed his rights to Armstrong-Whitworth, Ltd., for England, but his own country never bought a Lake submarine.

As early as 1898, Simon Lake advocated huge cargo and passenger submarines to link the continents of the Northern hemisphere by the shortest sea route—under the polar ice. When the German cargo submarine *Deutschland* ran the British blockade to the United States in 1916, Lake rushed to Baltimore to attach her for patent infringements. Captain Koenig, of the *Deutschland,* welcomed Lake with effusive praise. The Germans dined the inventor and toasted him as the creator of the *Deutschland,* which indeed he was. His preachings on cargo submarines had been marked well in Germany. The Germans talked about giving him a huge contract for cargo U-boats. Lake went away inflated, forgetting his libel. The *Deutschland* went away too, and that was the end of that.

The latest version of the *Nautilus* is the famous atomic submarine, created by Captain Hyman G. Rickover, U.S.N. He had to fight as hard as John P. Holland or Wilhelm Bauer against naval and political cliques. He was twice passed over for merited promotion by the secret Navy Selection Board and nearly forced to retire in the midst of construction. Clair Blair, Jr., Captain Rickover's biographer, said, "He was a controversial character; a thin, wiry, iron-fisted, tireless worker who wrote vituperative reports and drove men and machines to the breaking point. He was known as a man who could 'get the job done.' He believed the shortest distance between two points was a straight line—even if it bisected six admirals."

Rickover's planning battle went on four years before the keel plate was laid at Groton, Connecticut. On January 17, 1955, the signal that marked man's first use of atomic energy in propulsion was flashed from

Quartermaster Lyle B. Rayl, of the *Nautilus,* to Q.M. Gilbert L. Kerr, on the U.S.S. *Skylark*:

U. S. NAVAL DISPATCH
SND-GEN-1007

FROM:	USS NAUTILUS SSN 571	CLASSIFICATION UNCL	PRECEDENCE ROUTINE
ACTION:	COMSUBLANT		
INFO:			

```
NJOF DE NWCL
-T-YZZF
-R-171601Z -FM NWCL -TO YZZF GR 7/8 BT


UNDERWAY 1166R ON NUCLEAR POWER BT....


                    TOP /1133R      VU/ELT

                 F.L.
```

RELEASE	CY	TOR	TOD	DATE	D/T GR
			1133 R	17 JAN 55	171601Z

W	QW	3	4 X	5	6	7	8	9	10	11	12	13	14	15 X	16	17	18	19	20	21	22	23	24

SND-PSPO-(865)

6

Zero Nine Zero

THE U.S.S. *New Ironsides* sat at her station in the Charleston blockade on an October night in 1863. One of the brutal first-born of the U.S.S. *Monitor*, she was a ponderous three-master with a funnel before the mainmast and a wooden hull covered with four-inch iron plates. The Confederates had special reason to hate her. After the battle of Gettysburg that July, their own hopes of ironclads to smash the blockade were gone. In awe of Gettysburg, Britain and France, which were building a dozen iron ships for the South, decided not to deliver. But even with this comforting news, Lieutenant C. W. Howard, watch officer of the *New Ironsides,* was not the kind to relax. He inspected his guard. The rebels were always up to some desperate trick or another.

A sentry yelled a challenge. Howard ran to him. A strange object was moving toward them, an upright barrel-shape, low in the black water. It was not one of the Confederate drifting mines. It laid a white wake and sparks flared from it. Howard could not depress his two-hundred-pound Parrott guns low enough to fire on it. He ordered musket fire and sounded general quarters. The sentries snapped away, but the strange thing kept coming. There was a violent explosion a few yards off the *New Ironsides.* A towering waterspout roared into the air and, when it fell, Howard was dying of shrapnel wounds. The ironclad heeled in the explosion wave but rocked back to level, undamaged. Two Union monitors took up the chase of the mysterious craft, but it disappeared. Then a Federal collier found a young Southern officer swimming weakly in the bay—Lieutenant W. T. Glassell. The mystery was out. Glassell was commander of a Confederate steam submarine, the *David,* and he had tried Goliath with a spar torpedo, a mine on the end of an eighteen-foot pole sticking from the snout of his undersea craft. He had fired by a lanyard inside and misjudged his distance in the dark. He got out before the *David* sank.

Dutiful Lieutenant Howard was the first casualty of a submarine attack, although it failed to damage his ship. The Union Navy was thoroughly alerted for any further sneak attacks. In truth, the South was building several more *Davids*. Weak industrially, she could not even duplicate the fifty-foot Glassell craft, but built in New Orleans a smaller *David*, twenty-five feet long, designed by Captain Hunley. She was propelled by eight men sitting along the port side, turning the propeller shaft. Their officer navigated from a forward turret and manned the spar torpedo. When the Union Army took New Orleans, *David No. 2* was still incomplete, and was sunk to hide her from the foe. The submarine was salvaged long after the war and exhibited in New Orleans. Another *David* was laid down in Mobile by William A. Alexander, an artillery officer. She sank with all hands on her first run toward the federal blockade ships.

A fourth *David* was constructed and shipped by rail to Charleston. She was setting out for battle when the wake wave of a steamer swamped her with all hands. Only the skipper escaped. She was fished up and a new crew assembled. They started out from Fort Sumner and sank. Six men escaped. The *David* was salvaged again and began another attack from the Cooper River. This time she sank and drowned all nine men. The Confederates refused to give up the idea. The submarine was raised for the fourth time and a Lieutenant Dixon given command.

The pathetic attempts were now widely known. On January 14, 1864, the U.S. Secretary of the Navy wrote Vice Admiral John A. Dahlgren, commanding the South Atlantic fleet off Charleston, warning him that the Confederates had a new boat capable of much mischief. Washington took this very seriously, and Dahlgren redisposed his ships and put his men on their toes. He placed the newly built, heavily armed ironclad *Housatonic* as a guardship on the shoreward side of the formation. A month later, Lieutenant J. K. Crosby, watch officer of the *Housatonic* was going about his duties at 8:45 in the evening, when he saw a low shape gliding through the water toward his starboard. He sounded general quarters. In two minutes the object bumped the *Housatonic* midships near the powder magazine. Lieutenant Dixon made very sure of his contact. He held his mine against the side for a full minute before he pulled the lanyard. In the hellish flash the broken *David* rolled up in the waterspout and slid down stern first, showed her shattered spar for a moment and was gone. The great ironclad rocked far over and sank by the stern.

The submarine boat had sunk her first ship.

Five men died on the *Housatonic*; the others were saved by boats from the U.S.S. *Canandaiga*. The names of the men who went down with Dixon were Arnold Becker, C. Simpson, James A. Wicks, F. Collins, and Ridgeway, of the Confederate States Navy, with Captain J. F. Carlson, an artillery officer.

The Union Navy played with the idea of submarines, but placed most of its reliance on monitors, which steamed with decks awash. The engineers William W. Wood and John L. Lay, inventor of an effective spar torpedo, built an interesting semisubmersible, the *Spuyten Duyvil*, too late to see battle. She had a retractible spar torpedo under water at the bow. Lincoln boarded the *Spuyten Duyvil* in 1865 when he visited Richmond, the fallen Confederate capital.

For seventy-five years afterward no American submarine had a confirmed sinking of an enemy ship, until the U.S. *Swordfish*, out of Manila, destroyed the S.S. *Atsutusan Maru* on December 16, 1941, to begin the tremendous Pacific undersea offensive that sank eleven hundred Japanese ships.

After Charleston, the next combat period of undersea boats was 1914–18.

Britain's early submariners were a cheeky lot. A tall, grave, blond young man named Martin E. Nasmith, commanded H.M. Submarine *E-11* out of Harwich in 1914. He got himself into a three-dimensional battle on Christmas morning. It was a combined operation in the Heligoland Bight, in which three British seaplane carriers sent nine aircraft against the Zeppelin hangars at Cuxhafen. Lieutenant Commander Nasmith's boat was part of an undersea escort flotilla which hoped to bag any German vessels that came out after the carriers. He patrolled at periscope depth with a bright sky in the eye piece. The planes, however, ran into thick ground fog over land and droned around, trying to find holes to dive through. They stayed as long as they could and then made for sea. One came down, out of gas, and landed near Nasmith.

He surfaced, picked up the pilot and put a tow on the machine. Two more failing planes buzzed down and landed near him. He heard another disturbance in the air and there was a fat Zeppelin, chasing the mosquitoes. The angry sausage was loaded with bombs. Nasmith and his guests were sitting ducks. The submarine *D-6*, coming to Nasmith's assistance, crash-dived from the path of the airship. Nasmith refused to allow the German to capture the pilots or their bombsights. He brought them all on his deck as the dirigible came over low with the bomb-aimer bent over his cross wires. Nasmith took off his cap and waved to the Zeppelin. The startled German commander reacted fast. He stopped his bombardier, thinking the submarine was German. The big shadow crossed over the *E-11*. Nasmith's salvage tumbled down the hatch. He pelted after them,

bolted the hatch and crash-dived. The inflated knockwurst turned labor-
iously and ran back, dropping a rack of futile bombs on Nasmith's ballast
boils. Sadly the Zeppelin swam off to Cuxhaven. Then the *D-6* came up
and sank the planes.

The second ship sunk by a submarine after the U.S.S. *Housatonic* was
H.M.S. *Pathfinder*, which fell to a U-boat September 5, 1914. Then came
the catastrophe which had been dreaded by proper admirals since the days
of Fulton's subversive activity. Lieutenant Otto Weddigen, in the *Unter-
seeboot 9* sank H.M.S. *Aboukir, Hogue* and *Cressy* in one terrific attack,
taking the lives of almost two thousand men. Twenty-eight men in a four
hundred-ton boat sank forty thousand tons and got away unscathed.
Weddigen lived six months. He tried attacking the cruising Grand Fleet.
After missing one with a torpedo, he was rammed and cut in half by
H.M.S. *Dreadnought*. The initial surprise blow, the opportunity of the
aggressor, was repeated by the Germans in the opening days of the Second
Great War, when a tough little U-boat commander named Günther Prien
sneaked the *U-47* through Kirk Sound into Scapa Flow, the British
Home Fleet base. He surfaced and fired two torpedoes at the old seaplane
carrier *Pegasus* and the battleship *Royal Oak*. Prien observed no hit on
the battleship, so he coolly circled on the surface for eighteen minutes while
his crew reloaded the torpedo tubes. He sent two more into the *Royal
Oak* and escaped on the surface. Working out of the captured French base
of Lorient, Prien attacked a North Atlantic convoy in October, 1940, and
sank eight merchantmen out of the thirty-two that fell to seven U-boats.
Prien was defeated six months later in the North Atlantic, when he was
depth-bombed by H.M.S. *Wolverine*. This engagement finished three
Nazi submarine aces: Prien, Lieutenant Schepke, crushed against his periscope by H.M.S. *Vanoc*, and Lieutenant Kretschmer, rammed by the
destroyer *Walker* and picked up captive.

Long before the powerful long-range Nazi wolves marauded in the
forties, a saucy band of men of Harwich took their little boats in the Baltic.
One of them was Nasmith and the other was Max Horton, the master-
mind of Allied North Atlantic battles in World War II. Submarines were
towed submerged by North Sea trawlers, which were being sunk by
German surface vessels co-operating with the U-boats' starvation blockade.
A Scottish fisherman would lure an attacker up close and the submarine
would surface and sink him. One of these decoy tandems sighted the van
of the Kaiser's high seas fleet. Neither vessel had wireless. They used
carrier pigeons contributed by patriotic fanciers. The trawler skipper
scribbled the news in triplicate, ran down to the forecastle and inserted the
papers in the mail bags of three pigeons. He took the cage on deck and
opened the door. The pigeons positively refused to fly. They were too fat

from the loving care of the crew. The submarines went out with white mice issued from naval stores. Mice, as we have seen, have such a high metabolism that they die in noxious fumes much earlier than men. When the submarines returned from long patrols, medical officers inventoried the mice and required obituaries to gain information on breathing conditions during the cruise. This logical diagnostic failed utterly. Very few mice came back. The tenderhearted sailors gave them away to foster homes in ports of call. Submarining, in their opinion, was no career for rodents.

A U-boat commander, the imaginative and bold Lieutenant Otto Hersing, unfolded some more bad news for traditional naval thinkers during the Dardanelles campaign of 1915. The British and Anzacs had landed at Gallipoli with heavy naval support. There were no German or Turkish submarines to mess into the situation. The Turks asked their German ally for a submarine. To send one from the Baltic to the Bosphorus was an unprecedented undertaking. Before the war the Swedish submarine *Hvalen* had cruised from her Italian launching yards to Sweden, and in 1910 three British submarines had gone ten thousand miles to Hong Kong, but they were on peacetime ferries, calling frequently at ports and shepherded by escorts. Lieutenant Hersing undertook to sail the *U-21* to Turkey, through thousands of miles of enemy-dominated waters. He left Wilhelmshaven the day the Australians and British landed at Gallipoli.

He refueled for the Mediterranean from a Spanish tanker in Corcubión Bay and sailed on. Then he discovered the Spanish oil was no good for his Diesels. He figured he had enough German oil left to make the nearest Austrian port, Cattaro (now Kotor, Yugoslavia) if he cruised slowly the whole way on the surface. He pushed on through the Straits of Gibraltar. He was sighted four times by Allied ships and depth-bombed once, but crawled into Cattaro in nineteen days with a half ton of oil left.

He ran the Aegean and got into the Dardanelles, where British battleships were standing at anchor, bombarding the enemy shore. They were surrounded by antitorpedo nets, of course. Hersing's packet was the last thing they expected. He surfaced off the 11,800-ton H.M.S. *Triumph* at high noon and blew her into an upside-down roll to the bottom. The torpedo passed through the steel nets as though they were cotton seines. Three days later he drilled the 15,000 ton H.M.S. *Majestic*. She turned over and sank in five minutes. Commander E. K. Chatterton, the British marine historian, said, "Hersing had demonstrated the immense possibilities of one submarine's working independently, and had proved the uselessness of steel nets. Thenceforth no battleship could be safe unless anchored in harbor behind boom defenses or zigzagging at high speed."

Two years later, however, two audacious Italian underwater men showed how to sink them behind boom defenses, as will be described later.

British submarines delivered a countersurprise when Turkey joined the Germans in 1914. At Tenedos, a small island south of the Dardanelles, there were three outmoded B-class boats, launched in 1905. They had reeking gasoline engines and weak batteries, canvas conning towers and stronghearted men. Also at the island were three French submarines, whose commanders planned a raid through the strongly defended Dardanelles narrows. Lieutenant Norman B. Holbrook, R.N., commander of the submarine *B-11,* wanted to be first. The German battleships *Goeben* and *Breslau* were lording it over the Russians in the Black Sea, and the Turks were feeling their halvah.

Holbrook fitted the *B-11* with a jump wire, which the U.S. Navy calls a crash wire, a heavy cable running from the bow to the top of the periscope and down to the stern. It serves to ward off antisubmarine nets or mine cables. The *B-11* was also provided with curved steel fenders on her hydroplanes to serve a similar function. Holbrook set out slowly on the surface to conserve his batteries. They would have plenty to do when he tried to run against a five-knot current with a seven-knot boat. He got into the narrows, staying fifty feet down to pass under mines. He struck a jarring, drumming obstacle and surfaced to see what it was. A mine cable had twisted one of his fenders into a hook, sure to foul the next mine. The crew could not bend it back into place. Holbrook stayed on the surface while the artificers went into the water and removed the fender. He pressed on four hours under water until he reckoned he was about out of the narrows. He blew water ballast and went up for a peek. He was at the right spot, a mile or so off Cannakale, and there was a big warship looming two stacks over the town. He had only two torpedo tubes. A shot of a mile in the swift current would probably waste one. He dived and closed in. His next peep showed the current had carried him far off the course. He breasted the current to draw even, but it was too strong. Slipping away from the target, Holbrook fired his starboard tube at eight hundred yards. The torpedo leaped out and upset the little submarine's trim. The periscope went under and the skipper could not see what happened. The *B-11* rattled around in a thumping shock. Her people were just as happy to stay right down there and ride home in the lovely current.

Young Holbrook could not believe one lucky torpedo could murder a ship that size. He surfaced to look. The big ship, the Turkish battleship *Messudieh,* was definitely settling. Her guns and shore artillery were whanging away at the *B-11.* This class of submarine carried its compass on a binnacle on deck to hold it as far as possible from the electrical motors. One of the shell bursts wrecked the compass. The *B-11* stayed below, swept blindly in the current. Holbrook raised the periscope and saw they had been carried into Cannakale Bay under shore batteries. Down they went and made for what they fondly hoped was the bay mouth. The *B-11* thudded heavily and the crew went tumbling. They had struck a sandspit. The little boat bounced toward the surface. Holbrook flooded heavily to stay down. She kept bumping hollowly, and each time the depth gauges narrowed. He realized they were grinding their way to the surface on a shallow shoal. Then the *B-11* came to a soft stop and Holbrook looked out the conning tower ports at blue sky. The view was obscured by noisy walls of white water as the Turkish guns focused on them. He ordered everything the electric motors had left. The ammometers twirled over the danger mark. The *B-11* slid foot by foot on her belly, ringing with shell explosions, and dived heavily off the sand bar. The men frantically blew water ballast to trim off before they hit bottom. She straightened out at comfortable depth, where the shell bursts were muffled. None of the fifteen-man crew was injured but they did not know what was to come next.

Holbrook still had his periscope. He climbed and saw they were apparently surrounded by land, even further into the bay. The only landmark in sight was the one that he had recently fixed quite firmly, the *Messudieh,* standing on a shallow bottom. He passed out of the bay by peeping from time to time at the wreck. They reached the European bank and sailed home in the Marmara stream at a depth of eighty feet. B-boats were not supposed to go that deep. They passed under five mine barrages and came up safe from a nine-hour blind dive, wtih their air so far gone they could not light a match in it.

With the allied landings in Gallipoli there came several E-class submarines, including Commander Martin Nasmith's *E-11.* He continued past Gallipoli into the enemy-dominated Sea of Marmara, accosted a dhow and made her fast to his conning tower as a disguise. He trailed the bait off the Bosphorus, looking for targets, but nothing came out. He let go the dhow and her crew, hoping they would quickly report a submarine near Constantinople. Nasmith headed for the western Marmara Sea, where the Turks might feel safe to resume troop crossings to Europe. There the *E-11* sank a couple of small ships and doubled back to the Constantinople bight. Nasmith accosted a small steamer, whose crew bailed out rapidly, spilling their boats. A smiling man in khaki with a white armband came on deck and shouted, "Glad to see you. I'm Raymond Gram Swing of the Chicago *Daily News.*" "Charmed," said Nasmith. "Where are you bound and what are you carrying?" Swing was a neutral war correspondent and felt constrained not to provide information. The boarding party found the ship loaded with big guns and projectiles marked "Krupp." Nasmith escorted Swing and the crew into lifeboats and sank the ship with deck guns.

The E-11 chased another deep-laden ship into the port of Rodosto on the European shore and sank her beside a pier. The water was so shallow Nasmith couldn't get his periscope under. A paddle-wheeler came by and Nasmith stopped her to put on a boarding party. The spunky captain of the relic reversed a paddle and turned to ram the E-11. Nasmith was faced with a mortifying situation, like an aircraft pilot being shot down by a Montgolfier balloon. He ducked. When he surfaced again the target was waddling off in a hurry. He chased her. The sidewheeler deliberately ran aground. He closed in to land a party to blow her up. Thereupon a Turkish cavalry squadron arrived, flung themselves from their steeds and started rattling lively fire on the submarine. Nasmith had to dive. Standing off a ways he raised his periscope and skipped a torpedo at the ship. It ran up on the beach and exploded harmlessly.

Licked by a paddle-wheeler and cavalry, the red-faced lieutenant set his jaw and made for Constantinople. He dived into the Bosphorus Strait and came up beside a steam launch with a huge bemedalled pasha squatting on the stern. His Serenity did not see the periscope. The E-11 continued at periscope depth to the entrance of the great Ottoman harbor, the Golden Horn. It was like an enemy submarine arriving at the New York Battery and looking over the Brooklyn Navy Yard and the crowded piers of the North River for a good victim. Nasmith saw a transport loading at the Turkish navy yard. He lined up and fired one, but did not see any wake. His second torpedo hit true. As it exploded, Nasmith put a camera to the eye piece of the periscope and got a clear picture of his kill. The first torpedo, which had been running in a circle, now bore down on the E-11. Nasmith crash-dived and heard it explode a few minutes later—on a wharf, as it turned out.

He entered the swift current to get out of there. The E-11 bumped shoals several times but got off safely. Nasmith sank a supply ship and missed another. Torpedoes were a valuable thing to him and he devised a method for retrieving bad shots. Before then torpedoes were set to sink after they had missed. He changed them to float at the end of their runs. The next torpedo that missed Nasmith carefully overtook from behind. A seaman went into the water and unscrewed the detonator on the nose. Nasmith flooded his aftertanks until the forward tubes stood partially out of water. The sailor wrestled the torpedo back into the tube. They closed the outer hatch, blew water from the tube and pulled the torpedo into the submarine.

The E-11 had now been in enemy waters for nineteen days. She was urgently in need of overhaul. Nasmith made for the Dardanelles and started through the ten mine barrages. He had two torpedoes left which he hoped to deliver in the narrows. No targets were sighted. Instead of continuing on to base after his glorious patrol, Nasmith turned around, went back through the minefields and sank a transport with his last torpedoes. Going home very deep through the mines of Kalid Bahr, the E-11 swiped something. Nasmith climbed and upped periscope. He saw a large mine a few feet away. Its cable was fouled in his hydroplane. He did not mention it to the crew. He ran the periscope down and said matter-of-factly, "Take her down to ninety feet, Coxswain." The dive would keep the mine flying above the hull and give him time to think. He had been very lucky not to touch a detonator when he surfaced. But would the E-11 ever be able to surface again? It would be like landing a plane with an armed bomb hanging from the undercarriage. Perhaps Nasmith envied the happy crew, ignorant of the fact that they were cruising home through a minefield with a mine flying above them like a captive balloon. He decided he had gone far enough with this worry: "Full speed astern! Blow after ballast tanks!"

The orders were a gasping surprise. No one had felt a new shock, but the crew fell to automatically. The E-11 roared up by the stern at a steep incline. Nasmith peered in the eye piece and saw the mine being towed backward from his bow. It was safely clear of the boat. He ordered, "Blow forward ballast tanks. Easy does it." The bow slowly rose and the mine pulled its cable out of the hydroplane. The E-11 submerged and went peacefully home.

The raids practically drove Turkish ships from the Sea of Marmara. Submarines going in would navigate the bend in the narrows by crashing the nets. Turkish troops and supplies had to move clumsily by rail. Where the railroad skirted the sea, British submarines shelled line and bridges and once even a passing troop train. Nasmith's next patrol took the E-11 to the eastern extremity of the Sea of Marmara, the Gulf of Ismid. He went in and shelled an important viaduct on the Berlin-Bagdad railway. The bridge was hotly defended by gunners. The E-11 submerged. Nasmith and his executive officer, Lieutenant Guy D'Oyly Hughes, cooked up a one-man amphibious raid. They returned at night and surfaced under a cliff. D'Oyly Hughes swam ashore in his underwear, towing on an improvised raft his uniform, sixteen pounds of explosive, a stiletto and a whistle. He put on his uniform, not wishing to be shot as a spy, and climbed the cliff with his surprise package.

For an hour Number One floundered overland in the night before he found the railway. He followed it toward the viaduct, and stopped when he heard Turkish sentries yarning loudly on the tracks. He decided to cache his can of guncotton and detour the sentries to find his bearings. He proceeded through several farms, scaled a wall and landed in a chicken coop. The poultry shrieked deafeningly, but nobody awakened. He fled the coop and came upon the viaduct. It was all lighted up. Repair crews were working on the *E-11's* shell damage. D'Oyly Hughes was beaten. There was no chance of planting his stuff there.

He looped back for his explosive and searched for another vulnerable place in the Berlin-Bagdad railway. He found a culvert over a dry streambed between the sentries and the viaduct. He laid the guncotton and fired the fuse with a loud snap. The Turks started shouting. He did not want them to find the charge and snatch the fuse out before it exploded, so he ran noisily in the open and fired revolver shots to draw attention to himself. He ran a mile up the railway and slid down the cliff to swim to the submarine. The stone culvert blew up so beautifully that it bounced fragments on the *E-11*.

Unfortunately, D'Oyly Hughes had overrun the submarine. He swam out, fully clothed, and blew his whistle, but there was no sign of her. He returned to the rocks and rested under some bushes. He began prowling cautiously back in the direction of the culvert, hunting the submarine. Daylight grew. His only chance of escape was by sea. He removed his uniform and sank it with everything but the whistle and dived in again. He whistled and the *E-11* moved toward him with her fore and aft radio masts, conning tower and periscope gently parting the waves in the faint light. D'Oyly Hughes thought they were Turkish boats coming after him. He swam madly to shore again. He didn't think he had any more energy. But he did. When he saw it was the *E-11*, he shouted and leaped into the sea.

D'Oyly Hughes' classic raid did not change the course of the war. The culvert was repaired in a few days. His foray had a future meaning. One of the officers who sent the submarines on these raids was Commodore Sir Roger Keyes. In the Second World War he organized and trained the amphibious Commandos.

In a small office deep in "Main Navy," the labyrinthine building on Constitution Avenue, Washington, I met a slight, white-haired old man with a pink, worn face and bifocals with the magnifying part set in circles in the center of the lenses. They made his blue eyes look enormous and childlike. He was Admiral Julius Furer, retired, maker of one of the legends of underwater engineering. In 1915 he brought up a complete vessel from 304 feet, the greatest depth in the history of salvage. She was the United States Submarine *F-4*.

When I called, Admiral Furer was working on a history of naval

administration in the Second World War, but he took time out to re-
count the story of the *F-4.* "It was the valor of ignorance," he said. "If
I had known when I started out to raise the *F-4* what I knew five months
later, I believe I might have left her right there. I was not a salvage officer,
but an engineer-constructor, same class as Admiral King at the Academy.
In '14, I was superintendent of the Philadelphia Navy Yard, when the
Navy decided to build a base at Pearl Harbor in Hawaii. I was assigned to
set up the naval yard there. We built a big graving dock in Philadelphia
and towed her out around the Horn. The Panama Canal wasn't open
yet.

"The drydock was built like all the rest, a steel structure to be imbedded in the usual rock. Nobody thought of the fact that Hawaii is a
coral formation on lava. Very porous material. We excavated and put the
dock down. The coral was full of the hydrostatic pressure of the sea. It
busted right up through the dock. But, in the meantime, the wheels were
turning, and four new submarines of the F-class were sent on schedule to
the new base that wasn't there. They displaced 260 tons under water. They
came with their tender, the *Alert,* and I had my hands full. We had no
dock or shop machinery yet. I noticed in regulations that submarines had
to be inclined every year to check their stability. So I had to incline 'em. I
was never so thankful for a regulation in my life, because that check
eliminated one big probability for the loss of the *F-4.*

"In March, 1915, the submarines went out on a routine morning
exercise toward Diamond Head from the little old base at Honolulu.
They made a dive and returned, but the *F-4* didn't come back. The officer
of the deck sent boats and they found an oil slick two miles out. He called
me up at Pearl and said the oil was over a place a thousand feet deep. The
island inclines very sharply, so we started dragging up the slope hoping
the wreck was higher. We struck a likely object at 304 feet, but divers
could not go that far in those days. An electrician in one of the submarines
rigged a metal detector, two nails on a bridge with wires leading off to a
sounding wire. We poked around with this and got a buzz when a metal
plate closed the circuit. I started dragging with two tugs, hoping to lift
the sub and bounce her in to shallow water. We fished up some old sailing ship anchors but no submarine. The drag came up with paint smears
of a submarine and a bit of bronze from the conning tower. The Navy
Department was inclined to abandon her. Nothing had ever been raised
from that depth. I wanted to try it.

"We had some wonderful shallow-water divers on the other submarines.
One was a full-blooded Indian, Chief Gunner's Mate Agraz. The water
was clear, so Agraz volunteered to go down as far as he could, hoping to
sight the submarine. He did not wear a suit, only the helmet. He said that

was so he could get out fast in case anything happened. That Indian was ready to bail out naked at 200 feet and swim for it. The nerve of those people and what they'd do under water! Agraz went down 215 feet but he could not see through to the submarine. He was bothered by little fish that came up under the helmet and nibbled his neck and chin.

"The cruiser *Maryland* arrived with Chief George Stillson and four deep divers, Frank Crilley, Drelishak, Nielson and Loughman. Dr. French, the diving physiologist, was with them and they had a big recompression chamber. Those men were bugs on diving. Crilley was awful smart and built just right for a diver. Stillson had a funny attitude on the *F-4*. He thought we should leave it all to the divers. They were so sold on diving they thought it could do everything. He wanted to go down with an air hose and fit it in a salvage valve the submarines had, and blow her full of air. I would have taken any advice that would have brought that submarine up. But I knew that was not a good idea. A vessel has to have controlled buoyancy. If he'd sent her up that way, the air would have expanded ten times. She'd have exploded and sank again.

"The divers went down to that submarine—304 feet! As I remember, Drelishak was the only one not able to make it. They would stay down ten minutes at a time, seeing that my dragwires were being hauled under at the right places. They took water hoses and jetted trenches under her for the cables. They reported there were absolutely no holes or open valves in the *F-4*. Why did she go down? That question made me more and more determined to get her up.

"We had nothing to work with. The only cables I could find in Hawaii were nine inches thick and about as flexible as iron bars. We had no salvage tenders. Used two bottom-dump mud scows with enough buoyancy to lift the submarine. There isn't enough tide in Hawaii to make it work for you by tightening up your cables on the low tide and letting the high tide do the lifting. We had no winches. Made 'em on the scows out of shafts from sugar mills. The only machine shop in the islands was a little one that handled sugar-mill machinery. But we had good weather and made some progress lifting the *F-4* up the hill. One time Loughman was down and the current whirled him around and turned his air pipe several times around the shot line. Crilley went down two hundred feet and worked two hours to get him clear. The newspapermen came out every evening and they'd always ask me for an estimate when we'd have her in. I refused to predict. After two months we had the submarine up to eighty feet, almost into the main channel, and the next morning I was sure we'd jump her to forty feet. A reporter asked the usual question and I said, 'I'll say we will be in tomorrow afternoon.'

"It was three months from that day that we finally got her in. The next

morning a cable jammed and we had a delay putting it right. I always had
one eye toward Diamond Head, watching the weather. It had been
marvelous up to then. That morning I saw a big white comber away out.
A tremendous surf built up in a half hour. The scows swept back and
forth, anchored by the submarine. It looked like the whole works was
going on the reef. I had to let go everything and take the scows in. We
couldn't go back for three days. Agraz went down and found the submarine had a big gash amidships. If we tried draglines again the submarine
might break in half and block the harbor. The scows were finished. I had
to think of another method."

Commander Furer invented a classic salvage tool, which has been used
ever since. He constructed six huge metal drums, sheathed in wood to
reduce friction against ships' sides. Through the drums he ran hawsepipes
for chain cable. These drums were filled with enough water to sink gently
and permit the divers to fasten three on either side of the submarine. They
passed chains under the *F-4* and clamped the pontoons firmly. Then they
blew the water out of the drums with compressed air, carefully control-
ling the volume so that the submarine would come up evenly. The drums
worked beautifully. The same pontoons were later used on the sunken
submarines *S-51* and *S-5* and the *Squalus*. (Furer never did another salvage
job. He was rotated to stations in Brazil, London and many other posts in
Navy fashion.)

When the submarine was in his now-rebuilt drydock, Commander Furer
turned detective to penetrate the mystery of why she sank and was completely filled with water when not a hatch was open and all valves were
closed. The main clues were that the *F-4* had been found with her rudder
turned and there were several loose rivets in the inner pressure hull. This
was inside the exterior shell which formed the water ballast tanks. The
loose, corroded rivets were right next to the battery compartment, a well
in which sulphuric acid battery jars were nested. Of course, sulphuric
acid corrodes steel, but submarines had long lined the battery compartment
with thick plates of lead, which does not corrode from sulphuric acid.
The mystery grew more obtuse when Furer saw that the lead plates were
white and cratered through by some unknown corrosive. It had let the
acid through to attack the steel rivets. The Navy has never given an
official explanation of why the *F-4* sank, but Admiral Furer thinks he
discovered it.

"The batteries nested against each other in the lead-lined compartment,"
he said, "and were wedged even tighter by wooden splints. I heard that
telephone companies find violent corrosion in lead-lined underground
cables. Chemists found this was caused by acetic acid from vegetable
matter. I think the wooden splints in the *F-4* were green. They generated

acetic acid and cratered the lead. Then the sulphuric acid followed through to the steel.

"I had a picture of the last hours of the *F-4*. The lead was eaten away, unseen under the deck of the battery well. The rivets were already loose and seeping when she dived that day. Water started in by the gallons, still unseen. The commander felt her handle sluggishly. He had too much negative buoyancy and had to struggle to retain his trim. He decided to turn around and make for shallower water. We found the rudder turned. He was sinking slowly as he turned. There is a moment on the turn when the hydroplanes lose their lifting power and this sent him deeper. Then he might have seen water rising from the bilges. He acted fast and tripped his safety valve to blast all the water from his outside ballast tanks with compressed air. This blast only forced more water into the boat. He was laboring for shallow water. It was touch and go. She was going deeper and deeper until she ran aground where we found her. Then she filled up.

"We immediately ordered battery inspection in the other three F-boats. One of them also had corroded lead in the well. After that we changed the design." Commander Furer's determination to raise the *F-4* and find out why she sank, coupled with the stupendous dives of Crilley and his mates, saved a whole class of submarines from unknowable disaster. "The valor of ignorance is a great thing," the Admiral said, without smiling, and looked at me dead center through his magnifying lenses.

In World War II, United States long-range submarines, operating in the Pacific, sank 1,150 ships. Thirty of them fell in nine months to the U.S.S. *Tang*, under Commander Richard Hetherington O'Kane. The short career of the *Tang* climaxed in a patrol of Homeric clash and doom.

In her first four patrols the *Tang* sank seventeen ships. She set out of Pearl Harbor on September 24, 1944, for the fifth and last. There were eighty-eight men in the 300-foot submarine, and twenty-four torpedoes. She was O'Kane's first command. He had been executive officer of the *Wahoo*, under Commander Dudley W. Morton, a savage strategist, who would sit with his periscope up to guide onrushing Japanese destroyers and then fire torpedoes "down their throats." Morton was missing on patrol and O'Kane went out for revenge.

He proceeded to the Taiwan Strait between China and Formosa, the "safest" passage for Japanese ships hurrying to reinforce the Philippines. The decisive and greatest naval battle of the war was gathering in Leyte Gulf. The *Tang* sank two freighters, and tailed a cruiser and two destroyers, which forced her off with eight-inch guns. Two nights before the battle of Leyte Gulf, O'Kane raised three tankers in a column with two transports in line beside them, bound with escort vessels for the Philippines. The *Tang* ran ahead of them, turned broadside and lay in wait with six forward torpedoes pointing to where the tankers would pass and four after torpedoes ready for the transports.

The convoy came plodding on in the dark and started past on both ends of the submarine. The *Tang* sent two torpedoes into the first tanker, one in the second and two in the third. The first ship exploded with a vast flare of light while the torpedoes were still on their way to the others. The transports, which had not yet drawn up to the *Tang,* saw the submarine in the glare of flaming aviation gas and turned to ram. O'Kane had no time to dive. He yelled down the hatch to his telephone talker, "Stand by to ram! Collision Quarters! All ahead emergency! Right full rudder!" He sent everyone below and stayed alone in the conning tower. He planned to escape on the surface. The *Tang* circled to cross the bows of the outside ship. She turned in to cut him in two. O'Kane shouted, "Left full rudder!" and the submarine flicked her tail away from the angry ship. As the lofty side reeled past the Japanese fired machine guns at O'Kane.

The would-be rammer had to stay on this course to avoid her sister ship. That gave O'Kane a moment to maneuver for a shot. While she was set on this course, he fired the four stern torpedoes. As they neared the trooper he saw an incredible sight. The transports were not able to avoid collision. The ships mingled with a scream of men, a crashing, grinding roar of plates chewing and tearing, and then the *Tang's* four torpedoes exploded in the mound of wreckage, one by one, at ten second intervals. Five ships, the entire convoy, in ten minutes!

The next day, the day the distant battle commenced in the Philippines, as darkness came the radar scope in the submarine lighted up with splotches of orange fire to the north. Another big convoy. The *Tang* slipped in ahead of the procession and O'Kane studied its behavior. The flotilla had apparently received news of the catastrophe of the previous day. The escorts were racing back and forth along the outskirts of the convoy, firing into the dark, and nervously signaling to the merchantmen with big blinker lamps. The light allowed O'Kane to confirm the makeup of the convoy. The leading column consisted of two transports and a tanker. The *Tang* slid slowly toward the first transport, fired two; waited for the second, fired two; and emptied her bow tubes with two more into the tanker.

All torpedoes went home and exploded. On came another tanker and freighter and O'Kane maneuvered his stern tubes to get them. Now the Japanese had seen the submarine and the escorts were shooting at the conning tower. O'Kane fired three torpedoes, brought all his Diesels up full and the *Tang* began to run. As they retreated O'Kane saw a new ship, a big destroyer, coming out of the smoke and flames.

He carefully gauged her speed. Could he outrun the destroyer or would he have to dive and take a depth bombing? His first stern torpedo struck the transport. Another torpedo drilled into the tanker which exploded with an awful report and a column of flame. The destroyer was running by the tanker at that moment and she heaved up in a third explosion. Nine torpedoes and six ships hit! The *Tang* ran away from the smaller escorts and loaded her last two torpedoes in the forward tubes. O'Kane returned to see if there was anything left of the convoy. The *Tang* had left Pearl with twenty-four torpedoes and her commander did not intend to return any unused.

The fourth victim, the transport hit with one torpedo, was still afloat. She lay motionless in the water. Two small destroyers swept back and forth east of the trooper toward Formosa. O'Kane conned the submarine around on the other side into shallow water of the Chinese coast, and fired his penultimate torpedo at the sitting duck. To make good and sure of her he fired his last. Now they could go home from the most devastating submarine patrol in the history of warfare. The crew exulted. They yelled to each other, "Zero Nine Zero!"—the course to Pearl.

The last torpedo leaped out of the bow tube and commenced a tight circle to the left. "All ahead emergency!" O'Kane yelled down the hatch. The torpedo was likely to hit the *Tang* in a few moments. He had no time to dive. He would have to dodge it on the surface. "Right full rudder!" He and nine men stood on the bridge, watching their creature of terror drawing a phosphorescent circle in the dark water and speeding toward them in the conning tower. The *Tang* turned with maddening slowness, trying to haul her long port flank from the relentless robot.

The twenty-fourth torpedo struck aft, destroying three compartments. They flooded so quickly the *Tang's* stern fell like a rock. O'Kane was unhurt. He yelled down to his telephonist to shut the hatch. Black water fell upon the face of the telephone man. He disappeared. The conning tower disappeared. O'Kane was engulfed in a welter of water. He popped out in a slight chop on the surface. He felt a blow on the chest, the announcement of torpedo number twenty-three, and in the flash he saw eight human heads silhouetted in the water. The bow of the *Tang* still showed above the waves. The ninth man in the conning tower, Lieutenant Lawrence Savadkin, appeared after five minutes. He had sunk with the ship, caught below the conning tower hatch. He breathed for a minute from an air pocket in the overhead, then swam up through the hatch, drained another air pocket and proceeded to gulp from a third under the bridge, before he reached the surface.

With a final boil of air from the bow, the *Tang* disappeared. O'Kane was thrilled. The bubble meant that there might be living men in the submarine, who had expelled the air from a ballast tank to try to restore her to the horizontal. But no escape buoy came up. The water was warm. The bridge survivors swam toward China. O'Kane was picked up by a Japanese destroyer only a hundred yards from shore. The Japanese put them through the mill with clubs and fists. The captors knew who O'Kane was. His destruction had been so heavy that despite U.S. security and only nine months in his own command, Richard Hetherington O'Kane was a prominent devil in the Japanese hagiography. They even knew about the days he had spent at the periscope in the *Wahoo*, while Mush Morton, his dead commander, stood by without looking, just figuring and sending orders, reliant on the eye of Number One. An American-speaking interrogator arrived and the club wielders were dismissed. The Japanese said, "What kind of listening devices did you have in the *Tang*?" O'Kane said, "No savvy." The interrogator said, "Don't give me that stuff, Dick. I was a service engineer for Submarine Signal Company in Boston."

Whatever listening devices there were in the *Tang* were now 180 feet down in the Taiwan Strait, and O'Kane left his new friend wondering about them, as he was taken away to Japan. The submarine had settled upright on the floor and there were thirty men alive in her forward compartments. They had immediately dogged shut the watertight door to the after rooms, beyond which there was nothing but killed or drowned men. They fought home the lower conning tower hatch against a violent waterfall. The hatch was warped in the explosion and poured spigots, even when closed. Sea swirled above their boots, but friendly China was near by and they were confident they could go up 180 feet in oxygen lungs and swim ashore. The upset enemy began depth-bombing them. This occurred at night, while O'Kane's swimmers were still working toward the coast, and the Japanese did not know that the *Tang* had taken her own poison. The entombed men lay quiet during two hours of bombs.

They collected the secret papers and burned them in the control room like ballots of the College of Cardinals. The pyre bespoke their confidence and morale, but it filled their three remaining rooms with smoke and the papers consumed oxygen. Water started an electrical fire in the middle room, the forward battery compartment. The men went to the front torpedo room, where smoke, flood and fire seemed less, and where there was an escape lock. As the underwater bombing ceased, they shared out escape lungs. They shut themselves in their cell from fire and water, and opened ducts to slowly flood up to the sextupled pressure of the sea outside. The water rose over their knees and compressed the fatal carbon dioxide of their exhalations. The fire blistered their bulkhead. The rubber gasket in the door took fire. As pressure increased it shrank the gasket and gouts of evil rubber smoke puffed into the last room.

Thirteen men went out of the air lock in good order before the gasket collapsed. The seventeen men waiting in the queue for life nodded one by one, collapsed in the death gases and slid into the water.

Five of the escapees never reached the surface. Three more arrived too far gone and sank. The Japanese rescued five, which when totted to O'Kane's party made fifteen captives. Six survivors perished in Japanese captivity. Nine came home after the war. Dick O'Kane came home, starved and bruised. He wore the starry blue ribbon of the Congressional Medal of Honor as the victor of Taiwan Strait. Captain O'Kane is still in the Navy. William Ryan, an electronics engineer, took a cruise with him recently in a new submarine. They talked about the way the Japanese treated him. O'Kane said, "I don't really know what *I'd* do if I got ahold of people that sank all *my* ships."

7
Boutan's Drowned Camera

IN the cobblestone court of honor of the Sorbonne in Paris, inset lines of white bricks trace the foundations of the original college founded in 1253. Off the court, Escalier E leads up to a laboratory-office in golden oak, where a modern tradition of the great university resides, that of the diving professor. The present chair of zoology of the Paris faculty of sciences is occupied by Professor Pierre Drach, when he is not swimming to great depths with a compressed-air lung in the five oceans and seas he has investigated in the past eighteen years. He is the fourth generation of Sorbonne zoologists to descend into the sea, beginning in 1844 with Professor Henri Milne-Edwards, the first scientist who dived, if Aristotle is ruled out for lack of proof. In *Twenty Thousand Leagues Under the Sea*, an 1869 book considered to be fiction but actually Jules Verne's dramatization of existing techniques, Professor Aronnax tells Captain Nemo that Milne-Edwards was "my worthy master."

In 1883 the guiding figure among diving scientists, Louis Boutan, climbed Escalier E to report as assistant, or *préparateur*, to the incumbent, Professor Henri de Lacaze-Duthiers. Boutan was a powerful Whitmanesque figure, twenty-four years old, with shining brown eyes, a rough's beard, and the gait of long treks. He wore a neckerchief and an Australian bush hat upswept to one side.

Boutan had gone to Australia in 1880 in the warship *Finistère* as a member of a French cultural mission to the Melbourne Exhibition, but he did not attend many cultural receptions. He roamed out back, with two Irish outlaws named Joe and Tip collecting kangaroo foetuses and strange plants. His stay ended with an incident which made him a popular hero.

He was visiting the Geelong vineyards in Victoria when he saw a tiny root louse, *Phylloxera viticola*, chewing away on a vine. He recognized a native Californian which had ravaged the Napa Valley, traveled to Europe and almost annihilated French viticulture and was now in Australia, unknown to wine growers. Boutan raised the alarm and stumped the countryside, lecturing on how France had saved her vineyards by grafting immune California rootstocks and hybrids on domestic vines. On the voyage home Boutan dived naked with the pearl fishers of the Torres Straits. At Aden and Perim he plunged to gather giant tridacna clams, the "man-eaters."

Boutan became a lecture master of the Paris Faculty of Science, which entailed teaching in the summer at the Arago station at Banyuls-sur-Mer. There in 1892 he formed an idea which was to lead to one of his greatest works, the creation of underwater photography. It was a rash idea; photographs were still taken on glass plates with wet collodion emulsions. Boutan said, "Up to the present time the [marine] naturalist finds himself in a position analogous to a visitor from the moon who might make observations from a moon-ship floating on top of our atmosphere. If this lunatic [Boutan loved a pun] wished to do some research on the inhabitants of the globe, he would be reduced to using the means our own naturalists have used up to now: he would drag and net, and perhaps dive down the anchor rope of his balloon."

Boutan acquired a "Detective" camera, a fixed-focus box which would delineate objects ten or more feet from the lens. He then thought that focusing would be impossible under water. He fitted one external control, a lever which opened and closed the shutter. At the end of the lengthy exposure, which had to last from ten minutes to a half hour, the cameraman swung the lever in the opposite direction, which closed the shutter and dropped the exposed plate, leaving a fresh one in position for the next shot. He devised a copper waterproof box with three plate-glass ports, two for his view finder and one for his lens. The box lid was screwed tight on a rubber gasket, which slightly compressed the air in the case. Boutan was aware, however, that water pressure would probably crush the box at thirty feet down. He pressurized the case with an ingenious gadget that later divers thought they had invented, a tube from the box to a rubber balloon. When water pressure collapsed the balloon, it forced more air into the case.

Louis Boutan made his first photographic dives in 1893. He reported, in the Archives of General and Experimental Zoology: "This first apparatus was not very practical." He thought photography through from the beginning and arrived at a startling proposal: since the "lens of an ordinary camera is plunged in air on both sides, there is no reason why, in a more refracting element, the lens could not similarly be plunged in water." He imagined a drowned camera, in which water circulated freely through the mechanism; thus the need for pressurization and waterproofing were removed and focus and aperture could be handled as on land. The Lumière brothers, made him some specially varnished sensitized plates, which Boutan found were "negligibly" affected by salt water. He built the water-filled camera and tested it in 1894. He reported, "The results were very mediocre. Invariably a small wave or undulation is caused (by the shutter movement), somewhat blurring the image, and this problem seemed almost insoluble to me. I should like to point out, however, that however bad the results, the future of underwater photography may well lie in this direction.

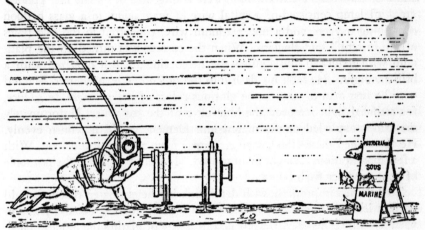

Louis Boutan makes undersea snapshot, 1897. (La Photographie Sous-Marine)

"So I went back to an arrangement similar to my first camera, a water-proof box containing both lens and plates surrounded by air." Boutan was solving the problems of underwater optics for the first time and overcoming factors that were to plague underwater photographers a half century later. He discovered that an underwater lens received a refracted image, in which subjects appeared one-fourth larger and nearer than they actually were. This is true also of the diver's eye behind a glass plate, and is due to the different velocities of light in water and in air.

The third underwater camera had an astigmatic lens which he could focus before diving. It took a photograph seven by nine and a half inches.

The third camera was a success. The big contact prints I have seen in his brother Auguste's collection, although sepiaed with age, are sharp and well composed. A newspaper ran an underwater cartoon showing a dotty old professor photographing the legs of bathing beauties. Boutan was amused. He took a submerged photograph of three sailors in striped drawers standing waist-deep in water. The undersurface of the water reflected their legs like a defective mirror. He sent the photo off to the papers and France laughed at the riposte. He published a *portrait instantané d'un plongeur*, which shows a stout naked man with his cheeks distended with breath, momentarily clinging to a staff planted in a weedy sea floor. The diver was Boutan, but he did not mention that. He climaxed his underwater photographic experiments with a technical coup described in his rare book, *La Photographie Sous-Marine et Le Progrès de la Photographie*, published in 1900. This final accomplishment was artificially lighted underwater pictures. At that time there were no submersible electric lamps, and flash bulbs and electronic flash were a long time off. "The first [photographic] lamp consisted of a spiral wire of magnesium in a glass balloon containing oxygen, and a fine platinum wire, connected to the two poles of the battery," said Boutan. "When the current was turned on the platinum wire reddened and ignited the magnesium, which oxidized with a brilliant light." He took his flash into the green depths of Barter Bay and was the first man to stare at the glorious colors of the *paysages du silence*, for artificial light removed the blue filter of the sea water. Unfortunately the lamps exploded or the magnesium filament would not burn evenly. He abandoned the method, saying, "I may have rejected it too soon. With a few modifications it might be improved." Indeed it was. It is the principle of contemporary flash bulbs.

To experiment properly with depth lighting he estimated that he would need at least ten thousand francs, which would probably equal $5,000 in what it would buy today. He saw no possibility of getting the money. Then, unannounced and unexpected, to Boutan's desk in the Sorbonne came a certain Monsieur Deloncle, president of a large optical manufacturing company, who proved to be also avuncular in deed. His engineers had built a two hundred-foot siderostat telescope for the coming Paris Exposition of 1900, and Deloncle wanted to pair pictures of the stars with photographs from the ocean deep. Boutan said, "Without ado, he told me his society was willing to give me all necessary equipment for creating underwater electric illumination on the one condition that I give photographs to be projected in the Optical Palace at the Exposition." Boutan felt that "this was perhaps the first time in history that a private commercial firm backed a scientific experiment."

Boutan built two storage batteries which could yield twenty-five amperes for one hour. They provided power for two submerged arc lamps, each with a gap of twelve inches to be leaped by flame. They would burn a half hour on a battery load. They tested in pressure equal to a depth of 330 feet, and were lowered only by the power cable. The gear was ready for im-

mersion trials at the end of August, 1899. The first test was at night.
Boutan sailed out in the evening and anchored. "There was no moon that
night," said Boutan. "The weather and the sea were very calm. Though
only a hundred metres from shore, we seemed lost in the night. The equipment was lowered to twenty feet. To test the connections we turned on the
lights. The sea floor glowed and objects could be seen much more clearly
than in the daytime."

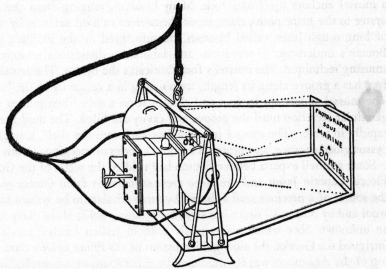

Louis Boutan's pioneer depth camera, 1899. Spheres containing arc
lamps flank the camera case. It photographed poster at 165 feet. (La
Photographie Sous-Marine)

They hauled in the arc lamps and camera and hastened to develop the
negative. It showed a ghostly cluster of gorgonian fans growing on a
clump of coral. "Satisfying, but not *too* satisfying," Boutan remarked.
"I decided to take some pictures at 50 meters [165 feet]. I prepared a
framework which held the camera and lamps on either side." He lowered
it to a depth of 165 feet with the shutter open and turned on his arc lights
for ten seconds. "I was worried about the result," he said, "and wondered
whether the camera had resisted the pressure. . . . It took a good hour to
bring the whole thing back aboard. I was genuinely relieved. For the
moment I didn't care whether the picture had succeeded or not, and when
the mechanic informed me that one of the lamps was full of water, this
news left me cold. Mopping my sweating brow, I resolved never again to
make experiments under such primitive conditions."

The plate was exposed—it was a sharp picture of the sign, *Photographie
Sous-Marine.* "The subject was a legitimate criticism," said Boutan. "How-

ever, now that the first step has been taken, genuine marine subjects should
be just as successful." He returned to Paris and, as it proved, never made
another underwater photograph. However, he had taken pictures at depths
which were not exceeded for forty years. He finished his experiments by
saying, "I have opened up a new field. It is up to others to follow, to clear
new paths, to reach the goals."

Boutan is the discoverer of one of the ocean's engineering secrets—how
a mussel anchors itself to a rock. Many bivalves, ranging from the pearl
oyster to the giant pinna clam, moor themselves to hard surfaces by a row
of long tough lines, called byssuses, manufactured by the mollusk itself.
Boutan's underwater observations and laboratory dissections revealed the
amusing technique. The mussel's foot fabricates the byssus. The retractable
foot has a groove along its length, terminating in a concavity in the "sole."
The mussel shoots out its foot and clumps it on a rock, then pumps out a
glandular secretion until the groove and cavity are filled. The fluid hardens
rapidly in water. The mussel jerks its foot back into the shell, leaving the
byssus glued in place, and proceeds to mold a series of moorings in this way.

Some seashell experts believe Bouton had riddled the secret of the Golden
Fleece. Captain Jason and the *Argo* crew sailed west from Greece to find
the source of a precious stuff believed by some scholars to be golden lambs-
wool and by others, a "fleece" or sieve for panning gold. More likely it was
an unknown fiber which was actually used in Italian knitted goods that
intrigued the Greeks, the silky golden byssus of the *Pinna nobilis* clam. The
log of the Argonauts was lip-mutilated by generations of minstrels, but the
prevailing version retains a salty smack—that Jason snatched the fleece from
a tree guarded by a sea monster. The malacologist Dr. William J. Clench
of Harvard told me that, "There has never been any question in my mind
that the byssus of *Pinna* was what Jason and his boys were after. I have seen
gloves woven out of the byssus."

Early in the First World War, Boutan and his brother Auguste, an artillery officer, designed a self-contained helmet diving dress and a one-man
chariot, which would be carried outside a mother submarine and be launched
under water by a diver who would emerge from an air lock in the bigger
ship. The chariot and diver could stay under twenty-four hours, sticking
mines on ship's bottoms by electromagnets. The idea was one war too early.
The baby submarine was never built, but its design was as advanced as the
Italian and British chariots of twenty-five years later. The diving dress used
compressed oxygen, which was regenerated in caustic soda by a clockwork
pump. The diver also carried a bottle of compressed air to keep up his internal pressure. The suit was successfully tested at Cherbourg in 1916 and
was accepted by the French Navy. The brothers offered it *avec un désin-
téressement absolu*, without profit.

A lion in the scholarly world, Boutan drew little popular notice until 1920, when he was suddenly precipitated on the front pages by an investigation he had pursued quietly for twenty-five years. The affair was touched off by a lean erudite Parisian named Lucien Pohl, an importer of oriental pearls and Chinese antiques, who had establishments in Saigon and Yokahoma. Pohl's father, who founded the business, had, in the late 1880's encountered a hustling Japanese noodle salesman named Kokichi Mikimoto of the village of Toba, near the Bay of Ago. The noodle man made a bit of money on the side by gathering mother-of-pearl and found an occasional round pearl, which he sold to Pohl. Around 1891 Mikimoto tried to induce oysters to make pearls to order—he knew that the Chinese for centuries had made amulets by inserting metallic beads and tiny carved Buddhas in the freshwater bivalve, *Dipsas plicatus*, which obligingly coated them with thin nacre. Mikimoto's Ago Bay oysters were of a different salt-water genus, *Meleagrina*; but he succeeded after several years in growing blister pearls—hemispheres attached to the inner shell—by introducing a crumb of mother-of-pearl as a nucleus between the shell and the mantle. Mikimoto obtained his first blisters in 1896. Across the world, Louis Boutan was doing exactly the same thing at the Roscoff Marine Biological Station in Brittany, and in 1898 reported in detail, in *Comptes Rendus*, of the French Academy of Science, on "Artificial Production of Pearls in the Shell of *Haliotis*." This was the ear-shaped abalone of Brittany, *Haliotis tuberculata*, a very different mollusk from the Japanese *Meleagrina*.

Mikimoto's blister pearls were exhibited at the Paris Universal Fair in 1900 and got yawns. At that time round pearls were worn in ropes by showy women, as they now wear Cadillacs. Paris was the pearl bourse of the world. Half pearls had no commercial promise. Fully rounded culture pearls resulted from Boutan's second paper, "The Real Origin of Fine Pearls," published in *Comptes Rendus* in 1903, in which he told the world, if it wanted to listen, how to induce nacreous mollusks to build round pearls. Nobody was listening except Mikimoto and alert marine biologists of the Japanese Imperial University, Professsors K. Mitsukuri and M. Miyajima.

Boutan described how he had succeeded in growing free pearls in the abalone. He pressed a crumb of nacre into the mantle, free of the shell, but not entirely enveloped in tissue. He left an open passage out to the shell. A pear-shaped pearl resulted. Boutan found that the foreign matter had to remain surrounded by the skin of the mantle, the hairy epithelial tissue which exuded the pearl-building substance. You could not simply insert foreign matter in the flesh out of contact with the epithelium. The idea persists that if you bury an irritant in the flesh of an oyster, it will build a pearl around it. The oyster will not do so, as Boutan pointed out.

Boutan said, however, that round pearls could be formed deep in the tissue if the foreign matter was wrapped in a sac of transplanted epithelial tissue. The only drawback was that, if you cut off a patch of skin, the oyster died. Mikimoto solved this by cutting a skin graft from one oyster, thereby sacrificing it, and burying the sac in another oyster whose epithelium remained intact. It made round pearls in four or five years.

Lucien Pohl broke round Mikimoto pearls in commercial quantity on the Paris market in 1920. No expert alive could screw his *loupe* in his eye and tell them from "natural" or wild pearls (*les perles sauvages*, Boutan called the accidental gems of nature). The Paris pearl market was desperate when cultured pearls arrived. The pearl syndicate had for fifty years maintained high prices on wild pearls, as South African diamonds are rigged today. One broker was said to be holding $30 million worth when Mikimoto's pearls came in in such volume and authenticity that they reduced the market value of his stockpile to one-tenth.

At that time $30 million (fr. 300,000,000) was a pretty fair bankruptcy, perhaps enough to flash TILT on the Paris bourse. The pearl king realized that his salvation lay in a vaster debt and wildly bought property on bank credits, until he was in hock for a billion francs. That amount could not be bankrupted, lest the French economy crash with him. Politicians, publishers and bankers rallied around him like epithelial tissue.

Newspapers called Pohl a dealer in "fraudulent pearls"—at that time you could buy news in French papers. Pohl sued for slander. The opposition arraigned him on a criminal charge, and the pearl war was joined. Boutan was called as an expert witness in the climactic trial and testified that the culture pearl was just as natural as the wild pearl; both grew the same way in oysters. It did not matter whether the sac were fortuitous as in nature or inserted by a clever man—the oyster did not care. This put the quietus on the wild pearl bonanza. Society women took their ropes off and pearls lost their mystique. In 1925 Boutan rounded up his knowledge in a monumental work, *La Perle*, which became a bestseller because of his newspaper fame. He is the Boswell of the pearl oyster.

Boutan retired in 1929 to a small isolated villa he built at Tigzirt-sur-Mer. He named it "Djouara," Arabic for pearl. He grew roses, wrote verse, short stories and plays and painted undersea murals on his walls. In 1934 his disciple, René Dieuzeide, saw Boutan for the last time in his lonely, almost inaccessible villa and wrote, "It was here, on a gray rainy day with a surging sea, in this calm Kabyle countryside, that I had the sad privilege of seeing him on his deathbed. With a broken heart I accompanied his coffin to the little cemetery at Tigzirt, from which the sea can be heard, and where reposes the mild and worthy scientist."

8

Undersea Snapshots

U NDERWATER photography burst out in color in the popular magazines of the 1950's. It was the realization of Boutan's beginnings sixty years before. The new photographers felt the same marvel as he did and now they had tremendous gains in techniques and equipment. The free-diving lung was a liberating tool for the photographer; suspended in space, he did not stir up dust with heavy boots and he could swim in three dimensions with fast hand-held cameras. Upward of forty types of submersible camera cases were on the market, from a die-stamped plastic box for the cheapest camera to a $6,500 professional cinécamera and a photographic torpedo with built-in lights and a propeller to push the diver.

Boutan inspired one serious follower, Etienne Peau, a semi-invalid with a large sandy mustache, son of a shipbuilder at Le Havre. Peau, an accomplished naturalist, built a cylindrical steel camera case and began taking pictures in the cold, dirty water of the Seine Bay around 1905. He studied the eyes of the Maya crab to pick up pointers on underwater optics. The crab had a sort of built-in conical lens shade which eliminated incident light in shallow water, so he put a conical hood on his lens. He had another striking idea—to seal a glass plate on the front of the cone and fill it with filtered water. That extended the camera eye far into the water, by pushing suspended dirt specks ten inches away from the lens, the nearest particles that block the view. He took round photos, which he felt had a "very peculiar charm" like a telescopic peek at a secret place. Peau did not dive with his camera because his feet would have stirred up silt. He lowered it on a weighted tripod to fifteen feet and snapped by remote control. He flashlighted his scenes by igniting magnesium powder in a submerged glass bell with a chimney to throw off combustion gases. He made clear shots of crabs, anemones, sea urchins and starfish. Peau disappeared during the Nazi invasion of Havre in 1940. He is thought to have sunk with five hundred French refugees on the S.S. *Niobe*, bound for England and never heard from.

The third underwater photographer was an obscure electrical engineer named H. Hartman. Around 1910 he began experiments under the patronage of Albert I, the "Oceanographic Prince" of Monaco. He took a working underwater camera to England, where it was patented in 1913. In 1916 Hartman turned up aboard U.S.S. *Vestal*, flagship of the Atlantic Train, with orders to test an astonishing robot depth camera. The huge rig consisted of three cylindrical housings attached to a vertical pipe. The top one held a motor, gyroscope and propeller, so that the unit could be turned completely around by remote control. Below it was an electrically driven time-lapse camera loaded with six thousand shots [sic], and at the bottom a reflector with seven fifteen hundred-watt lights. The root of the fantastic camera tree was a tripping mechanism that shed ballast if it struck bottom so the camera would return to the surface on buoyancy. The thing weighed seventeen hundred pounds and dwarfed the serious inventor. The *Vestal* tested it for seven weeks in the first underwater photographic experiment by a navy. The *Vestal* officers reported that the camera had obtained clear photos in midwater. Hartman claimed a field of twenty-five to sixty feet at a depth of seventy-five feet. The Navy did not adopt it and only re-entered underwater photography after the Second World War.

The man who put over submarine photography with the public was an energetic newspaper cartoonist of Norfolk, Virginia, John Ernest Williamson, the first undersea motion picture photographer. He was born in Liverpool of a Scottish seafaring father, who took his family to the States and started a ship-fitting business in Norfolk. Young Jack became a shipwright, studied art and landed on the *Virginian Pilot* as a cartoonist, photographer and reporter. All these knacks went to make the undersea cameraman, not the least ship-fitting. On his rounds one evening in Norfolk, he was walking on a narrow, old, waterfront street. He said, "Long, mysterious shadows filled the space between the ancient buildings, looming ghostly and unreal against the glow of the setting sun. Silence reigned. Above the crooked roofs and sagging chimneys was a fathomless green sky, and a strange sensation of standing at the bottom of the sea among the ruins of some sunken city came to me. I was seized with a sudden inspiration to make photographs of the world beneath the sea."

At the time, 1913, his father, Captain Charles Williamson, had just built a salvage machine, a sort of "hole in the sea." From a barge keel,

Captain Williamson hung a wide flexible metal tube through which one could climb down into an observation ball, look out through glass ports and work mechanical grabs on a wreck. Few fathers have found themselves in such good shape to indulge a boy's wild dream. The Williamsons towed the barge into Chesapeake Bay. With a press camera, Jack Williamson climbed thirty feet down the accordion folds of the tube to the observation sphere. "Streaming banners of light pierced to the floor of the bay," he said. "Clumps of seaweed were revealed, swaying in the current, while in the dim, pale green distance bloomed inscrutable shadows, hinting of mysteries further on. All about my chamber, undisturbed by the strange invader of their realm, the fishes swam lazily through the green sea water or stopped to peer curiously into the window." Miraculously Williamson's shots came out. There was big excitement next day in the news room when he turned them in. With the photos Williamson handed the managing editor a plan for an undersea moviemaking expedition! He had spent a feverish night planning it after he saw that his shutter speeds in under-water light were fast enough for motion pictures. No barnacles grew on Jack Williamson. His movie scheme was published with the pictures in the biggest scoop the *Virginian Pilot* has ever run. Unaware of the earlier work of Boutan, Simon Lake, Peau and Hartman, the paper crowed, "No one else has ever gone beneath the sea with a camera and brought back a suc-cessful photograph of life in the depths."

His shrewdly planted movie promotion brought Williamson offers of financial backing for a film that was to be made by a shipfitter who had never turned a movie crank. Hollywood was new and reaching for sensa-tions. Williamson rushed off to New York's First International Motion Picture Exposition with a half-dozen negatives. He blew up one fish snap to six feet, colored it with a sponge and collected the largest crowds of the show. He organized a company with Norfolk money and a New York dis-tributor, built a camera chamber he called the "photosphere" and fitted it with submersible mercury vapor floodlights. He sailed for Nassau in February, 1914, with a professional cameraman and his former managing editor on the *Pilot*, Keville Glennan, who had been so overcome with fish photography that he chucked his copy hook out the window and ran off to sea with his escaping cartoonist.

They let the photosphere down thirty feet to a dazzling white marl bottom. Williamson's first idea was to film Negro divers going down for coins. They reaped many shillings, but never appeared before his camera port. He discovered that coin diving took practically no skill. A coin side-slips so slowly going down that the clumsiest person might snatch it within six feet of the surface. Williamson saw to it that the coins were landing on the floor before the divers were sent in. That night he filmed with the powerful lamps. Both day and night shots came out perfect—the first undersea films ever made!

Soon he had a terrifying experience. The sphere was caught in a fierce, unexpected current and crashed a reef. The flexible tube gave with the impact and threw him about. When it bent back he was over the reef in calm water, with the window blessedly intact. The governor of the Bahamas arrived in his yacht, and he and his lady descended the hole in the sea. The barge moved slowly along the floor, affording the guests a scenic tour of waving multicolored gorgonians, spreading coral trees and flashing schools of fish. As a chaser, the window stopped near a barracuda which was hanging over a burrow waiting for its lunch.

Williamson had no idea what species of fish and coral he was filming. He heard of a neighboring marine biological expedition from the Carnegie Institute and Brooklyn Museum, so he invited the scholars to come over and call fish. In this way, naturalists discovered Williamson's marvelous observation chamber, which they were to employ for thirty years. An ichthyologist was in the chamber with Williamson one day when a parlous brute, a fish two feet long swam by. From its ugly head arose a staff with a white flag flying on it. Williamson filmed the astonishing animal so the scientist would not be embarrassed when he told his colleagues. The savants said the fish had the characteristics of the rare Spotted Horse, except for the flagpole. They thought it must have been a weird parasitic growth.

Williamson had promised his backers the ultimate in underwater sensations, a fight between a diver and a shark. This had sounded great in New York, but when the money men reminded him of it in Nassau he noted, "My promise must be made good, for time was getting short, funds were running low and the sharks were ready for business even if we were not." He pledged a bonus to two naked Negro divers to play hero and lowered a dead horse into the water to hire the villains. Big gray sharks collected around the carcass. When they struck the bargemen were to haul the horse out. The sharks were too quick and seized big bites before it was withdrawn. The frustrated sharks writhed about, slashing at each other. The first diver went down, admonished by Williamson to be sure and stay in the camera field. Since the actor had never seen a movie, the order was a bit hopeful.

Nor had the sharks attended the cinema. Knife clenched in his teeth, the West Indian slanted toward one in camera range. They circled each other close and wary, like a matador and a good bull, and passed off camera. Williamson yelled. The barge crew quickly slacked and tightened anchor hawsers trying to turn the photosphere to the action. Williamson witnessed the end, completely lost to the camera; the diver thrust his knife and ripped the belly open. He surfaced, smiling triumphantly, and demanded his fee. Williamson groaned and paid. He turned to the second volunteer and carefully explained the business. This one splashed in and descended very cautiously. A shark went for him. The diver zoomed for the dead horse and kept it between himself and the shark. Since Williamson was purposely keeping the horse bait out of the picture, this comedy bit was not helpful. Nobody else wished to take up the role.

Williamson removed his shirt, cut off his pantslegs, and announced, "I'm going to get that picture. I'll fight the shark myself." He wrote later, "No one had ever heard of a white man attempting the feat. I was going to my death, they felt certain. But they rubbed me down with their shark oil, which they declared was a secret compound. Perhaps it was. I have never smelled anything to equal it."

From the surface he counted twelve sharks prowling around the photosphere. He decided he needed practice and plunged to stalk a shark. "I didn't rehearse long," he said. "It wasn't comfortable after all down there with those skulking gray forms on every side." He looked down and waited for a shark to come on camera. He dived deep underneath the animal. "With a flirt of his tail the shark turned and was flashing open-mouthed at me," he said. While the shark was en route, Williamson glimpsed the camera window. He saw "the men feverishly working with the camera, and knew that whatever happened in the next few seconds, they at least would get the picture of pictures."

"My lungs seemed bursting. I had been underwater longer than ever before. Now the great gray body was almost upon me. I remembered the native diver's trick. Veering aside, I grasped the monster's fin, felt my hand close upon it. With a twist, I was under the livid white belly at the spot I was trying to reach. With all my remaining strength I struck. A quivering thrill raced up my arm as I felt the blade bury itself to the hilt in the flesh, and the next moment I was swung right and left by a lashing body. Then a blur, confusion—chaos. I believed I was swimming desperately, striving madly to reach the surface, but I couldn't be sure." He said, "Hands slapping my back brought me back to reality. Somehow I had managed to reach the deck. Everyone was shouting and congratulating me. I had killed the shark!"

The six-reel picture, *The Williamson Submarine Expedition*, was shown first at the Smithsonian Institution in Washington. One viewer termed it "the most remarkable photographs that have ever been made." It was a tremendous international hit. Although the picture had certain contrived scenes, it was a factual film, one of the very first documentaries. Without sex titillation or a story line, it gripped audiences with the reality of the sea. Williamson was so enthused that he planned to keep a Broadway house running on undersea films alone. He produced *The Submarine Eye*, a treasure-diving yarn, and *Girl of the Sea*, whose titles smack of Hollywood. His magnum opus was *Twenty Thousand Leagues Under the Sea*. It was made forty years before Walt Disney's version in the same Bahaman settings.

Williamson sought technical advice on helmet diving from the redoubtable Chief Gunner George D. Stillson, at the Brooklyn Navy Yard. The Chief was then testing the Davis submarine escape lung and figured it could be concealed inside a helmet dress to free Captain Nemo's floorwalkers from air pipes. Williamson bought fifteen suits and borrowed the Chief and his crack divers, Frank Crilley and his brother Lawrence, and Jack Gardner to act in the film.

Twenty Thousand Leagues was quite a production: Williamson had to promote a frigate to serve as Verne's U.S.S. *Abraham Lincoln*, a yacht to blow up, and a submarine, plus a fleet of work boats. With a war on, the Navy grudged him a submarine, so he built a wooden *Nautilus* with an underwater exit lock. On the way to Nassau, the yacht crew beached her on the Carolina coast and made off with everything they could steal. It was only the beginning. Two of the divers, Tuck and Gardner, were having fun playing gunners on the *Abraham Lincoln*. They touched off a muzzle-loader which did not fire. They looked into the touch-hole and it did. A ready surgeon saved their eyesight by covering them with cracked ice and sitting on their writhing chests to remove powder pocks from the eyeballs. The professional actors doing Nemo's guests refused to jump into shark-infested water, and Williamson scratched up doubles who would. Williamson was chauffeuring the *Nautilus* on what was meant to be a warning to ram on the frigate, and knocked off her rudder.

They had an imperfect understanding of the oxylithe used to repurify the oxygen in Sir Robert's escape lung. The divers stayed down too long during the preparations and retakes, and got drunk on fumes as the chemical weakened. They became "dreamily happy," as Williamson said, "and would wander off on their own, exploring coral caves and picking sea anemones. It was a curious experience to have these hardened veterans go off picking flowers like children." Another effect was worse. "They fell upon each other like maniacs," Williamson said. In one of these imbroglios, Lawrence Crilley's exhaust valve was knocked shut and he went up, ballooning. A gigantic Negro saved his life by plucking him from the water with one hand, a weight of 350 pounds. The diver foamed through black lips and it took five men to hold him down. His brother, Frank, came aboard in the same condition and yelled, "Let me at 'im! He needs a crack on the jaw." Another detachment bore him to the deck. Then the U.S. submarine *F-4* sank in Hawaii and the Navy divers pulled out to rush to her aid. Williamson glued together his expedition and continued. In a crowded anchorage one night a mess boy, starting a galley fire, left a can of gasoline on the stove. The work boats burned with much equipment and nine diving dresses. Williamson resorted to reserve gear he had set aside in case of losses by hurricane. (Some years later the original negative of *Twenty Thousand Leagues Under the Sea* was destroyed in a hurricane.)

For the big scene of the *Nautilus* blowing up the yacht with a torpedo, many sightseers arrived in boats, including the Royal Governor and his lady. Their launch inspected the doomed yacht before filming started. They saw technicians arm the load of dynamite in the old yacht, which was to be set off by a time fuse, allowing the men to get away. The signal for lighting the fuse was to be two shots fired by an assistant director. He fired a test shot. The dynamiters lit their fuse and roared off, leaving the gubernatorial party chatting away alongside the yacht. Williamson, on another boat, started the cameras. There was $25,000 worth of yacht going up, and he could not lose the scene. "The Governor was standing there with his wife and party," he said, "not knowing it would explode in their faces at any moment; and to add to my horror, the launch, Governor and all, must surely be in the picture."

The yacht exploded.

Williamson's luck turned. The Governor's boat was unharmed and it was not in the frame. There remained only one more photoplay divertisement for rapt Nassau—a beautiful passenger balloon ascension from the main square. With thousands gathered round, the balloon took fire and sent them scampering.

Twenty Thousand Leagues Under the Sea was a wow. John Barrymore told Williamson he had never been so thrilled as by the scenes of a diver battling a giant octopus. Williamson smiled but did not mention that the monster was his U.S. patent No. 1,378,641, a rubber contraption of coiled springs with halved rubber balls as suction cups and a diver inside at the controls. A Philadelphia critic said the scene was "one of the rarities of the camera. There can be no question of fake or deception." Williamson informed on the octopus in 1935 in his grand memoirs, *Twenty Years Under the Sea.*

The director was relaxing in victory when another monster reached a tentacle through his door, picked him up and contracted three thousand miles. It was Metro-Goldwyn-Mayer Pictures. The beast croaked, "We got a two-dollar idea for ya." In Hollywood talk that meant millions would school up with two dollars each at the box office. The idea was that Williamson should meld two Verne books in one to make a colossal color job. The scenario supplied Captain Nemo with a schizoid personality; he was to be inspired by a haunting female face cut in from time to time, and the setting would be Soviet Russia. "Give us two hundred undersea divers!" said M.G.M. and placed Williamson on the observation platform of an eastbound train.

Williamson assembled a company of fifty and sailed for Nassau. He learned then that he was Second Unit Director, under a newly imported French *maître*, who was to make the studio dream stuff. Shortly after

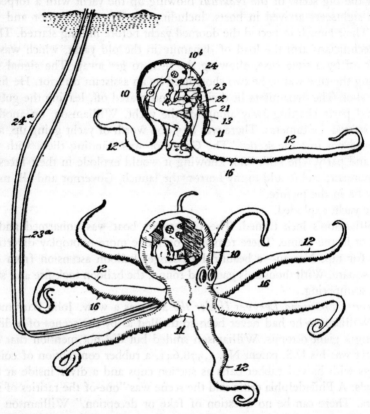

Williamson's patented octopus from *Twenty Thousand Leagues Under the Sea*, his film of 1915. (John E. Williamson)

Williamson raised the Bahamas, the Frenchman lost control of his exhaust valve and ballooned out of the picture. He was replaced by a fresh Danish artist, while Williamson was busy with a hurricane blowdown of the Second Unit. The Dane was caught in a script squeeze and went home to decompress. Williamson fought the picture out in his usual bold style. He surfaced with a two-million-dollar spectacle. Just as it was to open on Broadway, down the street Al Jolson sang "Mammy" from the screen and silent pictures were obsolete. Williamson said, "Instead of a grand super-spectacle, our picture was a hushed and silent specter."

Marine biologists remained fascinated with the photosphere and its cheerful, inventive skipper. Williamson may not have been able to name fish, but he knew more of their living habits than most ichthyologists. He joined scientists in transplanting Caribbean coral reef groups to the Brooklyn Museum and the American Museum of Natural History, and led his own expedition which lifted seven habitat groups for the Hall of the Ocean Floor at the Field Museum in Chicago. He took his wife, baby and kitten down the tube. The infant napped by the world's largest aquarium, as Williamson's tender, the *Jules Verne*, slowly trawled the photoscope across the floor.

Once beside a shipwreck swarming with little fish, they saw a colossal grouper emerge from the green ruin. "Like an ogre from a fairy tale," said Williamson, "this ugly denizen of the deep turned and made straight for our window. Slowly its great mouth opened like a yawning chasm. The ogre had no designs on us and soon his hypnotic eyes were fixed on a school of fish that huddled together a few yards distant. Sidling up beside them the big fish singled out one for his victim. Slowly under the power of the mesmeric glare this one fish swung out from the group and moved about nervously, the ogling monster following its fleeting movements. Then the huge mouth opened and the victim passed into the waiting chasm with no more concern than a person entering a subway. This performance was repeated until apparently the correct quota had passed the turnstiles; then, blinking his eyes and barely moving his ponderous tail, the lazy old fish sailed back into the shadows of the wreck."

In 1955, at the age of seventy-three, J. E. Williamson was contentedly living in Nassau, working in his marine and photographic laboratory. The *Jules Verne* was moored near by.

Scientists who gazed from Williamson's photosphere sought less expensive ways of photographing the new world, among them Dr. W. H. Longley, an ichthyologist of Goucher College, who worked at the Carnegie Institution marine research station in the Dry Tortugas, Florida. He returned to Boutan's system of man and camera in the water, and found a handy gear new to the market, the Dunn helmet, a big copper bucket with glass ports and an air pipe to a hand pump on the surface. The heavy helmet resting on the diver's shoulders was a diving bell, open to the water on the bottom, but kept dry by the pressure of pumped air. You had to stay upright. If you stumbled and capsized the bucket, you had to swim for the surface as fast as possible. Sixty feet was its extreme range. Most dives in the Dunn helmet were not more than fifteen feet. Longley built a heavy brass camera box with external focus, speed and shutter controls and secured 4x5-inch photographs on the brightly lighted floor of the Caribbean in 1917.

The experimenter next attempted underwater color photographs with Autochrome film. This French color plate was a varnished glass imbedded with millions of grains of tinted starch. In 1923 he succeeded in making long exposures of stationary subjects in natural light, the first color shots ever made under water. Longley was not satisfied; like Boutan, he wanted to catch moving animals. The only way was with a powerful flash, which would also wipe away the blue filter of water and reveal the sumptuous hues of tropical depths. He drew into the scheme Charles Martin, a photo technician of the National Geographic Society, which sponsored the effort. To raise light powerful enough to register in color at one-twentieth of a second, Longley and Martin used a tremendous charge, one pound of magnesium flash powder, fired on the surface. It would light the sea down to fifteen feet. Their explosion is still the most powerful illumination ever used in underwater photography. It was dangerous to handle. Longley had only a dory and two men. One pumped and the other held up the tray of flash powder. The camera trigger was connected by an electric cable to the powder. Sometimes Dr. Longley had to wait two hours before fish would swim into his camera field, while the man above held up the powder, never knowing when Longley would shoot. The boatmen also had to keep rowing after Longley's peregrinations on the bottom. When the charge went off it temporarily blinded them, showering sparks and a cloud of evil smoke. The system "was more than human nerves could stand," said Longley.

He built a triangular frame, resting on three cork floats with white canvas roof over it to act as a reflector. He hung a bag of magnesium powder from the contraption and wired the charge to his submerged camera. Longley towed the raft from the bottom and the boatmen were able to stand upwind at a safe distance. One day the Professor was arming the detonator when it exploded prematurely, fortunately with only an ounce of powder. The full charge might have killed him. He was back at work in six days.

The little expedition worked near the sepulchral ruins of Fort Jefferson, which once imprisoned the unlucky Dr. Samuel A. Mudd, who had set John Wilkes Booth's broken leg as Lincoln's assassin fled Washington. Longley's patience and ingenuity triumphed in 1926 with a series of beautiful color photographs of silver-lemon grunts schooled in staghorn coral, a banded hogfish among sea feathers, gray snappers, yellow and black porkfish and a gaudy parrotfish swimming among little slippery dicks. The pictures were slightly blurred at one-twentieth of a second, but Dr. Longley showed the rich palette of warm seas for the first time.

On a sedate residential street in Ardmore, Pennsylvania, there is a low,

ce sculpture in bronze from Roman ship sunk
80 B.C. at Mahdia, Tunisia.

"Thundering Zeus," bronze masterpiece of the Periclean Age, as he came
from the sea, shell encrusted, at Cape
Artemision, Greece, 1928.

fourth century B.C. bronze "Demeter"
ed from the Aegean in Turkish fishing
1953.

Aphrodite reborn from the sea. Underwater
photo of marble torso being drawn from
the floor off Rhodes, 1929.

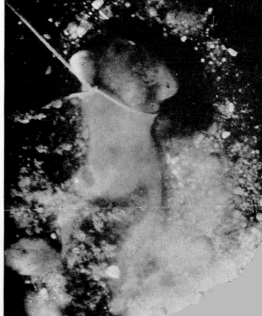

←
Rum bottles hauled out of British 1781 warship wreck in the York River, Virginia, 1934.

→
The Club Alpin Sous-Marin reconnoiters amphoras marking a buried ancient wreck at Anthéor, France.

Mariners' Museum

Henri B.

←
Frédéric Dumas and the perfect Ionic capital from the Roman first century B.C. wreck at Mahd Tunisia.

Harold E. Edgerton

About 205 B.C. a Greek wine ship crashed an sank on this cape, Grand Congloué Island, ne Marseille. Engine house used to excavate the wre 125 feet down was toppled in this gale, 1952, a fell on top of the wreck.

ronze dwarf from the first century B.C.
oman wreck off Mahdia, Tunisia.

"The Boy Jockey of Artemision," Greek genre
masterpiece found in the sea, 1928.

Thundering Zeus" in the lobby of UN Head-
larters, New York. Cast of the seven-foot mas-
rpiece of the Golden Age, recovered from the
a at Cape Artemision, Greece, 1928.

Bronze athlete, fourth or fifth century
Greek masterwork, brought up by divers
from 150 feet at Antikythera Island,
Greece, 1901.

Florida free diver exploring a wreck in he Keys.

British midget submarines (X-Craft) invade enemy anchorages from Altenfjord to Hor Kong. Skipper is Lt. Jack Smart.

Royal Navy chariot riders, Lt. M. R. Causer and Seaman Harry Smith, sank the cruiser *Bolzano* in February, 1944.

Philip Nash—Gustav Dalla Valle

Veteran international free diver, Gustav Dalla Valle, spears a Mako shark, Haiti, 1952.

Ed Fisher

Crowded undersea studio in Florida. Black angelfish and a barracuda stroll past the photographer.

Ed Greenberg

Thousands of wet photographers are attracted to the clear, warm, populous Florida reefs.

A Southern California masked hunter has driven detachable spearhead through his prey, securely holding the fish on a line.

Chuck Peterson

London Illustrated News

Norbert Casteret in the first siphon of Montespan Cave, 1922. Beyond lie the oldest sculptures yet found.

Norbert Casteret and the 20,000-year-old clay bear he discovered in the inner rooms of Montespan Cave, 1922.

London Illustrated News

R. Corfield, *Manchester Evening News*

After a dive in Peak Cavern, Derbyshire, 1949: Dr. R. E. Davies (right), leader of the British Cave Diving Group.

British Cave Diving Group member emerges after seven hours inside Peak Cavern, Derbyshire, 1949.

R. Corfield, *Manchester Evening News*

Dr. Harold E. Edgerton, son Robert, and Captain Cousteau with electronic flash depth cameras used aboard the *Calypso*.

Archeologists aboard the *Calypso* watch on television divers digging in 2,200-year-old Greek wreck, 125 feet down off Marseille.
↓

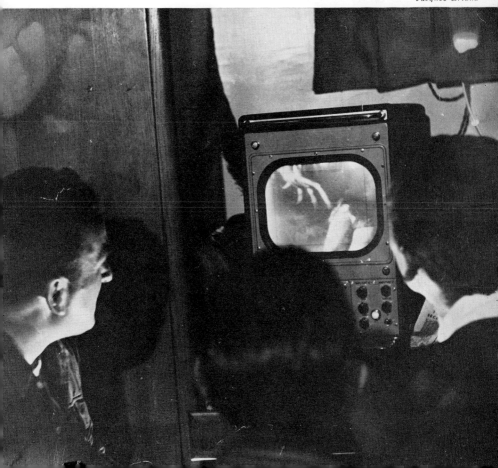

Louis *Malle*

Jacques Ertaud

Underwater television camera with floodlights and hemisphere lens developed by Siebe, Gorman-Marconi

Siebe, Gorman

TV cameraman of *Calypso* Expeditions swims into wreck of a Greek freighter sunk 205 B.C. Depth 125 feet.

↓

J.-Y. Co

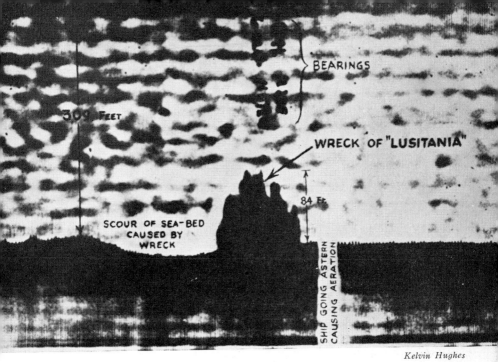

Kelvin Hughes

Echo sounder draws a picture of the *Lusitania* standing on the sea floor, 309 feet down.

Is this the Loch Ness monster? The famous echogram of the Peterhead trawler, *Rival,* showing a weird object among crags at the bottom of Loch Ness.

Daily Herald

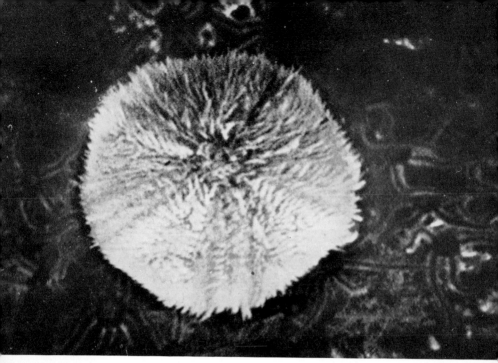

Television view of *Echinus esculentus* in the Firth of Forth. Sharpness of Scottish TV camera may be judged by fact you see echinoderm through six "filters"—TV camera, monitor, still camera negative, photo print, engraver's halftone, and this picture.

Television finds the sunken submarine, H.M.S. *Affray*. The conning tower photographed from the TV screen.

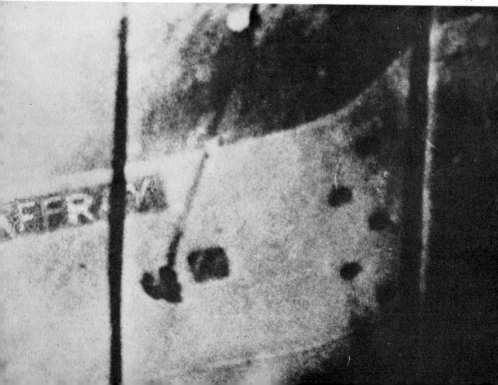

Captain Cousteau briefs his *Calypso* team before a winter's dive. Left to right: Falco, Laban, Davso, Cousteau, Kientzy.

"The real environment of petroleum-building." Dan Feray's geological team delves the bed of the Gulf of Mexico.

British Petroleum Ltd.

On the floor of the Persian Gulf a *Calypso* diver checks a marine gravimeter, recording the gravity of the earth.

French Air Force pilot, Lt. Pierre Vanleur, riding his underwater glider, the *Manta,* at Cannes.

Henri Broussard

Navy Aqualung divers and Hydrographic Office experts dive under Bering Sea ice, 1955, to chart navigable channels for Coast Guard ship *Northwind*.

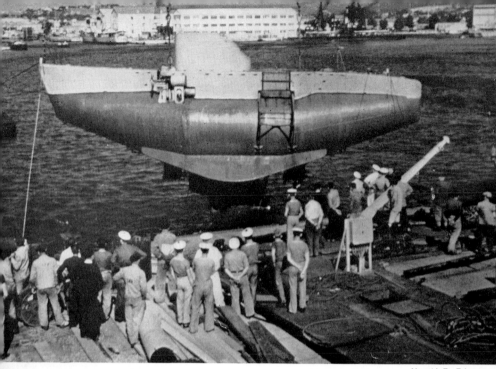

Harold E. Edgerton

The French Navy bathyscaphe, *FNRS 3,* in which Houot and Willm reached the record depth of 13,287 feet.

Professor August Piccard's bathyscaphe, the *Trieste.* Stripes indicate bulkheads in the envelope, for damage detection and placing cradles in drydock.

Troncone-Jacques Piccard

unassertive brick building, the plant of the Fenjohn Underwater Photo and Equipment Company, the oldest firm making underwater cameras, founded by tall, elusive Commander E. R. Fenimore Johnson. He screens his name by the "Fenjohn" and by having himself called "John Fenton" in the few published references to his amazing career under the sea. Johnson's Captain Nemo complex is for the public prints; personally he is a warm and helpful man. He is the main contributor to American undersea photography since 1928. Heir to the Victor Talking Machine fortune, he is perhaps the least publicized millionaire in the United States, despite his having won a professional reputation in a scientific field.

In 1928 he was yachting off Florida and decided to try underwater photography. He "read one of Beebe's glorious descriptions of the beauties of the undersea gardens and the complete ease with which they could be visited and photographed," and got a Dunn helmet. He built a cylindrical case for an Eyemo cinécamera. "The result of several weeks' work was very mediocre," said honest Johnson. "We found out that if one can see forty feet that does not mean that he can take good pictures at more than ten." He pondered diving bells and baby submarines; he made inverted periscopes to bring an image up to camera, shot through glass-bottomed buckets and lowered cameras with telescopic viewfinders on the surface. "But pictures from an unsteady base are unattractive and tend to make the audience seasick," he found. He worked three years on a cast aluminum housing which made good films on the Vanderbilt-Gilks Oceanographic Expedition in 1931. Johnson then attempted the deepest photographs ever taken. He constructed a depth housing with a quartz window that rested on a lapped steel rim without gaskets. The hatch through which the camera was inserted had a soft copper gasket designed to give in the tremendous depths he was challenging. The case, without camera, was lowered in a test in the Brownson Deep of Puerto Rico by the Johnson-Smithsonian Deep Sea Expedition in 1933. It went to eighteen thousand feet, into pressure of eight thousand pounds per square inch, and came up without a leak. He inserted the camera and lowered it. Far below the cable parted and Johnson's camera was gone.

He was one of the first underwater explorers to use the Aqualung, and his laboratory has contributed many ideas to diving equipment, cameras and lighting. After losing money for years developing gear for the small scientific and Hollywood demand, Johnson's plant boomed with orders from amateurs in the 1950's.

Commander Johnson's wealth of experience in the sea, numbering thousands of hours of observation and experiment, may never be recorded: he is content to be the shadowy "John Fenton." A few bits of his adventures are known. In 1931 he led an expedition to the Matto Grosso, Brazil, and became interested in the voracious little piranha, a fresh-water fish which

infests the Orinoco, Amazon and Paraguay rivers. The animal has a small
mouth, but, said Johnson, "when the lips are pulled back and the teeth
are exposed their jaws are simply terrifying to the beholder. The teeth are
triangular, something like a shark's, and are so set that they interlock."
When Johnson's party was near the headwaters of the Paraguay River, a
Brazilian was brought in with part of his big toe cleanly removed by a
piranha. The man had been fording a stream on horseback and let his toe
dangle in the water. Johnson and Sasha Siemel, the "Tiger Man," had been
swimming in the same waters in one-inch visibility. "I cannot honestly say
I enjoyed the brief dips the heat drove us to take," Johnson confessed.

"The people up home regarded us as intrepid explorers, but the people
of Brazil regarded us as a bunch of tourists who would probably get into
trouble if we were not watched pretty carefully," said Johnson. He flew his
amphibian to Corumbá, and took aboard General Candido Mariano de Silva
Rondon, an Indian expert. Johnson saw that his anchor was fouled in a pipeline twelve feet down on the river bed. He stripped, dived and freed the
anchor cable. "I glanced upward along the line," he said, "and felt my
entire body change from warm to that icy-cold feeling which instantly
possesses one shocked by mortal fear. Around the anchor line above me,
arranged like spokes on a wagon wheel, were layer after layer of full-
grown piranhas. Instinctively I reached the conclusion that a sudden move
might precipitate an attack. Fortunately I had plenty of breath left, so I
started slowly hand over hand, squarely through the center of the coldly
staring fish. A most prominent feature of the piranha is its large, round,
light-colored eyes, with their dark pea-sized pupils. By the time I climbed
aboard the plane I was in such a state of shock, I couldn't speak." Commander Johnson noted that the river was also furnished with crocodiles and
anacondas. One time the Fenjohn Company sent a catalog to a South
American amateur diver. It was returned with a notation, "Undeliverable:
addressee eaten by a crocodile."

Fenimore Johnson sold underwater film sequences to Hollywood in the
thirties, but a handsome, laughing adventurer named John D. Craig actually made a living out of underwater heroics for the antebellum cinema.
Born in Cincinnati, Ohio, Craig grew up in Canada and California. Before
he was twenty he struck oil and took off on a dashing *Wanderjahr* around
the world. He was captured by the Riffs, lived in a French girls' finishing
school, and stalked and shot a man-killing tiger in India. The uproar lasted
four years and then the oil money ran out. Sailing home he stopped off in
Tahiti, where a Hollywood troupe was shooting *White Shadows in the
South Seas*. The director told Craig he belonged in Hollywood.

The only job he could find in dreamland was chauffeuring prospects to a
blue-sky real estate promotion. He offered to remake some sea-fishing se-

quences for a studio which had lost its first expedition to the bottle. Craig was so eager he agreed to make the stuff on speculation, and organized an expedition on borrowed money. He crammed for several weeks and passed the examination for a yacht master's license. He got married and took his bride with four men, to Cape San Lucas, Mexico, where he began work from a friendly Japanese abalone boat. The Japanese company, Shim Shimbata, then had commercial abalone canneries in Baja California. It used helmet divers to gather the monovalves, which were canned and shipped to Manchuria. The inquisitive Captain Craig told diver Sinjji Yamanoto that he'd like to give it a try. "So one afternoon," said Craig in his exciting book *Danger Is My Business,* "I climbed into the weighty, cumbersome dress, wrapped a towel around my head to keep perspiration out of my eyes, and the tender of the lines, an old Mexican named Antonio, smiled and nodded to give me confidence. Then I let go and drifted slowly down." He quickly knew that diving was the grandest adventure.

Craig learned to decompress in the unscientific Japanese manner; at the cannery there was a great wooden tub full of hot water in which the divers sat for hours discoursing amiably. One time Craig shucked his clothes and got in with the camp cook, whose smiling face showed above the water, for a good soak and pleasant talk. Presently the chef said a polite *adieu* and clambered out. The cook was a lady.

The Japanese guided him in the submerged topography, taught him how to play currents and not be ruined, and how to take precautions in the strangling forests of kelp. Craig described a dive:

"One of the Japanese divers offered to guide us into the ravine from a safe place at the lower end where the water would be eighty-five feet deep, and we went down with him. He led us to a slope at one end of the gulch, where there was an easy ascent up to the narrow entrance. The Jap went first, I followed. As we neared the rocks I felt the pull of current. The tidal currents are very strong in the straits south of Cedros, and the ravine had probably been scooped out by them. I braced myself against the drag. Suddenly I saw the Jap ahead of me lifted off his feet, as though by some giant invisible hand.

"He was swept around a jutting pinnacle of rock. Helpless, dangling in midwater, he was crashed time and again against the face of the rock.

"Somewhere above, his air line fouled as the current pulled, swayed, and slammed him about. I saw coils of his loose air line come drifting down about us.

"Then he seemed to change, to shorten, to telescope into a dwarflike figure. The tons of water pressure were crushing his torso into his helmet. His faceplate was smashed. I saw coming from it something that looked like gray smoke. The gray smoke was blood.

"It all happened so quickly that we could hardly realize a tragedy had occurred. A diver had been killed before our eyes.

"We signaled to be pulled up. Antonio was already hauling up the Jap by means of the life line.

"The body was a mass of pulp. It was placed on the stern of the boat. In stunned horror, we sat some distance away staring at it.

" 'Like strawberry jam,' I heard Antonio mutter."

The Japanese were fatalistic about pressure accidents because they didn't know what caused the squeeze, bends or other accidents. Nor did Craig. He questioned Antonio who had been tending Japanese undersea peasants for a quarter century. The explorer pieced together Antonio's accident data with his own rough ken of physiology. It was a sobering conclusion.. Then he found a Japanese divers' graveyard on Cedros Island with twenty-two tenants.

Twenty years later Captain Craig was still at it. He put on an Aqualung and dived to make an underwater television serial.

New beginnings in French underwater camera work came in the early thirties from a thin, hawk-faced naval officer, Commandant Yves le Prieur. He devised 16 mm. movie units and 35 mm. candid cameras to use with his independent compressed-air lung, a fine aid for submarine photography. The documentary director and naturalist, Jean Painlevé, used the lung to make films beneath the Mediterranean with a studio camera in a ponderous box. The French Navy built a big brass Leica box that Padré Poidebard used in surveying the sunken ancient harbor works at Tyre and Sidon. This case intrigued an underwater enthusiast, Lieutenant Philippe Tailliez, who came upon it in the naval research center. Made for a man plodding on the floor, it was too heavy for a free diver's delicate trim. Tailliez buoyed it with cork slabs, sank with it, wrestled it and made pictures. He realized that a much lighter unit was needed by swimming divers. Tailliez took to movies in 1939 with a Pathé Baby 9.5 mm. camera in a glass jar, as he formed an historic trio of submarine explorers with Cousteau and Dumas. "I remember that year," said Tailliez, in his captivating book *To Hidden Depths*, "with the terrible vividness that attaches to momentous periods of one's life. Our undersea existence was never so carefree and so exciting as that summer; never had we been so full of plans." But, "In the north a storm was brewing. Behind the low, black clouds it seemed to us that a giant hand in an iron glove was lifted to crash down upon the town."

The war held a caprice for them. Cousteau and Tailliez went to sea and Dumas was an army muledriver in the Alps. The fates brought them together in Toulon as France was falling. Tailliez said, "As an escape from the moral disintegration, the creeping paralysis of inactivity which affected everyone round him, Cousteau had even more enthusiastically than before taken up his undersea activities again. He had rigged up an old movie camera picked up in a junk shop in Marseille, a 35 mm. Kinamo with a first-class lens."

"Hunters of submarine pictures today," Tailliez said, "with all kinds of highly developed cameras available to them, perhaps have little idea of the difficulties, the disappointments, the horrible waterlogging of our apparatus which accompanied our first pioneer experiments." They could not buy 35 mm. movie film, so they bought up hundreds of rolls of Leica negatives, which Mme. Cousteau unpacked under bedcovers and spliced into movie lengths. They hadn't enough to eat on Nazi-occupation rations. Cold water is a terrific drain on caloric heat. Each of the trio was normally lean and lithe, without a sign of body fat, but Cousteau presented such a cavernous appearance a lady asked him, "Were you shrunk by pressure?"

Their camera loaded eighty feet of film, but would run through only twenty feet before they had to rewind. They camped on islands, priming wet open campfires with gunpowder, subsisting on Dumas' skill at shooting groupers without expending more energy than the fish would restore. The area was occupied by Italians, who fired at them from shore. They were interrupted when the Germans dynamited Dumas' house to clear a line of fire for coast artillery. Allied planes bombed the café they used as head-quarters. Tailliez had to hide out from the Germans as a forest ranger. Cousteau led a doubly dangerous life; he was chief of a counterintelligence group of the Resistance. The team persisted.

One of the compelling scenes in their first film, *Par dix-huit mètres de fond* (Sixty Feet Down) 1942, shows Dumas swimming through a tunnel forty-five feet under an island without breathing apparatus. The shot took patience and hardihood. Cameraman Cousteau stood above one end of the tunnel with Dumas on the other side. They were unable to see each other because of an intervening hill. Atop the hill, in sight of both, was a signal man. When he gestured, Cousteau dived forty-five feet and trained the camera. The starter waved to Dumas who plunged into the tunnel, shot a fish and swam toward the camera.

In 1948 aboard the ship *Élie Monnier*, of the French Navy Group for Undersea Study and Research which they had founded, the trio made the first color movies in the blue zone, below a hundred feet. In the silvery reflected gloom of a sandy floor of Tunisia, among the Ionic columns of the famous Mahdia treasure argosy, they filmed divers in natural light in Agfacolor at a depth of 130 feet. The quality was grayed but fairly clear. On this cruise Dumas swam down to more than 200 feet with a powerful floodlamp on a trailing cable to where Cousteau waited with a movie camera. Dumas played the reflector on a lush reef wall and turned on the light. They saw something not seen or suspected by all men before them.

The reef, buried in timeless blue, was a blaring opulence of color. They stared at ruby gorgonian fans, yellow sponges, and vivid orange and green algaes as fresh as paint. Cousteau wondered, "Why did nature put this color here, where it could never be seen, even by fish?"

In 1950, after a decade of moviemaking, Cousteau turned to color still photography. He built pressurized reflectors holding eight G.E. 50 bulbs, which could fire one, two, four or eight at a time, or almost as many lumens as Dr. Longley's powder raft in the Dry Tortugas. The three-man team dived in cold numbing winter water to make their set-ups in the blue reefs. Dumas was the subject, Cousteau the cameraman and Jacques Ertaud, the mountain climber and cave diver, was the flash holder. Ertaud trained the cumbersome reflector on Dumas. The thick glass reflector port collapsed in pressure. The weightless object turned into an anvil. It tore out of his hands, ripped out the camera cable and fell, ringing on the reef. They swam down after it. The brass bowl lay face down. Ertaud tried to lift it and couldn't. Dumas curved down and touched his air regulator to the rim. The others heaved up one side. Dumas filled the bowl with exhalations and it went up easily.

Dmitri Rebikoff had no idea he would be an undersea photographer in 1950. He was a Parisian designer and builder of electronic flash lighting units, a follower of Professor Harold E. Edgerton, of the Massachusetts Institute of Technology, who had devised working speedlights a decade before. Rebikoff was working on color flash, when the diving leader, Henri Broussard, of Cannes, asked him to consider its underwater applications. Rebikoff went to Cannes and was converted and baptized on his first dive. Since then he has built ingenious *torpilles sous-marines,* which contain camera, electronic flash and even electric propulsion to carry the photographer along on the show.

The undersea photographers were hampered by the fact that the field of vision was reduced by about one quarter. In the late forties Dr. Edward M. Thorndike of Queens College, New York, who was working with the pioneer depth photographer, Maurice Ewing, evolved a lens which corrected underwater distortion and restored things to normal. His study was refined in a lens by Marcel Dratz of the French National Scientific Research Center. Another Parisian, Alexandre Ivanoff, designed a variation of Dratz's lens.

Hans Hass, a personable blond Viennese and an energetic pioneer of underwater photography, was inspired by seeing Guy Gilpatric hunting at Cap d'Antibes. Hass and his young friends obtained de Corlieu fins and went on a gay fish-spearing expedition in the Adriatic. He began underwater photography during a visit to the Dutch West Indies in 1939. During the war Hass conducted diving experiments for the Germans and adopted the Draeger oxygen lung. Afterward he made several vivid motion pictures, which contained contrived perils. One showed his wife with her leg seized by a tridacna clam. Frau Hass was also depicted in an underwater grotto with her oxygen running out, as sharks besieged the cave. Fortunately, Herr Hass was able to come to her rescue. His underwater cinematography is characterized by enterprise and exciting scenarios, although he has been handicapped by the shallow depth-range of the oxygen lung. Hass has published several books on his experiences, illustrated by fine still photographs.

Britain's precurser in submarine cinematography was the late Commander H. J. Hodges, R.N.V.R. Who was the first foreigner to check out of Dumas' diving course at the G.E.R.S. and learn underwater film work from Tailliez and Cousteau. Hodges shot marvelous stuff for the Royal Navy on the French themes—men escaping with Davis lungs from a bottomed submarine, torpedoes starting from the tube and sunken ships. Retiring from service, he worked for Siebe, Gorman as a development expert, but he liked diving better than the shop. Early in 1954, he resigned to join Hans Hass' Caribbean film expedition as first cameraman.

At that time I was in Toulon, shivering in the snow, waiting for the *Calypso* to sail for the Indian Ocean. I sympathized with Hodges' drive for the clear summery seas. Some months later the *Calypso's* radio man brought Captain Cousteau a personal signal from Admiral Lord Louis Mountbatten, then Commander-in-Chief of the Mediterranean North Atlantic Treaty Forces. Mountbatten, who knew that Cousteau and Hodges were friends, reported: HODGES LOST HASS CARIBBEAN EXPEDITION.

Later in London I heard what happened to Hodges from his old diving companions. During the war Hodges had twice convulsed on oxygen dives. When he joined Hass he promised his wife, Jacqueline, he would not dive on oxygen again. In the Dutch West Indies, Hodges came up from the eighty-foot oxygen dive with Hass, removed his mouthpiece and yelled for help. A boat made for him rapidly, but he sank unconscious, without replacing his breathing tube. Hass dedicated the film to Commander Hodges.

Until free-diving cameramen appeared, nobody knew the actual behavior of commercial fishing nets and trawls. For thousands of years fishermen cast their nets by luck and hand-me-down theories of how they worked. A film of a trawl sweeping across the floor was made by Cousteau and Dumas in 1943 for the Mediterranean fishermen who carried them on offshore explorations. "Perched above the grassy floor I saw the towline of the net arrive," said Cousteau. "It looped back to the rigid gate which scraped along the bottom, breaking down grasses and spreading destruction to the tiny creatures of the prairie. Fishes leaped away like rabbits running from a reaper. I was astonished to see how many fish escaped the monster and how much it destroyed of future fish stocks and pasturage."

Commander Hodges was asked in 1952 by the Marine Laboratory of the Scottish Home Department at Aberdeen to film the action of the Danish seine trawl, the favorite bottom-fishing net of the North Sea fleet. Hodges' movie proved the Danish trawl remarkably effective. It came upon him with its meshes fully inflated. The towline, running ahead, stirred fish from the bottom, which schooled directly in the path and were carried into the deep end of the net. The open meshes allowed young fish to escape, but very few adults dodged free from the wings of the trawl.

Several years ago, Richard Crosby, a Long Island diving enthusiast, introduced me to a long, lean professor of marine biology named John F. Storr whom Crosby said had made fine 16 mm. undersea films in the Caribbean. The pictures showed beautiful ballets of tropical fish against coral décor; octopuses swimming and crawling across sand spits; green morays jutting their unlovely snouts from clumps of sea fans, and a butterfly fish wearing its funny falseface—a large staring false eye painted on the tail. I wondered how this happened at Adelphi College, a most estimable institution, but not one suspected of harboring an underwater movie virtuoso. Dr. Storr said, "It was an accident. In 1949 two faculty people took a diving holiday in the West Indies and they wanted somebody to identify the fish and corals. So I went along. What I saw made me crazy to photograph it." Dr. Storr quickly went through the blundering experimental period. He built a vast diving bell on a tripod, under which he could shelter. It did not survive its baptism. He acquired an U.S. Navy shallow-water breathing rig, a triangular face mask, ventilated by a surface pump. It worked. He proceeded to stereo movies. His clear articles in camera magazines led others into the field. Few could resist his description of the first dive:

"I stood on the bleached sand in this valley, under whose greyed sloping walls grew golden-topped cones, their sides covered with striped broad crinkled leaves of some strange plant. Broad leafless yellow trunks raised themselves from the floor of the valley, each branching repeatedly to a flat-topped tree. I noticed two bulging eyes, like those of an enormous frog, protruding from the sand. The sand heaved upward and with a lunge an animal broke free from its camouflage and with a swift motion of its broad undulating wings, sailed gracefully away. It disappeared into the blue-green mist. With unperturbed slowness, part of an overhanging ledge glided into the wavering sunlight, to become a moving ball of inky black spines. I grasped a bush on the rocky wall for support. Its velvety pink branches turned at once to purple, the branches themselves decreasing

rapidly in diameter. This is not the beginning of an astounding tale of adventure on another planet, but my actual experience full fathom five beneath the surface of the semi-tropics."

A remarkable Australian explorer named Noel Monkman has been diving and filming in the Great Barrier Reef for many years.

Monkman is a robust, goateed, self-educated scientist. He escaped from
school in his native New Zealand to play in the sea with Maori boys. At
nine he got a microscope and became engrossed with watching microscopic
marine diatoms. "I was a diatomaniac," he says. He learned to make time-
lapse films of the life cycles of plankton. In 1929 he started an educational
film company and journeyed to the Great Barrier Reef for his first subject.
Ever since then, he and his lively wife have wintered on the reef "just like
two castaways." In his thousands of dives, Monkman has witnessed out-
landish dramas, such as the partnership of the slivery fierasfer fish and the
ponderous sea slug, *bêche-de-mer*. The little fish lures prey to the sedentary
colleague, then dives into the *bêche-de-mer* and hides in the rear intestine.
When the two have had lunch, the little one peers out to see if the coast is
clear, before sallying forth. Monkman has never speared a fish. He says,
"I don't like killing them—and maybe that's why they haven't killed me."

Inevitably Hollywood took the plunge. The studios were not handicapped by the reality of the sea; they simply drowned the regular scenarios
and strapped lungs on the production crew. The fright script was immersed
in *The Creature from the Black Lagoon*, which turned into a series like Pa
and Ma Kettle. Jane Russell was taken down and Esther Williams learned
to dive. The submersible leading man appeared, typified by Gilbert Roland,
who has not been dry for several years. Actors had not been so put upon
since they were lashed to buzzsaws and dangled from cliffs. Business was
good in rubber octopuses and motorized mantas. Prop men found themselves standing on the sea floor with captive fish in cages to release on cue.
Gustave Dalla Valle, who made an underwater television serial, described
a typical creative headache, which occurred while he was shooting in
Weeki Wachee Spring in Florida: "I tried to get the cooperation of the
fish to make the underwater scene more realistic, but they would not come
near us. The one time that the fish were attracted to the scene was when
were were filming the submarine. Then the little fish ruined the effect by
making it obvious that the submarine was only a three-foot model."

One night in the Ritz Bar in Paris, Cousteau and I had a drink with the
enthusiastic director, John Huston, who asked Cousteau's advice on how
to film *Moby Dick*. Huston recounted an earlier attempted by Warner
Brothers to film the story. Several hundred thousand dollars were spent on a
rubber white whale, crammed with machinery for producing a spout, moving

the flukes and rolling the eyes. On his first diving trial the architect said he would pilot it alone, omitting the officers in command of flukes and spouts. It was just as well.

The whale submerged handsomely. Seconds later the inventor broke the surface in distress. He was picked up but the whale kept on sounding. The furious studio canceled the film. Now, Huston wondered, why did he not film actual whales? Cousteau said, "It would take an expedition to the Antarctic with a crew of specialists capable of diving under the ice. If they were very lucky they might get one minute's playing time for each month of work."

Huston built a mechanical whale.

9

Professors with Fins

O FF Southern California, four free divers popped in and out of the water with optical instruments and measuring tapes instead of spear guns. They were conducting an experiment in water visibility for the Scripps Institution of Oceanography at La Jolla and the Navy Electronics Laboratory at San Diego. Two were Navy divers; two were from Scripps, Fred Snodgrass, an engineer who specializes in waves and currents, and Conrad Limbaugh, a marine biologist. Their ocean research center has the largest and most active group of diving scientists in the world today.

In the depths they took sights, measured limits of visibility and entered data on waterproof plates. Suddenly a shape as big as a fishing boat appeared above them. Limbaugh recognized the silhouette of a whale shark, forty feet long. Such a sight is enough to empty the water of men—if they don't know about whale sharks. Limbaugh knew that they are lazy, harmless plankton-eaters. He beckoned to his companions and they swam up to the huge, white-spotted gray creature and boarded it. "You could swim up and grab his tail or one of his fins and hold on. He would pull you along without apparently being fully aware that you were there," said Snodgrass. "We climbed all over it," Limbaugh recalled. "It was accompanied by a large number of pilot fish and on the body clung many shark suckers, or remoras, a small fish with a suction cup on its head. I saw the whale shark open its mouth. I was curious to see what was inside. I looked in and saw it was black. I placed my hand inside to feel the texture and put it on a remora, clinging to the inside of the mouth. This startled me."

Limbaugh, who is chief diver at the Institution, introduced free diving there in 1949. He is a blond, blue-eyed, supple individual, a diver since he was twelve. On his original compressed-air dives, he used one of the first two Aqualungs to be brought to the United States from France by Commander Douglas Fane of the Navy Underwater Demolition Teams. Limbaugh was then a graduate student at the Institution, which is a branch of the University of California. Enchanted with his baptism, he at once felt that the Aqualung was "to become an extremely important tool to the ocean scientist." His enthusiasm caught on among Scripps' researchers. A fellow zoology student, Andreas Rechnitzer, plunged in with him. Limbaugh set up a training course and was soon leading an academic procession into the ocean, including Professor Carl L. Hubbs, the distinguished ichthyologist; biologist Theodore Walker; biochemist Wheeler North; physiologist Robert B. Livingston; oceanographer Walter H. Munk, and many others.

La Jolla is a casual, wealthy, cultured colony seated in an amphitheater facing the ocean. It is an American Monaco set in sandstone bluffs and coves, with white beaches and cliff houses rising among redwoods. Its landmark is the long Scripps Oceanography Pier, which lets you down in one of the most fascinating and varied of undersea terrains. Scripps Canyon, a tributary of the rich, many-branched La Jolla submarine canyon, reaches almost to the pier. Off Spindrift Beach is flat desertic floor, and further out is a populous undersea jungle of great stands of kelp.

Each environment has its adherents. Geologist Francis P. Shepard, a world expert on submarine canyons, has directed hundreds of dives to study the undersea ravines. In some places Scripps Canyon is so narrow a man can touch both walls at once. Diver Earl Murray said, "You get a greater sensation of depth in those steep rocky walls, traveling up and down with the ease of a fly on a windowpane." It was the same delight in scaling cliffs without touching them that led Henri Broussard, of Cannes, to name the first Aqualung society the *Club Alpin Sous-Marin* or Undersea Mountaineering Club.

In Scripps Canyon, Limbaugh captured a live fish of a new species, which he and Professor Hubbs christened *Icelinus cousteaui*. The watery mountaineers turned the gully into a field laboratory. They marked the walls at the depth borders of various sedentary life forms to see if the habitats change from year to year and season to season. They installed current meters and thermometers on the floor. "There is generally a greenish cast to things in the canyon," said Limbaugh. "Some of the fuchsia sea fans appear violet, the pink sea fans look white. The bright orange Garibaldi fish appears yellow." He found that in summer there is a deep cold layer in the canyon, when the sea around about is uniformly warm from surface to bottom. When the labs need cold-water fauna and flora during the summer, divers virtually go out of the window to get them, instead of traveling hundreds of miles to cold waters.

One of the prowlers of the desert, Earl Murray, diver of the division studying shore processes, said "Your first trips out on the sand you say it is very drab and uninteresting. We have some difficulty getting people to dive out there because they get bored with it. But when you get down close to it, you see it is just teeming with life. There is an abundance of little shellfishes that have a busy game of life in the sand. Down deeper there are giant sea pansies, sea pens and sea cucumbers; and large halibut, diamond turbot, little shellfish, hermit crabs and sharks, sluggish angels and giant blues. Tiny stingrays fly around like birds. There are crabs that look like pingpong balls, and a small octopus that builds his home out of seashells. He's a very timid little fellow, but always pleasant."

The kelp forests are composed of *Macrocystis,* or long bladder kelp, a towering seaweed anchored to rocks on the floor and held upright by gas-filled floats. Scripps Forest has some stands of *Macrocystis* a hundred feet tall. It has been found twice that height. One of the undersea foresters at Scripps is Charles Fleming, a tall, blue-eyed engineer who has been diving since his boyhood in Lake Michigan. He knows the coral wonderlands of the tropics, but prefers the kelp jungle. "Coral is beautiful for about a week," he said, "and then, because it is immovable, it becomes boring. Your reefs are almost all the same, your fish the same. As a result you don't even look at these things after a couple of weeks. But the kelp is always in motion. It grows on boulders as big as a house." Among these undulating brown Jack-in-the-Beanstalk plants, the divers pursue fish with butterfly nets. They have studied over a hundred species in Scripps Forest, gliding in and out between the thin stalks. The floating fronds break up wind chop and make the jungle a quiet place for fish-watching.

Once Limbaugh, Rechnitzer and a graduate student named Ramsey Parks went out in a rowboat and dived into the ocean fringe of the weed bed. They followed one of the stalks to the floor. The sandstones were covered with enormous sea urchins ten inches in diameter. The divers avoided these marine porcupines. Their needles are mildly poisonous. Limbaugh spotted a rare fringehead fish, of which science had obtained only three specimens before the Scripps team brought up nine in butterfly nets. He saw a gaudy little sculpin four inches long, "very brilliantly colored in pink and browns and whites." With his hand he chased the sculpin into a jar and capped it. Parks speared a fifteen-pound sheephead, and they gathered a burlap sack full of red and pink abalones and a cousin called the Northern Green.

When they had been down twenty-five minutes, Rechnitzer drew his hand across his throat. The throat-cutting signal meant: my air is nearly exhausted, time to surface. They swam out of the forest toward the open sea, which was shining blue beyond the dull golden stems of kelp. They surfaced and looked for the man in the rowboat, who had been instructed never to take his eyes off their bubbles. There was no rowboat. Their eyes were only inches above the water and a moderate swell was running, carrying them into the entangling fronds. Several divers have died in kelp entanglements. A swell lifted them and they saw the rowboat. It was about twelve hundred yards away. They yelled as loud as they could and waved their arms. There was no sign from the boatman. Perhaps he could not hear them; perhaps he had lost his oars. Riding up in the waves, they watched the faraway boat for several minutes. Then they knew they would have to swim for life. They were three-quarters of a mile from shore. Between them and the beach lay the great kelp barrier. It stretched too far on either side to swim around. They would have to struggle through it.

Limbaugh ordered that they drop their belt weights. He regretfully jettisoned his pretty sculpin in the jar and advised the others to drop their collections. Parks loosed the sack of abalones, but did not want to give up the fish he had speared. Limbaugh had to talk him into dropping that and the speargun. Rechnitzer's and Parks' air bottles were exhausted. That made them buoyant, which would help their fight through the entangled fronds. Limbaugh, however, wore a two-bottle lung which still held enough compressed air to be heavy. He was also wearing a rubber suit. He made these two encumbrances work for him. He took off the lung, inserted the breathing tube into the cuff of the suit and inflated it. The three struck out, keeping together, using their knowledge of the architecture of kelp to avoid swimming into the crotches of the long branches. Two hours later they dragged themselves out on the shore exhausted. Limbaugh said, "The guy in the boat was still looking for us three hours later when another Scripps boat got to him. He had lost our bubbles in the first few seconds we were down."

Scripps divers have driven stakes in the sand offshore to measure the sand level periodically for scientists studying beach erosion and shoaling. They have furnished valuable data to marine botany by laying down plastic plates and regularly checking them to identify which algas grow on them and at what rate. They have planted wave measuring instruments on the shallow floor, and plunged into such picturesque researches as observing sewer outfalls for coastal cities. Earl Murray said, "The sewage coming up from the outfall is like a big black umbrella." They caught live angel sharks for their aquarium by swimming up to a shark dozing on the sand and lassoing its tail. The next step consisted of "the diver getting the hell out of the way of the threshing animal as it was hauled up to the skiff."

They took specimens with rotenone, an agricultural insecticide which has the power to kill fish when you spread it in the water. The poison constricts the gill capillaries and suffocates the fish. One of Scripps neighbors is a fish called the Sarcastic Fringehead. It lived in empty seashells until the pioneers arrived in the Golden West and began hurling empty whisky bottles into the sea. The Sarcastic Fringehead moved into these fine new homes. In comparison an abalone shell was a mere awning. The tribe increased as more and more prefabs arrived with the rise of south Californian civilization. The diver put a thumb over the bottle mouth and carried Mr. Sardonic Fringehead to the aquarium.

Dr. Theodore Walker, the biologist, learned to dive at forty and said diving was "a wide-open field to anyone interested in the reactions of fish." He had long worked in laboratory tanks to find the function of the fishes' "lateral line," a strip along their sides which many scientists believe is nature's ultrasonar, tuned in on high frequencies to locate fin beats of other fish. Dr. Walker found that the sea was much better than a tank for fish-watching. The divers bring him interesting reports. Every diver at Scripps—there were twenty-five regulars in 1955—writes a comprehensive log of each descent, which is combed for information useful to the various studies: geology, water visibility, beach erosion and the several approaches to fish behavior. The Navy Laboratory obtains information on under-water sound and submerged explosion effects on swimmers.

Biochemist Wheeler North studied a marine anemone, which looks like a ball of cotton. Although it had no eyes, he found it responded to light. He tried to find out what substituted for eyes by establishing an anemone ranch on a canyon wall.

The adventurous Limbaugh and a student of marine vertebrates, named John McGowan, spent many hours on the canyon floor in winter, watch-ing and filming a fantastic drama of nature, the mating and death of squids. Millions of squids arrived from the ocean at a regular time each winter and hovered over sandy patches in the gully floors 45 to 150 feet down. Accompanying this mass honeymoon trip were the animals that eat squid —sea lions, whales, many fishes, crabs and lobsters. The hovering squids paired off, male and female, and there were writhing battles of males over a female. The triumphant male turned bright mottled red and squeezed his pale mate with his tentacles. She dropped the eggs, about three hundred of them at a time, in a white capsule shaped like a Lima-bean pod. She attached the egg cases to the sand. Then all the adult squids died and the predators crashed into rotting beds of them. Even the fixed anemones got in on the feast.

But among the corpses of the dead generation the egg cases swelled to more than twice their original size and became discolored with infinitesimal brown diatoms which came to live on them. And when the tiny squids hatched out, smaller fishes came to gobble in the nursery.

Limbaugh filmed under water in a colony of sea elephants at Guadaloupe Island, off the Mexican Coast. As a cameraman he was disappointed that the one-ton bulls stayed ashore, guarding their harems, but, as a diver, he thought it was just as well. He was filming among the pups, which weighed only a thousand pounds apiece, when one swam toward him in playful curiosity. He pushed it away with the camera. Then he felt something brushing against his balding head. "At first I thought it was some sea-weed," he said, "but it was warm. Then I felt the points of teeth." The sea elephant pup had the top of his head in its mouth. "I reacted quickly," he said. He twitched out of this situation and put the camera between himself and his unnecessary playmate. He surfaced at the first opportunity. His scalp was not marked, but he found tooth marks on the cast aluminum camera case.

Scripps Institution launched the first free-diving expedition of American science; to Polynesia in 1952–53 went Capricorn Expedition in the research ship *Baird* and a tuna tender. Six diving geologists and naturalists declared their aim was "to apply underwater man as an oceanographic tool." Before the cruise was over, everybody wanted to be a tool. The planners of a general oceanographic voyage must divide time, personnel, equipment, stowage, working deck space and plot stations, so that each branch of science gets a fair crack at useful work. You must give the depth photographer as much winch time as the bathythermograph man, and promptly clear the deck of mudpies dredged up by the geologists so the biologists can sort their slippery hauls. It takes a long time to lower collecting gear and bring it up, and you will be in deep water of no interest to the divers. Unless the planners are experienced and firm, a disruptive tug-of-war may take place at sea between various specialists, each trying to do his job and maybe wangle a little of the other fellow's time and equipment. Oceanographic voyages are much more complicated than any other type of civil seafaring. The ship does not merely pack and go to the next port; she works her way by sea stations, constantly stopping, breaking out gear, stowing it and trying to make the best of time, weather and human personality. When hove to for lowering traps, samplers and cameras, even the mildest swell sets up oscillations that rock her like a going ship in a gale. Moreover, the oscillations are sharp, rapid and unpredictable, unlike the rhythm of rolling under way. It is a hard bruising life, but it is the grandest way you can sail the sea. There is never a dull moment on a research ship, unless you are a dull fellow.

So the Capricorn divers had their allotted time and island sites in the over-all plan. After their first dives at Ocean Island far out on the equator to survey the reef structure around the limestone islet, the dry scientists wanted to get wet. "There was so much interest and enthusiasm for the diving techniques," said the team in a report, "that an equal number of auxiliary divers could have been recruited and effectively employed if diving had been a more prominent part of the over-all program." They came up with geological facts that could hardly have been discovered in any other way. They found that there were no submerged ledges on the coral reef, which might have been formed by a sinking of the island. They found no raised coral formations on dry land. There was no evidence that Ocean Island had subsided or the sea level had risen over it in recent geological history. It was another nail in the coffin of the sunken city romance.

Around Alexa Bank, a submerged reef, they dived to 120 feet seeking clues on the mystery of the building and destruction of coral islands. The *Baird's* scientists left their two days at the bank convinced that no previous oceanographic resource could have served this type of survey as well as diving. A lot of big sharks circled the sunken students, but came no closer than ten feet.

In the Cannibal Islands, they dived with the spearmen of Fiji, who used rubberband sling spears and goggles with plastic frames. The Scripps team reported, "They swim along the surface, inspecting marine life beneath them, proceeding slowly and without much disturbance of the water. When they see an interesting prey, they stalk him to a convenient location or actually drive him gently toward a region favorable for spearing. When the fish is well located, they scoop water with one hand, to duck their heads under, then swim downwards, usually spearing the fish beneath a rocky or coral ledge. These men look like Charlie Chaplin walking as they tread water." The scientists could not resist taking a small bow: "Their dives do not demand prolonged breath-holding and they seemed no abler than ourselves in this regard."

In Tonga they met the redoubtable Prince Tungi, the tall, progressive heir to the throne of Her Delightful Majesty, Queen Salote of Tonga, who won London crowds during the Coronation of Elizabeth II. Tungi, already a skilled naked diver, had introduced fish weirs to the islands. On Christmas morning he took the Aqualungers in a horse-drawn cart to a lagoon, where Tongan spearmen were clearing a trap at low tide. The islanders ducked under, pranged a fish and paralyzed it by biting into the spine. They strung one fish after another on plant fibers, and jumped with delight when they found a 350-pound ray, the caviar of Tonga. The divers emptied the trap each morning and evening tide and found it filled with fish at the next day's harvest.

The Scripps team went beyond the fringing reef and dived with the naked Tongans. "Here for the first time we encountered impressive swimmers," they said. "They dived deeper and stayed submerged longer than the divers of Fiji, attaining depths of forty to fifty feet with obvious ease and remained there for a full minute." A diver took down three spears and left two beside a cave mouth in which he had speared a big fish. After he had surfaced to breathe, the spears were at hand if he needed several casts on a fish. The Tongans paid no attention to wandering barracudas. "No sharks enter the lagoon waters, but divers warn emphatically about their hazard outside," said the scientists. Prince Tungi was delighted with the air lungs and ordered several from London.

The Capricorn geologists next experienced the unique adventure of diving on the drowned peaks of a live volcano. It was Falcon Bank, which three times in the last seventy-five years has exploded and thrown up lava islands as high as six hundred feet and two miles wide. The islands eroded rapidly into the sea afterward. The last eruption was in 1938. The divers did not mention personal risk in the report, although vulcanists have died investigating sea-borne Pacific volcanoes. In 1952, at the birth of Myojin, "Bright God," 250 miles south of Tokyo, the Japanese research vessel, the *Kaiyo Maru*, was blown up, dismembered and consumed with nine scientists and twenty-two sailors.

The Falcon Bank party consisted of Robert B. Livingston, Willard N. Bascom, Philip E. Jackson and Walter H. Munk. They rowed a skiff for a mile and a half toward a patch of green water, which they thought betrayed the crest of the submerged volcano. It turned out to be an underwater mirage. Usually, light green patches in the sea are caused by light reflected from shallow bottom, but here they sounded three hundred feet. Suspended volcanic particles in the water caused the pallor. They sighted the volcano in blue water. Fifty feet down were sharp pinnacles rising out of a ridge of lava. They harnessed up, swam down and came upon an astonishing thing: young healthy coral antlers and clumps were growing as high as two feet on the lava. The coral "was as vigorous and fresh-looking as any we saw in the South Pacific," they reported. They had to pull hard to break off antlers. These polyp structures could not have started to form before 1938, when Falcon last erupted. They had discovered dated coral. No one had known before at what rate coral grew. They estimated that if the coral was spread over the entire lava surface, it would form a half-inch crust, and if it continued to compact and build toward the surface without further explosions of molten rock, there will be a coral island on Falcon Bank in about twelve thousand years.

In Pago-Pago Harbor they swam upon a 200-foot American tanker, which had been scuttled during a dock fire in 1949. They reached the deck 163 feet down and examined the big rifles and antiaircraft guns standing intact in blankets of silt. They found her name, the *Chehalis*, on the stern. Livingston's air bottles were nearly empty when he started up after a lengthy inspection of the wreck. They were too buoyant to allow his to rise slowly and decompress. He swam into an after cabin and carried off a metal chair to ballast himself for the ascent.

In the Tuamotus the Scripps team descended to watch the pearl divers, who plunged naked in the lagoon from outriggers, wearing only metal-framed goggles. They went down weighted lines with a rope basket to gather three or four shells at a time, sometimes to 140 feet. During the pearling season, the Takaroans dive up to 100 times a day five days a week. Whereas the Scripps team had found the Tongans unconcerned about barracudas, the Takaroans were quite scared of them and cleared out of the water when barracudas were sighted. (You cannot say that such conflicting views of marine predators are due to blissful ignorance on one island and exaggerated fear on another. The fact is that the carnivores have differing appetites for man in different places. In Australia, for instance, a dozen bathers a year are taken by sharks, while there is no record of a swimmer being molested by sharks in New Zealand. The diver's book on dangerous animals of all seas is almost a blank. In the Mediterranean, nurse sharks are regarded as harmless dopes and the Australians fear no species more.)

A legendary undersea hunter of the Palau Islands in Micronesia, a giant named Siakong, was swimming beyond a fringing reef with a companion. It was raining and they could not see bottom because of a layer of *schlieren* on the surface. This is the blurred mingling of rain and salt water, fluids of different densities. Siakong called, "Nechan, come see here." They dived beneath the turbid layer and saw through clear water a tridacna clam on the floor. This is the giant bivalve accounted to be a man-eater. Siakong ventilated his lungs and dived. Nechan reported, "I followed, swallowing to adjust my ears to the increasing pressure. I've never measured how deep I can dive, but I know that more than twenty feet under, my mask cuts into my head and my ears and nose feel uncomfortable. But this time I followed Siakong until I felt I was well below my usual limit, and knew my breath wouldn't last descending any deeper. From the depth I did manage to reach, I could see Siakong far below me getting smaller and smaller until he reached the clam.

"Then I saw it was truly a giant.

"Siakong looked like a midget beside the clam which seemed nearly four feet across. I saw him give it a kick to close the huge jaws which could have held all of Siakong with ease. And then I had to shoot for the surface."

On his second dive Siakong stayed down a long time. Nechan ducked under the *schlieren* with the boatman, Niraibui. "As we descended I made out a sight that sickened me with horror," said Nechan—"Siakong was caught in the clam. The jaws of the gigantic mollusk were clamped tight and Siakong's arm was in it up to the elbow." Nechan yelled for Niraibui to help the trapped diver. The boatman merely laughed. Nechan could not dive that far. "Short of breath and good for nothing, I nevertheless ad-

justed my mask to dive again. Just then Siakong popped up beside us—
panting but grinning! He lifted his arm out of the water, the one that had
been in the jaws of the clam, and held up the biggest adductor muscle I
had ever laid eyes on."

Siakong had realized that the clam was much too heavy to lift. Nevertheless, he wanted the adductor muscle, a great delicacy in the Palaus. This
muscle at the hinge of the shell was also the one that clamped the jaws.
He reached in with his knife and was trapped for a moment while he cut
out the muscle. Then the shell collapsed open. Nechan said, "Soon we all
sat contentedly in the boat, munching on a delicious adductor muscle the
size of a man's thigh."

The tale is not from Jack London, but the true relation of a small, beautiful American girl. "Nechan" is the Japanese nickname of the ichthyologist, Dr. Eugenie Clark, director of the Cape Haze Marine Laboratory
in Florida. She dived with Siakong in her chosen line of work, which
is hunting in far seas with spear and mask in pursuit of her specialty,
blowfishes. She mask-dived in the Atlantic, Pacific and Red Sea, before her
profession took up mechanical lungs. Dr. Clark's charming book, *Lady
with a Spear,* is the story of a Japanese-American child growing up in New
York City, becoming fascinated with a home aquarium, and going on to
study fishes at the University of Michigan, Scripps Institution, Woods
Hole and New York University. She was introduced to diving in 1947 by
Dr. Carl L. Hubbs, the famous ichthyologist of Scripps Institution.

The urge of naturalists to visit the marine world goes back a century,
at least. A strange complement sailed on the little, brightly painted Sicilian
fishing boat, the *Santa Rosalia,* out of Cefalù one spring day in 1844.
Seven rowers sat around the gunwales. On a tiny deck at the bow stood a
large brass fireman's pump with rocking bars. In the stern sheets sat two
professors, fighting *mal-de-mer.* They averted their noses from the fumes
of garlic which the boatmen chewed to avoid seasickness. The passengers
scratched themselves, for the *Santa Rosalia* was infested with blood-thirsty
insects. For three days the boat thumped in the waves and dashed spray
over the uneasy savants as they pressed on for Cape Milazzo, near the
Messina Strait. The professors had wished this on themselves. They were
making the first scientific diving expedition. One of them was A. de
Quatrefages, a naturalist, and the other the distinguished zoologist of the
Sorbonne, Professor Henri Milne-Edwards, forty-four, a stout, solemn
man with a monocle. They planned "to pursue marine animals into their
most hidden retreats," and, instead of dragging haphazardly from the surface, were to descend into the sea "in the enjoyment of perfect liberty of
action."

This feat they hoped to accomplish with an open helmet with a glass visor and a padded leather corselet. Both it and the pump had been devised by Colonel Paulin, Commandant of the Paris Fire Brigade, for use in flooded cellars. At Milazzo the scientists staggered up to a hospitable villa and restored themselves. History's first scientific dive took place in Milazzo Harbor, when Milne-Edwards buckled on a chest harness attached to a line carried up through a yard of the *Santa Rosalia*, donned the heavy helmet and plunked over the side. Four men seesawed on the fire pump as the professor sank down thirteen feet and commenced to study the zoophytes in the teaming, brilliant landscape of the sea. He was so entranced he stayed down a half hour on his first dive. His colleague in the boat watched him move about, kept his air pipe clear and held the signal line tightly. Quatrefages said, "God knows with what anxiety I watched its faintest motion. The slightest mistake might have proved fatal to Milne-Edwards. It certainly requires an amount of zeal very uncommon among naturalists of our day to risk so perilous an undertaking."

At last came the signal to be raised and the crew heaved the heavy scholar. It took them two minutes to bring him aboard. They went out to sea again on the long journey through the Straits to Taormina. There Milne-Edwards ventured below twenty-five feet with a pickax and stayed down forty-five minutes, dislodging living specimens of the large gaping clam, *Panope glycimeris*, which had been known previously only from dead shells. He also collected sea slugs, rhapsodizing over the "spangled veil of finest gauze stretched over the head of these lovely little creatures." On one of these dives in an agitated sea, the yardarm cracked under the strain of lifting the professor and he had to be heaved up the hard way without tackle. The three weeks that Milne-Edwards dived around Sicily turned him to embryology, of which study he was one of the founders.

Milne-Edwards was forty years ahead of his colleagues; the next wet biologist was Professor Berthold, who dived to eighty-five feet in the Bay of Naples to study marine plants. In 1908, the Norwegian scholar Peterson dived in a helmet suit in the Limfjord to study the distribution of oysters, and returned to the same sites seventeen years later to find the oysters greatly decreased.

Several free-diving scientists of today began with helmet suits: Professor Pierre Drach, Dr. Carl Hubbs and a trim enthusiastic geologist of the U.S. Geological Survey, Preston Cloud, Jr. In 1949 Dr. Cloud went down off Saipan Island in a helmet suit on a geological study for the army. He encountered the Aqualung in Hawaii two years later. His free-diving teacher was Vernon Brock, Fish and Game Director for the Hawaiian Board of Agriculture and Forestry. Brock had been diving for twenty-five years, without apparatus, in open helmets, helmet suits, oxygen lungs and finally air lungs. Before the war he covered the U.S. Pacific Coast from

Oregon to Mexico, and since then had ranged widely in the Pacific, to the Line Islands, Guam and the Palaus. He was a leader of a hardy group of scientific divers scattered in the great Pacific.

Brock's Hawaiian diving team evolved a method of taking sample censuses of the fish in the open sea. They laid a five-hundred-yard cotton line on the floor, tagged every hundred yards. Two divers with large plastic pads and pencils started down the line abreast, each man watching fish on his side of the line. They wrote down how many there were of what species, and the average length of the fish. They recorded depth, described the type of bottoms, and discounted schools of fish that crossed their field twice. Each man covered an area twenty feet to the side of the line. There are about 125 species of fish around Hawaii and Brock's students learned to spot each kind instantly. These censuses threw some light on the "food chain" of Hawaiian marine life. Brock was trying to find out if more edible fish could be produced by dumping into Hawaiian waters alien fish which would strengthen weak links in the piscatorial economy. In 1955 Brock went out to the Palaus in the United States trust territories of the Pacific to look for species that might be transplanted to Hawaii. The oceans are vast and some big nomads swim ceaselessly around the world through all of them; but reef fish are provincials and will not investigate greener pastures across the open sea. (Brock's idea of forced emigration was not new. The coastal waters of ancient Rome were heavily depopulated by fishing with small meshes that killed off the spawn. The Emperor Claudius was fond of Ballan wrasse, a fish frequenting only the Aegean. Claudius constructed salt-water tankers and transported thousands of living wrasse from Greece and dumped them in the Tyrrhenian Sea at Ostia. He prohibited wrasse fishing for five years to give them a chance to catch on. The fish did not flourish, but Italian fishermen still catch a few exiled Ballan wrasse.)

At Guam on his way to the Palaus, Brock met an extraordinary middle-aged man named Bert Bronson, who had found a harmonious life. Bronson sells seashells by the seashore as souvenirs to the ship and airplane passengers passing through Guam. His Shells of Micronesia Company sells just enough shells for him to live modestly. He shutters his shop for weeks to go off diving in the islands. He is a seasoned naked diver, devoted to observing the habits of fish. Although he has no academic training, Bronson "has a lot to teach the professionals," according to Dr. Cloud, one of his admirers. Dr. Louis Brann of the University of Cincinnati had Bronson write on Micronesian shells for a forthcoming monograph on cone shells. Bronson's easy manner of doing business was the despair of shell collectors in the States. There is, for instance, a Philadelphia croesus, who owns the largest private shell collection on earth—and who endowed a chair of conchology in Philadelphia so he could have a handy expert to call shells. This connoisseur waits months and years for Bronson to take an interest in his orders for rarities.

It is much too early for Vernon Brock to know whether his selected Palauan fish will strengthen the food chain in Hawaii. This highly experienced student told me, "Our knowledge of the process of production and of the ecological relation in the food chains of plants and animals is so slight that even if we had the means, we would not know how to manipulate the ecological complex to our advantage. Fundamentally fisheries are a thousand years behind agriculture and remain behind until man effectively manipulates the environment of fish."

Brock introduced rotenone poisoning to collect deep specimens on dives. One time he spread root poison on the floor and returned to put the dead fish in a bag. He saw a huge moray lying motionless on the floor and thrust his spear in it. The eel did not move. He left it there, pinned to the floor, while he gathered his fish. He started up with the moray on the spear. Suddenly the eel convulsed and came writhing up the shaft. It bit Brock's elbow through his rubber suit. He arrived on the surface unconscious, but was quickly pulled out. The eel wriggled off the shaft. After a hospital stay, Brock came out with a great scar on his elbow and a respect for dead morays. The teeth marks indicated an eel eight feet long.

Robert Owen, who aided Brock on Koror Island in the Palaus, was sent there in 1950 to make war on the rhinocerus coconut beetle, a two-inch living tank which was eating up the coco palms, the main economic resource of the islands. The bronze-armored rhinocerus beetle had incidentally been brought by Japanese troops in 1942. After five years the entomologist had licked the beetle, but didn't go home. He signed a new contract to remain on Koror because he had discovered diving. Owen dives around one of the most fascinating and varied island groups on earth. The Palaus are on the "Wallace Line," the boundary between life forms of the Pacific and Indian oceans. The eighty-mile chain has everything geologically except mother rock.

Inside a vast barrier reef there are coral atolls, volcanic islands and limestone peaks. Owen, an athletic thirty-nine-year-old from Seattle, Washington, thinks the islands contain in small compass the widest variety of marine habitats on earth. He entered the sea because of his concern with the economic fortunes of the Palauans. Having mastered the palm-eating beetle he wanted to investigate the second product of the islands, the *Trocus* shell, which yields fine mother-of-pearl. His employer, the U.S. Department of the Interior, did not see why it should buy diving gear for a bug man. Owen put his own money into lungs and compressors with Bronson and Sydney Seid, of the Western Carolines Trading Company. Owen set up a general biological laboratory in a ruined Japanese weather station and fitted up an apartment for transients. Soon the three amateur oceanographers were entertaining visiting Elks with the proper degrees, among them Dr. Eugenie Clark.

They dived among groupers large enough to swallow a man. Owen believes Dr. Clark's Palauan diving companion, the famous Siakong, was engulfed by a grouper. Siakong dived after a turtle in 1952 and never came up. "No trace of his body has ever been found," Owen told me. "That's unusual. Sharks, morays, or anything in that line, rarely make off entirely with a body. The grouper has no teeth. It just opens wide enough to take you right in. I know a fifty-year-old man on Babelthuap Island who was swallowed by a grouper. He made his escape through a gill, and is badly scarred on the chest and face."

The Palauans say the grouper stays inside a cave, looking out with its weak eyes and getting hungry. Something comes along and the big fish leaps out with its enormous mouth wide open and the prey slides in without even a bruise. The talent is shared with its Mediterranean cousin, which the French call the *merou* and Italians the *cernia,* a fish which comes big enough to have swallowed Jonah. The report in the Book of Jonah states that, "Jonah was in the belly of the fish three days and three nights." This may have been merely sloppy reporting by an excitable country correspondent. The true story may have been something like this: Jonah was swallowed by a *merou,* and got out through the gills. He swam to safety and exclaimed, "It seemed like I was inside for three days!"

Bert Bronson spears octopuses in their grottoes and leaves the spear in place, as the octopus braces tentacles against the walls, attaching itself too firmly to be withdrawn by human strength. Bronson takes a hunk of coral and hammers it on his spear shaft. The vibrations shatter the octopus' nerves. It relaxes its muscles and comes out limp. Bronson says, "If you are in a narrow hole in the reef and sharks are after you, don't worry. They can't swim backwards. They are inefficient in narrow places." Once he and Owen were competing with a band of sharks for dynamited fish specimens. Dead fish drifted into a cliff niche a few feet from the divers. Owen said, "The sharks drove in the hole and bounced out by their noses time after time. Bert and I held hands and climbed the cliff to the surface, feeling fairly secure against the reef." Dr. Owen said Bronson still wore goggles. "He started out with them in Hawaii years ago and won't change over to the mask." He estimated that Bronson spends thirty hours a week in the water, an extraordinary feat, exceeding that of any professional I know of.

Bronson's octopus trick is a variation of the technique used by Gilbert Island divers, who hunt the cephalopod as food in the reefs at low tide.

Sir Arthur Grimble described it in *We Chose the Islands*. A Gilbertese dived and offered his bare arm to the octopus. It reached out of the crevice and the diver hung there until he had all eight tentacles wrapped around himself. Then he popped to the surface where a confederate bent the octopus' head back and bit it between the eyes. The animal let go dead. "This is nothing but child's play for a seventeen-year-old Gilbertese," said Sir Arthur.

Walter McCray, a helmet diver in Puget Sound back in 1922, had less understanding of octopus traits. Fifty feet down, he unwittingly offered himself in Gilbertese fashion. The octopus curled a reconnaissance tentacle around his air pipe. McCray phoned up for a steel wrecking bar and requested that he be hauled most urgently. He grabbed the bar in mid-water and jabbed it repeatedly into the octopus' sac. When he came swinging out of the water, the animal was well entwined with him and his ganglia. A dock watchman drew his revolver to deliver McCray, but wiser hands held him back. Workmen surrounded the wriggling tangle of man, lines and *Octopus vulgaris,* and pried and hammered. The poor beast was no match for them. It gave up and fell into the water. Picking up the menu and ordering lunch is very difficult for octopuses.

Occasionally scientists have been able to wrangle military submarines for basic research. The physicist Dr. Vening Meinesz, traveled on a long cruise in a Dutch submarine recording the earth's gravity with a pendulum instrument. The device would not work on a rocking ship, but the undersea craft furnished a stable platform. In 1931 Sir Hubert Wilkins attempted to cross the North Pole in an ex-U.S. Navy submarine renamed the *Nautilus* and refitted by Simon Lake. The noted Danish oceanographer, H. U. Sverdrup, went along and made valuable observations. H.M. Submarine *Acheron* set out on a six-month world cruise in 1955, carrying Lt. J. C. Harrison, R.N.V.R. and a pendulum apparatus to make gravity surveys in the South Atlantic and Indian oceans. Harrison, a Doctor of Philosophy, previously operated gravity surveys in U.S. submarines off California. H.M.S. *Acheron's* chore was a contribution to the great international scientific effort centered on the Geophysical Year—1957.

In 1947 Frédéric Dumas began an Aqualung diving course for the French Navy at Toulon, to which a civilian applied,—a stocky, balding, fair-complexioned Norman with glasses and a boyish grin that moderated his air of incision and learning. Professor Pierre Drach was a fighter of the Resistance and the heir of Milne-Edwards and Louis Boutan in the Paris Faculté des Sciences. He had begun zoological diving in a helmet dress before the war and he wanted to learn the Aqualung. Dumas said, "Professor Drach believed that direct observation of marine life was necessary to complete information gathered by other methods." The middle-aged savant dived with the Navy novices, on whom Dumas made spectacular demands. In midsemester the pupils removed masks, mouthpieces and lungs 75 feet down, and exchanged them with each other. Professor Drach graduated *cum laude* 125 feet down, by removing his lung and returning to the surface naked.

His main study is the ecology of fixed fauna on the reefs—the coral-builders, the million-in-a-foot animals who live as flowers and die as grains of rock. Pupil Drach in turn taught much to Professors Tailliez, Dumas and Cousteau. They knew the beauty of corals, but little of their science. They stayed after school with the student, diving along the vertical cliffs of Cassis, where they showed him explosions of fixed fauna. Drach impressed them with his collecting gear. He strapped a depth gauge on his wrist and took precise notes on a board with a ball-point pen. He slung a housewive's string shopping bag on his belt and filled it with animal clusters, pried from the reef with a burglar's jimmy. On his first deep dive at Cassis, Professor Drach came up with his mask half swamped with nose-bleed. Dumas said, "He took it off and his eyes were shining. He said, 'Now I can die!' " Professor Drach led the scientific party on the *Calypso* Red Sea Expedition in 1951, where he swam down 220 feet on the Abu Latt reef and busied himself with his jimmy and notebook as sharks patrolled past. He came up the ladder from one of these deep studies and burst out, "That dive was for me the top!" Everybody laughed. He looked blank for a moment and joined in. I called on Professor Drach last year at the Sorbonne, where he occupies the bureau of Milne-Edwards on Escalier E. He said, "When Le Prieur perfected his diving apparatus, I was an assistant on the Faculté. I thought to myself, now there's the best means for getting to know the *peuplement rocheux* [peopling of the rocks]. Now, of course, at that time, there was not the same kind of mental climate as now. My idea was considered a desire for *l'amusement sportif*. I was not able to dive seriously until 1947. I was working in a laboratory in the Boulevard Raspail, when Commandant Cousteau called on me. It did not take me long to be convinced that I should try his *scaphandre-autonome*. I went through my baptism at the G.E.R.S., with the cave explorer Guy de Lavour. We were immediately *enthousiasmé*. At the Rocher de l'Empereur at Cassis I gazed along this hallucinating cliff, a single drop of two hundred feet straight—what a vision! For five years I dived on my own. For the last three years I have had young people along with me, and Dr. Ernst, my Viennese assistant at the Roscoff Laboratory."

During Professor Drach's cruise on the *Calypso* in the Red Sea, the divers were without compressed air for some weeks due to the breakdown of a compressor. He and Cousteau swam out with masks on a submerged coral plateau about fifteen feet deep, until they came to the drop-off. Professor

Drach said, "Vision suddenly plunged into a blue-violet depth, quite rich with fish, an extraordinary density of fish. Far below there suddenly materialized a mass of sharks. They must have risen toward us in two seconds from a depth of 150 feet. You know sharks can swim at sixty kilometers an hour, perhaps more. The sharks were not very big, but even so . . . Cousteau flapped his feet and this movement scared the sharks. They plunged as quickly as they had come. We know very little about sharks' behavior. What was extremely curious—we would often see these Red Sea sharks swimming in the middle of huge schools of fish, and the other species showed not the slightest fear."

Professor Drach watched Arab commercial fishing methods to report to the Food and Agricultural Organization of the United Nations, which has been working to increase the fish yield in protein-deficient Islam. Drach told me, "The kind of fishing done by the Arabs—on a family or artisan scale—is completely insignificant. It scarcely feeds the fisherman's own family. Their methods are a great waste of time and energy. From diving at many points in this region, I would say that trawling would not be practicable—too many sharp reef heads protruding from the sandy floor to rip trawl nets. But I am optimistic about another method. Perhaps a kind of artisan fishing could be organized that would be very efficient, even providing enough fish for export, if the fishermen were taught to use *filets tournants*." This is a round net stretched between four or five small boats and drawn in. He continued, "The reefs drop vertically for at least a hundred feet, consequently you could put your net quite close to the great concentrations of edible reef fish without much risk."

I asked Professor Drach what he felt to be his most important diving observation. "Well, it's a large question," he said. "After all I've dived in many different areas—the Mediterranean, the English Channel, the South Atlantic, the China Sea, the Red Sea. Nothing has impressed me so forcibly as the fact that everywhere—and this was always true—the walls of the sea are covered with an incredible blanket of living matter."

One of the new school of diving scientists is the American biologist, Talbot H. Waterman, who has been trying to find if aquatic animals find their directions as certain land animals do by sensing polarized light from the dome of the sky. In 1950 Waterman showed that the horseshoe crab (*Limulus*) established a sense of direction by an ability of its many-lensed eyes to analyze polarized light from the sky. This was discovered on land. Dr. Waterman went diving off Bermuda with optical instruments, and in the scattered rays of the sun he found that "underwater light is polarized in a complex pattern." On land only the dome of the sky is polarized, but under water "the complete visual background of an animal is polarized." His work may lead to knowledge of how fishes fix their uncanny courses on long migrations, such as the tuna's round-the-world swim on regular routes. It appears that the mammals, the porpoise and whale have a sort of organic radar, but there may be a polarization factor as well.

In Britain lung divers were at work for marine research centers by 1951. The Scottish Marine Laboratory at Aberdeen maintained a four-man team of diving biologists, who used a two-man underwater sled to ride ahead of trawls, building up knowledge for fishermen. At Edinburgh, the Scottish Seaweed Research Institute deployed a diving photographer to study the distribution of seaweeds for commercial kelp pickers. At the end of 1955 the Institute dissolved itself because its researches were too successful. Lord Bilsland, the chairman, reported that in ten years the researchers had created a $3 million annual industry, which harvested 40,000 tons of seaweed a year. Scholars at the Marine Biological Association of the United Kingdom at Plymouth started down in bucket helmets in the early thirties and today use lungs to collect marine invertebrates.

Among the newly discovered faunas of the California floor is a species of diving geologist, a sleek, hump-backed animal with a crew haircut. The first specimens were H. W. Menard, R. F. Dill, E. L. Hamilton, D. G. Moore, George Shumway, M. Silverman and H. B. Stewart. The diving geologist crawls out on land occasionally where its favorite habitat is an oil company laboratory. Most of the group comes from the busy and enterprising Navy Electronics Laboratory in San Diego, with some from Scripps Institution near by. Their baptism came in 1953 when the Ordnance Test Station at Inyokern requested information on the bottom topography off San Nicolas Island, and the N.E.L. concluded that "one possible method, indeed the most obvious one, was to put a field party on the sea floor." The party went out on the *E. W. Scripps,* the research ship, laid buoys and leaped in backwards, carrying burlap sacks of geological picks, compasses, light sledges and inclinometers. They were entranced with the undersea terrain and attained heights of geological prosody in describing it: "San Nicolas Island is composed of more than 2,000 feet of Eocene sandstone and shale intruded in a few places by Miocene diabase dikes and covered extensively by Pleocene terrace capping. The sandstone and shales have been folded and now form part of an anticline which plunges toward the southeast."

The converts to wet geology scoured the labs for anything they could put in a watertight case and take down, including cameras and other instruments. They marveled at the speed with which they could obtain bottom data: "Only six minutes were required to take a dip and strike and collect a hand sample in 63 feet of water at Station Baker in area A-1." They built new gadgets such as sediment samplers and ripplemark measurers. The original team set up a company called Geological Diving Consultants. In the first year the consultants logged 2,000 dives to 150 feet, inspecting underwater pier structures and sewer outfalls, finding the best beds for pipelines and cables, and surveying offshore oil concessions.

Underwater pipelines called forth a venturesome engineer who arrived in a black air-conditioned limousine with an office in the back seat, donned an Aqualung and swam down with his staff to check the situation. He is a small, hard-driving Texan, S. V. "Sammy" Collins, the Hephaestus of submerged pipelines. Collins learned pipelining as a boomer and tool pusher in the Texas oil fields, and, when the Texas towers paraded out to sea, he was ready to connect them up to shore. His first coup was a pipeline in Matagorda Bay in 1948. A vast aluminum corporation was wringing its hands and crying for help. It had a $140 million smelting plant ready at Port Lavaca and a production lease expiring on its only fuel source, an underwater natural gas well twenty-six miles out in the bay. There was no pipeline to the well and the lease expiration was four weeks off. Collins said he could run the submarine line in time. The actual pipe length was forty-five miles. Collins and his ardent young engineers tortured the clock and welded the line on the smelter conduit twenty minutes before the option expired.

When Collins began to run wet pipe, milelong lengths were loaded on a train of barges, blockading busy harbors and straits which trunk pipelines usually cross. The anchored trains fussed around for hours, welding to the upheld mouth of the previously laid pipe and ponderously lowering the extension. That was the way Collins strung the Matagorda pipe. Three months after it was laid the wrapping was being riddled by marine organisms. The company called Sammy.

He already knew the sea secret of the Greek marbles at Antikythera: that if an object merely lies on the bottom, sea animals consume it, but if the object is buried in the bottom, it is embalmed for ages. Pipeline engineers, since the beginning of submerged lines, knew that too; they always wanted the pipe covered in an expensive trench cut by dredgers. Collins and his staff spent a month on the bottom of Corpus Christi Bay, tinkering with a different trenching principle. He called it the Collins Jet Trencher, a sled-shaped skeleton clamped over the head of a submarine pipe. The trencher bristled with powerful water jets, which ploughed the ditch while air jets broke up clods and scattered them. By now Collins had rejected the barge train and was plunging pipelines down from the shore on submerged relieving pontoons. Tugs dragged the line along the floor to the other shore. Shipping passed above without concern. The jet trencher buried two miles of pipe eighteen inches deep in twelve hours in the first test. On a job in Copano Bay, Collins ran into tougher bed mud. He and his assistants, Billy Glasscock and Jean Johnson, spent six weeks under water, redesigning the jet trencher. The second model entrenched nine miles of pipe three feet deep in thirty hours.

The Texas team was soon operating around the world. They ran the world's longest sea-loading oil line, two and one half miles long, at Accra, on the African Gold Coast; an 84,000-foot line in Bombay Harbor; and a phenomenal line across Mackinac Straits, Michigan, which reached depths of 250 feet in water. Four miles of twin pipes, twenty inches in diameter, were dragged across in sixty-five hours. Collins burrowed a pipe across the Narrows in New York Bay, without impairing ship traffic. He was called in on a "pipeliner's nightmare" on a trunk gas line already buried under the North River floor at 134th Street, New York City. It was the main line from Texas to New York and had to keep transmitting gas while Collins attempted to plant it deeper. The pipe was thirty inches in diameter. It was interred fourteen feet down in a dredged trench, which did not fully protect it in the thin mud of the river bottom. The pipeline company wanted to bury it at least twenty feet. Collins and two staff engineers dived sixty feet to a point where the silt cover was its thinnest. They jetted their way down to the pipe and straddled it with a traveling jet trencher. This huge special model had an attachment to blow off the top mud cover. They uncovered ninety feet a day. When the pipe was exposed, the trencher shuttled back and forth on the tube at a hundred feet an hour, ploughing deeper, without damaging the pipe or stopping river traffic. When they were finished, the trunk line was sealed off thirty-five feet deep in the river bed.

10
Gifts of Aphrodite

THE past is a hovering presence over the Mediterranean Sea. You would not blink at a trireme flapping oared wings in the spray; you frown at the water skier and his speed boat. Young Gustave Flaubert wrote his friend, Alfred le Poittevin: "I am moved to the depths of my being when I think of the Roman keels that once cut the changeless, eternally undulant waves of this ever-young sea. The ocean is perhaps more beautiful, but here the absence of tides which divide time in regular periods seems to make you forget that the past is far distant and that centuries separate you from Cleopatra."

The collapse of time in the Mediterranean is no longer an emotion. Men are reaching arms around Roman keels in the clear depths and picking up wine cups dropped by fellow sailors two thousand years ago. Ship archeology in the twentieth century is reaching back for the Golden Age. Free divers are hunting the floor for sculptures which once came up only in the fisherman's trawl. The net has recovered many beautiful works, among them:

A bronze torso and four portrait heads, including Homer and Sophocles, netted off Livorno in the eighteenth century.

A fifth century B.C. bronze Apollo, hauled off Elba a century ago, now in the Louvre.

A bronze head of a youth, netted off Sousse, Tunisia, in 1890.

A bronze Gorgon, netted at Rhodes, now in the Louvre.

A bronze figurehead of Medusa, netted off Sanary-sur-Mer in 1877, sold for scrap metal.

A sack of bronze coins, netted recently off La Ciotat, now in the Borély Museum, Marseille.

A gold cup, sold by a Dodecanese fisherman to the yachting Comtesse de Bearn, 1908.

Two Roman gilded silver dishes dredged at Bizerte.

Around 1907 the god of the sea, Poseidon himself, arose dripping from the waves in southern Greece. His effigy was a bronze masterpiece of the fifth century B.C., now in the National Museum in Athens. It appears that Poseidon was not a diver. The image stood in a shrine on the shore, which toppled into the sea and remained partially visible for centuries, until fishermen heard about archeologists and fished him up for sale. To be sure, this was not archeology, only chance finds. Marine archeology requires systematic search and disciplined digging.

The young science was founded in 1900. The circumstances were appropriate. A storm was blowing like those which sank the old ships, and in the storm were two Greek sailing galleys, each carrying twenty-two oars for use in calms. In the galleys were Greek seamen and divers from the little island of Syme in the Dodecanese, which has produced *sphoungarades*, or sponge divers, for thousands of years. The galleys were commanded by Captain Demetrios Kondos, master diver. He had completed the sponge harvest in Tunisia, had been paid off and was skimming home to Syme. The galleys tried to run the Elaphonesou Strait between Cape Malea and Kythera Island. A howling northwestern wind, coming on the beam, pushed the little ships out of the passage and they took shelter behind the small island of Antikythera, the tentacle of the Grecian archipelago which almost reaches Crete. There is a little village called Potama on the northeast of Antikythera, but, as Captain Kondos did not want to lose any men to the wineshops, he conducted the galleys around a headland to the south and they lay up in the lee about seventy-five feet off an ugly cliff. Above was a burnt shelf which supported a poor goatsherd, and near the galleys there was a notch in the cliff from which a yellow mineralized stain ran down into the sea, an unmistakable landmark.

While waiting out the wind, Captain Kondos thought they might as well see if there were any sponges below. Diver Elias Stadiatis got into his helmet suit and jumped into the sea. He sank rapidly through water of extraordinary clarity. Had his vision not been cut off by the helmet, he might have seen just under the surface what awaited him 150 feet down. Stadiatis landed in a nightmare. Around him in the sand stood monumental white horses and human figures in the blue gloaming. Some of the horses rolled hoofs up, and nude women, sunk to the waist, stared at him with sightless eyes. Among the white figures he saw the dark, reaching limbs of bronze statues. In a trance Stadiatis trudged on his leaden boots and took hold of a black hand. A heavy arm came up in his hands. He tugged four times on his signal line, "Pull me up," and was hauled on deck carrying the enormous arm.

Captain Kondos looked at it and called for his dresser. As they bolted the helmet and closed his faceplate, he clutched a tape measure in his hand. He dropped over the side. The tenders whipped out air pipe and lines and the pumpmen pumped hard. The captain was down for some time. When he came up, he wrote some measurements on a piece of paper, then he looked at the wind. The gale was dying. He ordered sails up for Syme. He put the arm behind his bunk. At home the crews scattered with the wonderful tale. Captain Kondos called a mighty moot of the elders of the island and showed them the big arm. They decided that the best thing for Syme was to take the arm to Athens.

Captain Kondos and Elias Stadiatis arrayed themselves in their church clothes, shoes and all, and went off to the capital with the arm. They arrived at a good time. For two thousand years, Greek masterpieces had been carried off by foreigners, sometimes to "protect and preserve" them, sometimes with no excuse at all. Now there was a law keeping archeological discoveries in the country and the foreigners were coming to study, not to steal. British, French and German archeological schools were running and native archeologists had been trained, notably Panajotis Cavvadias and Velerios Stais, who were sorting the national collections. The sea peasants of Syme met an enthusiastic reception. They made a deal to recover the statuary at a bonus for each piece, and the Greek Navy joined with a ship capable of lifting the great weights Captain Kondos had measured. It was the first time Greeks had run a Greek archeological expedition.

The summer went by in preparations and it was late November before the warship and caïques got to work under the notch by the yellow stain. The situation was hard enough without winter weather to boot. (The *Calypso* divers surveyed the Antikythera wreck in 1953 in summer. It was apprehensive work to keep a ship moored to the cliff in treacherous winds that veered around the compass without warning. It was more difficult for the 1900 expedition.) The first station lasted only three hours before the wind forced them to untie and take shelter. They continued to steal hours from the weather with the ships in danger the whole time.

Under water it was no easier. The wreck site was steeply pitched from 150 to 170 feet, very bad footing for a helmet diver trying to work stiff lines over a big stone. The depth was greater than the working range of the Symiotes, but they have a reputation for audacity. Aegina Island may turn out more divers, but Syme makes up in reckless courage. They used six divers, who could not stand the depth for more than five minutes. When the weather was right, a man dived twice a day. On the best days one man-hour was the total effort on the bottom.

During the first brief station they brought up a life-sized bronze head, two big marble statues and some smaller pieces. It was typical of the initial zeal on an underwater dig. The men go crazy for statues and glean the loose ones right off. Then they come harder, tenaciously rooted in the hard compacted floor, and the men have to dig. When a marble was finally slung, hauling it up was risky. If it slipped and fell, it might destroy others below or roll down the slope to unattainable depths. There were long days without yield as the sponge divers lifted rocks off the site to look for buried pieces. Throughout the nine months of exertion the weather was against them most of the time.

In the spring of 1901 they recruited four more divers as replacements. Two men had been disabled for life with bends and one died. Professor George Karo, who inspected the objects when they arrived in Athens, said, "Yet, these illiterate fishermen, totally ignorant of archeological techniques, treated the finds with quite remarkable care and delicacy. I was amazed at the insignificant amount of recent damage. Not only had the sculptures been handled with evident gentleness, but even pottery and glass vases had been brought up intact."

In the National Museum the recoveries of Antikythera occupy a long gallery. The big bronzes included broken parts of a group of five or six men, one of them owner of Stadiatis' magic arm. Their leaden bases were ripped and bent, telling how the looters had torn them from stone bases in a sanctuary. Two superb bronze statuettes of the Periclean Age were recovered. The finest bronze is the fourth or fifth century *ephebos*, or athlete, of Antikythera, a noble naked youth, life-size, with gemstones set in the eyes to delineate the pupils. Scholars differ on whom he represents. Some say Perseus, others Paris or Hermes; so he is called the athlete.

The athlete was found in a great many pieces and was reconstructed by the celebrated antique welder of the Louvre, M. André. Many experts were dissatisfied with André's interpretation. The athlete has been dismantled several times to try for more natural posturing. When I was in Athens a couple of years ago, the athlete was at the doctor's again. An archeologist remarked, "You can tell when a new curator has arrived—the *ephebos* goes into the workroom." Harold Edgerton saw him on display again in 1955 and reported, "The esthetes stand around, looking at him curiously."

The marbles, twenty-five huge figures and groups, are not on exhibition at the Museum. They lie in an open court among the workshops. At twilight you may see them almost as Stadiatis did, awful monsters of the floor. They have been eaten away by shellfish. Coming upon a naked goddess, you see a scabrous front and a fine silhouette, and the back is smooth as silk where she lay in the protecting sand. Karo described them perfectly, "They look like lepers in advanced stages of the disease." The stones are commercial copies four centuries younger than the bronzes, which poses a curious question about the sunken ship. She was undoubtedly bound from Athens to Rome in the last decades before Christ was born, and had worse luck in the Strait than Captain Kondos. The crew were no better art connoisseurs than they were sailors. They stole a very good antique—the athlete was then four hundred years old—and some nice old statuettes, and raided a temple for a male group about a hundred years old, whose artistic quality cannot be judged owing to its incomplete state. The raiders loaded forty tons of newly carved brummagem. It was like a smash-and-grab raid on New York in which the mob lifted a Rembrandt from the Metropolitan, tore down Atlas at Rockefeller Center and then stole all the window dummies from Macy's.

We know one more thing about them as sailors: they used a bronze astrolobe to fix their position by the stars. The Symiotes found it in the wreck. It is the only one surviving from pre-Christian times.   •

The Antikythera Expedition aroused great hopes for submarine archeology, but no one came forth to carry on the dangerous and expensive science. The most important consequence was the simple fact that Greek seafaring peasants heard about the hullaballoo over objects they had been netting beyond memory. Henceforth they turned many of them in for a reward, instead of melting them for scrap.

Among the scholars fascinated with the possibilities revealed at Antikythera was Salomon Reinach, the most influential classic antiquarian of the time. He had just published his *Apollo,* a monumental history of the plastic arts, and was eager to float a diving archeological effort when an opportunity offered. It came in 1907, when another Greek sponge diver discovered a second Roman plunder ship full of Greek sculptures. He was canvassing a rather barren sandy floor, 130 feet deep, three miles off Mahdia, Tunisia, when he saw rows of long cylindrical objects covered with shellfish and algae. He thought they were cannons. He looked closer and discovered they were marble columns. About him other objects protruded from the sand, bronze figures and stone carvings. The Greeks pelted down and picked up the most accessible sculptures.

Alfred Merlin, director of antiquities in Tunisia, found an unusual situation in the Arab *souk.* The market was offering genuine Greek art objects. He quickly looked into their source and came upon the Greeks happily recovering what the Romans had taken from them two thousand years before. However, these were French waters and the harvest was over. Reinach shifted into high gear. He convinced an American friend of the tremendous opportunity at Mahdia—a tall, erudite millionaire living in

Paris, James Hazen Hyde, who contributed $25,000 and was joined in the patronage by the Duc de Loubat and Édouard de Billy. The Marine Prefect of Bizerta, Admiral Jean Baëhme, contributed the tug *Cyclope* and the harbor board lent the diving tender *Eugène Resal*. The Tunisian Government and three French ministries and institutes also gave money. Altogether the dig was well backed. An underwater archeological project costs at least ten times as much as one on land, the difference lying in ships and crews, buoys to mark out the area, lifting power, auxiliary boats, the short time divers may do effective work on the bottom, and the fact that the diggers must be well-paid professionals, not low-paid unskilled labor as is the case with Middle Eastern archeology. Time lost due to weather with the full force standing by is another added cost of wet archeology.

Greeks did the diving, with one hard-working Turk. They discovered that the ship had been badly overloaded. She held huge kraters, the ornamental marble basins in which the Greeks and Romans reconstituted their dehydrated wines with water. She carried many bronze and marble figures and at least sixty fluted Ionic columns with capitals, bases and lintels, suggesting that she had carried off an entire temple. Sunk five hundred miles off course, her last days must have been a desperate round of bailing, trying to close seams and trying to beach. There was a very nice beach three miles from the wreck, which the old sailors might have seen as they went down.

Reinach saw the first hauls and declared, "Nothing comparable has come to light since Pompeii and Herculaneum." The sculptures were mainly of a late decadent style. The finest piece was a fifty-inch bronze Eros with a bow and arrow. Here, unlike Antikythera, most of the marbles were buried in the sand, which protected them from mutilation by shellfish. The excavation was pursued for five seasons and yielded enough ancient objets d'art to fill five rooms in the Alaoui Museum at Bardo, Tunis. Few architectural parts were lifted, and many are still there. They were loaded on the eight-inch-thick main deck, which the divers breached to get at the art cargo in the hold, most of which was found between decks. The Greeks dug two shafts fore and aft, according to Merlin.

Forty years afterward the Mahdia wreck served as the first school of archeology for free divers, when Cousteau, Tailliez and Dumas relocated her from the *Élie Monnier*. They spent three days lifting out a half-dozen capitals and columns. The finest capital is in the Naval Museum at Toulon. The free divers worked with comparative ease in a one-knot current that had been extremely bothersome to the Greek helmet men. The *Élie Monnier's* divers left with the conviction that there is still cargo in the wreck. They were frustrated because the ship itself was still there and should be excavated to learn more about ancient navigation. In 1954 Cousteau and Dumas had another look at the Mahdia argosy during a cruise of the

Calypso. They found amateurs from Tunis excavating under the direction of the chief of antiquities. The group was attempting to dig a shaft deep into the bilge of the big argosy on the assumption that there were still buried sculptures. They recovered several statuary fragments in priestine state which encouraged this theory. Dumas carefully surveyed the litter of Ionic columns on the floor and noticed an interesting thing. There were no sponges growing on them. Apparently the Greek sponge divers had continued to visit their museum.

The family of the gods, arisen from the sea in our century, is ruled by the Greek lord of the Universe, thundering Zeus. His nude representation in heroic scale, with legs and arms outspread to hurl a thunderbolt, came from twenty fathoms in the bay between Cape Artemision and Thessaly in 1928. It is considered the finest Greek bronze ever found, the work of a great master of the Golden Age. A cast stands in the main lobby of the United Nations headquarters building in New York, a gift from Greece to the family of nations.

Zeus arose from the sea with the help of a Greek sponge diver who found his massive left arm; Professor George Karo, of the German Archeological Institute in Athens, who campaigned for an expedition to search the site, and Alexander Benakis, a Greek art patron, who put up $3,000 for the effort. The salvage was conducted by the Greek Navy and sponge divers.

Diving six hundred yards off the Cape in strong current, the helmet men found the great body that fitted the arm. They also came upon an unique bronze figure of a stable boy half-flying from his horse. They found the horse's head and neck and some distance off smaller bits of the mount, swept away in the current when the ship crashed the floor. The little jockey was the work of a genre master, full of fun and sport, not so much "classical" as human. Surviving Greek sculpture consists mostly of Olympians endowed with immortal majesty like angry Zeus or grieving Demeter. There was no divinity in the little rider; he and the sculptor were having a whale of a good time. The piece smiles over twenty-four centuries.

Karo tried to maintain diving discipline at Cape Artemision. The sponge divers were working far deeper than usual, but they refused to decompress under water and spurned the new helmet suits he had bought for the job. One of them demonstrated how silly it was, this underwater loitering, and rocketed to the surface from 140 feet. He climbed the ladder and laughed as they unbolted his helmet. He fell dead of an embolism. The death discouraged the divers and the money was running out. Karo was halted on the edge of perhaps more discoveries. His two figures, he said, "were evidently not the only spoils taken from some great sanctuary, and the facts simply cried out for intensified research, but nothing could be done.

The only really adequate diving apparatus produced at that time in Europe, by a firm in Luebeck [the Neufeldt and Kuhnke Armor Company—J.D.] cost 600,000 gold marks and was too heavy for the salvage vessels which the Greek Navy could provide for the purpose. Moreover, as competent authorities very truly remarked, the rest of the treasure is quite safe, guarded for a better day in twenty fathoms of water."

The old harbors of the Mediterranean invite archeological search. None are on the mouths of rivers which carry off sunken objects or bury them hopelessly in alluvial silt. The raucous Vieux Port of Marseille has thrived for twenty-five hundred years. During the last war the Nazis dynamited a medieval labyrinth on the north side in a vain attempt to destroy patriotic hideouts. They leveled Marseille's oldest quarter, but later archeologists dug into the clearings and found oaken pilings of the sixth century B.C. port of Massalia. They uncovered traces of the wooden hards upon which vessels once were hauled out and singed with straw to kill shipworm larvae. Near the water they unearthed a huge Ionic capital, the only Greek building stone ever found in France. In 49 B.C. Julius Caesar destroyed Greek France as thoroughly as a Carthage or Lidice. His legions slaughtered a million Gauls and enslaved at least as many. You have to look for Massalia elsewhere, by diving on the Greek wrecks heaped along the white rocks of Marseilleveyre to the east, and digging thousands of amphora shards scattered inland beyond the springs of the Rhone River system. Archeologists believe the mucky bottom of Marseille's Old Port is a book of Greek history, to be opened, page by page, perhaps to statuary which the water hid from the smashing hammer of Rome. (Lake Nemi in Italy was drained in the thirties to reveal pleasure galleys in which Caligula perhaps took his outings. The Germans burned these ships in 1944.) A lock across the narrow gate of the Vieux Port would allow it to be pumped dry, even if it would evict the rubberneck boats which trap country people to see the fictional cell of the Count of Monte-Cristo at Chateau d'If.

The port-pumping school vividly remembers finds at Piraeus, the port of Athens, in 1931. A dredger struck in shallow water the burned-down hulk of an ancient ship, which was loaded with marble reliefs of the second century B.C. Artistically the carvings were no match for the bronzes of Artemision and Antikythera; they were commercial copies from an atelier catering to the Roman trade. Apparently the ship burned just before departure. The marbles were cracked by fire; perhaps the shipper fished up one or two, decided to leave them there and bade his stonecutters make some more at so much per horse and less for humans. The reliefs, however, told something about a major artistic puzzle—the colossal ivory and gold statue of Athena Promachos by Phidias which stood in front of the Erechtheum and Parthenon on the Acropolis. Unveiled by Pericles in 438 B.C., Athena was to the Greek hoi polloi their greatest work of art. Contemporary writers have left many descriptions of the colossus. Nothing of the statue remains today but the lowest course of stones in the base. Over the goddess's enormous golden shield spread a sculptured battle between Greeks and Amazons which must have been copied and recopied by the pieceworkers in the commercial studios. The reliefs from the burned ship showed Greek and Amazon warriors in a scale suitable for the great golden shield. Unfortunately, says Professor Karo, "the portraits of himself and his great patron, Pericles, which Phidias had included in the Greek host, apparently were not copied for the decorative reliefs—unless they are still imbedded in the deep slime of the harbor."

The landmarks of Mediterranean ship archeology are terra cotta cargo jars called amphoras, the jerry-cans of antiquity. From Homeric times well into the Roman era, amphoras were the universal carriers of wine, oil, perfume, water, grains, tiles, ores—anything that would flow through a four- or five-inch mouth. Ancient ships were loaded like baskets to two or three upright layers of amphoras on the main deck. Their conical bottoms allowed the jars to be nested upright. The old ships seem to have been usually dangerously overloaded and top-heavy judging from the thousands of amphoras found by divers from Gibraltar to the Golden Horn. Thousands have also been found in net hauls. Until recently fishermen knew them as "those old jars" and chunked them back in the water.

In ancient times shipwreck was a common occurrence; in a few weeks of archeological surveys in the Aegean in 1953, the *Calypso* divers looking for wrecks on likely capes and reefs along the ancient trade routes, found amphoras on every single dive, dating from the Phoenicians to the late days of Rome. Some jars were isolated falls, perhaps deck cargo hastily thrown over while drifting on the rocks, or amphoras which broke loose in a blow and fell overside. But fifty places had masses of amphoras, strongly indicating the grave of a vessel. Ship casualties must have been enormous. But merchant venture profits were huge, too. An eight-gallon amphora of concentrated red wine from Greece brought the price of a slave in Marseille. So the shipowner overloaded and the sailors sailed them.

The number of wrecks is so high the extent of shipping must have been far greater than was realized before diving archeology brought the evidence. Ancient sea commerce has been conceived as a matter of galleys, rowed by slaves and soldiers. Greek myths, mosaics and reliefs deal with war galleys and it was assumed that rowing was also the principal means of cargo navigation. Two ancient ships that have been found, photographed and excavated on the floor at Mahdia and at Grand Congloué Island, were not galleys, they were much too big to have been rowed. The Grand Congloué ship displaced at least a thousand tons. She probably voyaged under a great square sail of bull hides, which did not permit sailing close to the wind and was a menace in storms.

Amphoras are usually dated and located by a morphological table worked out by the German archeologist, Dressel, who studied and classified them according to shape of body, handles, lips and composition of the fireclay. He worked from jars and broken pieces found in the Roman city dump. Diving has knocked Dressel's tables galley-west, for in the same wreck have been found amphoras hundreds of years apart in the Dressel chronology.

Finding an amphora is now almost commonplace. They may become tourist trophies like scarabs in Egypt or the millions of bullets that met in midair at the battle of Gettysburg. By law in Spain, France, Italy and Greece, underwater archeological finds must be reported and turned over to the government. In most cases, if the type is not unique, the state archeologist graciously permits finder to have it. The important thing is to record the location of the find, not to gather mountains of old jars. Many divers neglect to fix the site. There are also amphora poachers, who clean up a group, thereby obliterating the evidence of a buried wreck. They peddle the jars to tourists who do not care to get wet. The amateur archeologists of the Club de la Mer at Juan-les-Pins, have elected themselves submerged museum guards. Once they heard that a group was cleaning up an ancient wreck without reporting it to Professor Fernand Benoît, the state archeologist of Provence. The Club planned a game of underwater cops and robbers. They tracked the recreants in a fishing boat and assembled a posse of divers and prepared to send relays of men into the wreck to pick it clean. They would erect a sign on the bottom reading, "This wreck may be seen in the Borély Museum, Marseille." The fun was spoiled when the Club doublechecked and learned that the furtive expedition had actually reported to Benoît.

The classic wreck is found interred in a mound of fossil mud, surmounted by half-buried amphoras, often standing upright in the order of stowage. It is doubtful whether any sea save the Mediterranean has the natural conditions to preserve wrecks in this manner. The sea is almost tideless, generally rock-girt, and has gentle underwater circulation. The silent old shipmound tells the story of the fallen argosy. She was overloaded. She was laboring under her clumsy squaresail in sight of the coast. A storm fell upon her. She began shipping water. Her crew fought to sail her to shelter. She humped up and down in the surf, nearing the rocks. The men tried to fend off the rocks with oars, boathooks, and even the heavy rudder sweeps. Her stern rose in a wave and came crashing down on a rock. She was stoved through her lead plating, her Aleppo pine sheathing and her ribs of Lebanon cedar. She crashed and ground again, as tons of water roared into the breach. The men leaped for the lonely rocks, clung and were washed off and battered unconscious in the smother. A few hauled themselves up to safety.

She sank upright, like a falling leaf, heavily and slowly, hitting shelves and jutting rocks beneath, shedding parts of the hull, which flew off in dreamy slow motion. Her bottom struck with a dull, enormous impact that swelled and split her sides and amphoras and potteries issued forth, bouncing and rolling lazily. A white cloud drawled forth from her skirts, spread softly and suffused the water until the ship was hidden. The last sound was the hollow break-up of an amphora that had rolled deep and struck. It sent up a purple plume of Delian wine. Then the patient ages ruled her fate.

The white cloud settled as a shroud on the ship. Animals arrived from all about to claim her; octopuses and morays moved into the empty jars. Clams, gorgonians, coral polyps, starfish, came to nibble. The bodies floating under the bull-hide square sail were eaten to the bones in a week and the sail as well, and bacteria began dissolving the skeletons of men and ship. Time—there was lots of time—overlaid the wreck with generations of plankton and polyps who died and filtered into the ship like snow, building the mound. Shipworms riddled the standing wood, but as they ate down the mound grew, covering and preserving the lower part. Nothing could eat the amphoras, the eternal fire clay, and nothing could eat the earthenware dishes. Her lead and bronze hardware resisted all corrosion. A thousand years passed and there was a mistral, which upheaved rocks from the cliff above and they tumbled down upon the grave. A five-ton rock landed so gently upon an amphora that the jar did not break. She became a city of fish. So many animal forms thrived that the ship mound became a place of beauty, a grave laid with everlasting flowers, waving red gorgonians, yellow sponges, bright pigments of algae.

That was her history for two thousand years, until a man in a mask swam upon her. Perhaps this century is the last one before the little skeletons cover the toploading of amphoras completely. Frédéric Dumas believes it is the last century.

As submerged archeological finds increased, the techniques of search spread slowly. Only a few dozen men were learning how to find ancient wrecks. There were four main archeological diving groups: a Marseille team led by Georges Beuchat, teacher and patron of many fine divers; the Navy G.E.R.S. group with liaison in Marseille, mainly through Dumas, the wide-ranging scout of the Maures and Esterel coasts. From Esterel to Monaco was the province of Henri Broussard and the Club Alpin-Sous-Marin of Cannes and of Louis Lehoux' rival, Club de la Mer of Juan-les-Pins. The latter two clubs kept wrecks secret from each other, although both reported to Professor Benoît. One good wreck was discovered by an individual who refused to tell his own club where it was located. He was expelled. He bounced into the rival club and divulged the secret.

Fishermen told Broussard of seeing huge worked blocks of stone in shallow water off Saint Tropez. The Cannes divers inspected them and found nine sections of Roman columns six feet thick, and an architrave eighteen feet long and five feet square. They came upon three Doric capitals in the same gigantic scale. The divers scraped away the biological encrustation and found white Carrara marble. In 1951 the Club organized an expedition which lifted several of the great stones. Experts who have studied them believe they were cut in Italy, and shipped by the Romans to erect a temple at Narbonne. The freighter was wrecked at Saint Tropez.

Academic archeologists have been slow to learn free diving and it has not yet become part of the curriculum in archeological schools. Professionals have encouraged and supervised diving salvage, but from the boat. None have visited excavations such as Mahdia, Antikythera or Grand Congloué. The nearest that academic archeology has come to the sites is in the dives of the learned French journalist, Philippe Diolé. In a way, marine archeology is a science founded without scientists. The initiative for the first Underwater Archeology Conference held at Cannes in 1955 came from amateurs, Henri Broussard and the Club Alpin Sous-Marin. The conference heard reports on the current excavations, on the Grand Congloué argosy by Professor Fernand Benoît, and on a pre-Christian wreck off the Ile de Levant by Commandant Philippe Tailliez of the G.E.R.S. The Navy research group had spent several days digging with a suction pipe on a very promising wreck. It was discovered in 1953 by Dr. (of medicine) Jacques Piroux of Cannes.

Piroux was diving with his wife and young daughter, Ondine, from their boat, La Provençale. He used a narghile, an Aqualung adaptation with an air pipe to the surface. Ninety-three feet down in very clear water he sighted large clusters of amphoras standing upright in a ship-shaped mound of sponge, coral and thick algaes. Morays poked their noses from some of the jars and a conger slithered past him. Piroux fastened an amphora to his small anchor and hauled it up. The jar was elongate and as tall as eight-year-old Ondine. It seemed to be Roman of about the first century B.C. The explorer kept his discovery secret from everyone but his friends, Broussard and Dmitri Rebikoff, the underwater cameraman. He said he wanted to prevent "pirates and submarine adventurers" from despoiling the wreck. It lay far off the island and the odds were that prowlers would not chance on it.

The next spring Piroux conducted Rebikoff's boat, the Louis Boutan, to the wreck in bad weather. Mme. Piroux sighted the wreck mound through the agitated surface. They dropped a small float and sheltered three days at Porquerolles before the wind fell. When they returned, the buoy was gone. Piroux and Rebikoff searched the floor for two days before they found the mound again. Rebikoff saw it first, and reported "as far as I could see there was nothing but upright amphoras." The next year Commandant Tailliez secured navy permission to excavate professionally.

The Cannes Conference heard a melancholy report from Professor Nino Lamboglia, the able young Italian state archeologist of Liguria, on an ancient ship dig excavated off Albenga, Italy. In 1925 two Roman amphoras had come up in a fisherman's net, a good sign of an ancient wreck. Other hauls were made near by in a depth of 130 feet. After World War II, Lamboglia vainly tried to secure government funds to work the wreck. The Italian Government was backing several land excavations and could spare nothing for the sea. Lamboglia then tried to recruit a group of amateur free divers, but "they were interested only in shooting fish and hunting treasure." The postbellum air was full of glistening rumors that Mussolini's personal getaway gold had been sunk in the sea. Divers preferred to chase a will o' the wisp rather than labor on actual historical treasure. Ian Fleming, of the London *Sunday Times*, said the young Italian divers' "parents and schoolteachers had brought them up on the contents of the local museums and they have no enthusiasm for risking their lives for more 'pottery and statues'."

Lamboglia then received an offer of free aid from the Sorima Salvage Company of Genoa, which had recovered the gold from the *Egypt* in the deepest diving operation. In February, 1950, *Artiglio II*, the famous salvage tender of the firm, moved over the Albenga wreck and lowered helmet divers. They saw a profusion of amphoras, gathered loose jars, bent lines around their necks and sent them up in series. When the floor was cleared a bit, the salvage ship lowered a Galezzi observation chamber with a man to direct by phone the movements of a huge clamshell grab called the "benna." This voracious beast gulped into the buried ship, chewing up wood, jars and metal fittings. The benna grabbed one hundred amphoras in a single day, and smashed up the wreck disastrously.

I visited Lamboglia's Roman Naval Museum in the Palazzo d'Aste at Bordighera a few years later to see the finds. There were four types of slender amphoras among the two hundred impressively lined up in tiers, and a lot of shattered ship timber. The claw brought up three brims of bronze helmets, a curious horn made of solid lead, maybe part of a figurehead, and also leaden hull plates and sections of lead pipe. Here was the same mysterious pipe later found in the Grand Congloué wreck. Was it the drain for a lavatory, or part of the ship's pumping system? Albenga will never tell, but the answer may come from Grand Congloué or Ile de

Levant. I asked the distinguished British classical scholar, Professor M. Cary, what he thought of the lead pipes and lead plating from the Congloué ship. "It seems to me fairly certain," he said, "that the lead on the sunken ship came from the mines at Laurium at the southeastern tip of Attica. They were chiefly exploited for silver, but the ore in which the silver was imbedded in small quantities was sulphide of lead, and the lead residue far exceeded the silver product."

Cargo clues established that the ship sank about 75 B.C. Lamboglia gave me a large splinter of the ship. I sent it to the Arizona State Museum which operates a radio-carbon laboratory. Professor Willard F. Libby, at the University of Chicago, evolved a technique for dating the creation of organic materials such as wood, bones and natural cloth fibers. They contain radioactive Carbon 14, which loses energy at a slow, measurable rate per year. At Arizona scientists had been estimating the age of 7,750-year-old campfire coals of early Americans, and welcomed a more recent piece of wood given an age by archeological deduction to serve a time check on the archeological clock. If the splinter from Albenga burns down to the radioactive year near to Lamboglia's attribution it will furnish a minute hand for the endless clock. It will certainly fix fragments from other Mediterranean wrecks as sunk before or after Albenga. Professor Benoît sent to Arizona wood from the ship at Grand Congloué. Its thousands of classified potteries carved out by the *Calypso* divers with their suction pipes establish the best burial date in ship archeology—205 B.C. The wreck could furnish the scientific time clock with a sweep second hand.

Since the publicity of the Albenga excavation, Italian free divers have become interested in archeology and amphoras are turning up everywhere. In 1952 the Young Diver's Club of Genoa found an ancient wreck, with wine jars and Campanian dishes; another was located off Cape Mele and one off Cervo in 1951. Every year sees more indications and proved ancient wrecks on the French and Italian rivieras—now about twenty have been reported to Professor Benoît in his jurisdiction of Provence, and a dozen in Professor Lamboglia's sector of the Ligurian seacoast.

A veteran amateur ship archeologist of Juan-le-Pins has warned however, "Sometimes scattered pieces of amphoras in shallow water do not prove a wreck. People living along the coast use the sea as a trash basket. Earthenware jars break easily and are cheaply replaced. The Greeks have been storing things in clay jars for a least three thousand years, and still do. Amphoras often fell overboard owing to the way the Greeks overloaded their boats. Sailors dumped them over by the dozen when a boat was swamping. In port cooks threw empty amphoras over the side, like so many empty tin cans and bottles. The surprising thing is that most piles of amphoras are actually the grave markers of ships. However, a piece of the ship itself is the only assurance and this means digging, not just looking."

A strategic archeologist, grand marshal of his profession, was Père A. Poidebard, a magisterial French Jesuit, who died in 1954. Father Poidebard searched for the past on land, in the air and under the sea. His main campaign was to trace the route of ancient commerce from Spain and the German amber road to China. In 1925 he trekked through the desert of Syria, scouting from the air for the ruined villages of the caravan road, dating to the time of Alexander the Great. Six years of digging in the wastes led him to the site of the Phoenician port of Tyre on the blue Mediterranean.

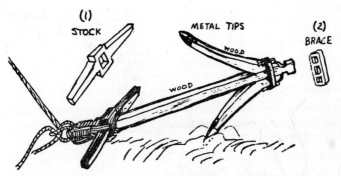

Reconstruction of a classic anchor, showing leaden stock and brace. (Author's *Calypso* Journal)

Here once came great ships from Tarshish with solid Spanish silver anchor stocks, when all the sea ships were sailed by Phoenicians and the Greeks had not yet ventured out of sight of their islands. The seamen of Tyre carried Ligurian Sea red coral to the mandarins of China, Arabian frankincense to Iberia, Cornish tin to make bronze to Greece, Damascene wine and white wool to Egypt, and Israelite honey and Greek sponges to Morocco for a mother to soak a sponge in honey and give to a crying baby.

Poidebard stood in the tiny fishing village on the rocky island which had once been great Tyre and looked west over the sea that the Phoenicians had made their lake. "Thy rowers have brought thee into great waters: the east wind hath broken thee in the midst of the seas," the prophet Ezekiel chanted in his Lamentation for Tyre. "Thy riches and thy fairs, thy merchandise, thy mariners, and thy pilots, thy calkers, and the occupiers of thy merchandise, and all thy men of war, that are in thee, and in all thy company which is in the midst of thee, shall fall into the midst of the sea in the day of thy ruin."

Poidebard reflected, "The planes which helped us find the ruins of the desert, would they help us pierce the water to discover forgotten ports?" He sent military reconnaissance planes over Tyre. The photos "immediately showed that divers would be perhaps the most essential members of our teams. Our work would be simultaneously aerial and submarine." He hired a local naked diver, who had prowled the coast for sponges. The man could go down forty feet and "do hard work there for one and a half minutes," said Poidebard. The Syrian was able to dive deeper but could stay only a few seconds. There were also helmet divers on the job, but the naked man was ideal for shallow searches over a wide range. He was the scout, leading the clumsy helmet men to the submerged ruins.

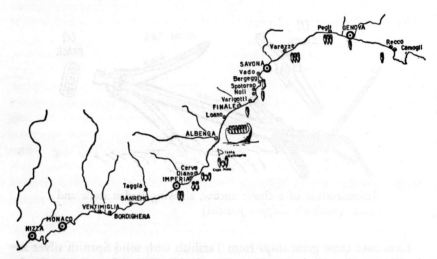

Ship archeological sites of the Ligurian Coast, showing location of the Albenga argosy, excavated 1950. (Institut International d'Études Ligures)

Poidebard read William Beebe's diving reports and consulted Commandant Yves le Prieur on how to photograph under water. Le Prieur designed a brass box for a Leica and a waterscope called a *lunette de calfat*. Held in the water from a boat, vertical photographs could be made through the *lunette* with a Leica and a stereoscopic camera. Stereophotos proved the most useful evidence on the submerged harbor. Before his three years' work at Tyre (1935–37) was over, Poidebard was also making underwater movies. He discovered "a vast and judicious construction work" to shelter ships from prevailing south west winds. The Phoenicians had laid huge stone blocks as breakwaters, cleverly utilizing natural reefs in the system. Poidebard was unable to find when it was constructed.

Father Poidebard in 1946–50 proceeded to uncover the ancient jetties and moles of the other great port of Phoenicia: Sidon, now Saïda, Lebanon. His historic achievement was not only in these discoveries, but in the way he pulled in many techniques and scientists to his operations. He used photoplanes, divers, underwater cameras, big floating derricks, cartographers, archeologists, seamen, naval engineers, geologists, governments, navies and ministers. The *Missions Poidebard* have never been emulated.

No one knows how many bronzes have come up in the nets of Mediterranean fishermen in two hundred years and have been melted down as scrap metal. It was the fate of Greek statues found in earth in the Dark Ages, and so it must have been for those plucked from the sea. Archeology itself is only a century old, slow to be known to country people, and marine archeology is an even younger branch. Yet Mediterranean fisherfolk are hauling in wonderful sculptures and turning the finds over to museums.

In the summer of 1953, Professor G. E. Bean, classical philologist at Istanbul University, heard of a bronze statue drawn up by Turkish fishermen of Bitez, near the site of ancient Halicarnassus. He hastened to Bitez, which took four days on the roads (for 450 air miles) and was escorted by the populace to the beach. There, propped upright against a log, was the hollow upper half of a majestic figure of a mourning woman more than life size, "a work of the full classical period of Greek art, almost certainly an original of the fourth century B.C.," he felt. All the experts who have seen the figure since agree with him. "The sponge fisher's strange catch," said Bean, "seems likely to rank with the most remarkable artistic finds of recent years."

The woman's slightly bowed head, wearing a sweeping veil, had a gaping hole in the forehead, which did not mar her grave beauty. The drapery was encrusted with fossils, but the face was clean. Who was she? Professor Bean remembered a marble statue in the British Museum, which had been found in the earth at Cnidus on the next cape to the south, another pensive veiled woman, that of gentle Demeter, the wandering corn-mother of Greek myth, mourning her abducted daughter, Persephone.

The fishermen said she had come up from a depth of four hundred feet off the cape where the British Museum Demeter had been disinterred. But another fisherman told Bean she had been found off Cape Bozburun, sixty miles east. These disheartening conflicts are heard all too often by archeologists, trying to locate a net haul. The fact is that Aegean fishermen do not know their exact position at any time and on long trawls they do not know when an object tumbled over their otter boards and went along in the mesh.

The curve of the draperies at the waist suggested the figure was seated. What else was down there? And how did it get there? The heroic proportions bespoke a statue made for a cult-shrine of Demeter, whose worship in autumn fertility rites survived in Turkey until modern times. Perhaps she had been ordered by Mausolus, the Persian connoisseur, who founded Halicarnassus on the Greek model in the middle of the fourth century. King Mausolus' tomb, from which we get the word "mausoleum," was one of the Seven Wonders of the World, adorned by statues by four Greek masters. The Crusaders finished it off; the Castle of the Knights of St. John, still standing on the site, was built of the stones of the Fifth Wonder.

Demeter might have been commissioned by the Cnidians, who had bought some pretty good stuff for their new city founded about 350 B.C., including an Aphrodite of Praxiteles and the British Museum Demeter, thought to be by Leochares. The ship carrying the bronze was considerably off course, whatever her destination and place of sinking, but that is Mediterranean weather as it was and is. The bronze Demeter's wreck would be hard to reach. Four hundred feet is a very serious depth. Searchers would have to employ armor or helmet men breathing helium-oxygen. However, the Elba Comet salvage, using television, has demonstrated marvelous possibilities for archeology. If a net bouncing along the floor could scoop up a bronze almost three feet high, one of the heaviest archeological hauls on record, then there may be other protruding sculptures that television could detect.

Professor Bean could not resist a charming speculation in reporting the masterpiece he was the first expert to see: "It is not impossible that our Demeter was sunk on her way to Cnidus from the sculptor's workshop, and was therefore never erected there. This would account for the total absence, otherwise rather surprising, of extant copies, and of works apparently inspired or influenced by ours. If this is indeed what happened, we may imagine that we now have the opportunity, surely unique, of admiring a statue that the Greeks themselves never saw."

England got into the business of extracting Greek art from the Mediterranean in a curious way. In 1802, Thomas Bruce, Earl of Elgin, Ambassador to the Ottoman Empire, grew concerned over the safety of the surviving friezes of Phidias on the Parthenon. The Greeks were taking up arms against the occupying Turks, who had been party to the mutilation of the Parthenon in 1687, when they stored gunpowder in the great temple. Venetian artillerymen scored a hit on the magazine and blew off the roof of the Parthenon.

Lord Elgin proceeded to collect Phidias' panels, the friezes of the Temple of Victory and those of the Acropolis wall, packed them in sixteen huge cases and shipped them to England in the brig *Mentor*, in the care of his secretary, W. R. Hamilton. The second evening out the *Mentor* was on the same course as the Roman plunder ship which sank at Antikythera, running

Cape Tainaron in a rising west wind. The gale veered suddenly to north-west. The brig was blown off course and began to ship water. By morning there was nothing to do but seek haven. The Greek pilot nominated Kythera Island, the big sister to the north of Antikythera. To anchor on these islands obliges a vessel to come very close due to the sheer under-water drop. The captain threw out two anchors, which did not hold. The *Mentor* ran up canvas and cut her anchor cables, but could not escape. She struck and sank, another art export ship in a long roll that failed to carry Greek sculptures away to the safe-keeping of a foreign phil-Hellene.

Hamilton and all souls escaped. The brig was in sixty feet of water, he informed Elgin in Constantinople. My Lord wrote back, declaring that he considered the carvings "of personal, more than intrinsic value," and said he was dickering with Basilio Menachini, an Italian from La Spezia, for a salvage job. He appointed the Speziote as a British vice-consul, an office that he could depute if necessary. But if Menachini did not fish up the marbles in three months he would no longer be a vice-consul.

Hamilton remained on Kythera, keeping a diligent eye on the water that covered Lord Elgin's personal indulgences. The secretary was surrounded by guerrillas, pirates, tall-story tellers, and Russian naval officers who were hanging around to embolden the Greeks against their mutual Ottoman enemy. Then the war of independence came in earnest. Hamilton tried to bring H.M.S. *Victorieuse* and Menachini's *Speziot* over the brig to lift her bodily, but the plan failed. The Russians told Hamilton they could lift the marbles, but Lord Elgin wanted none of that. The Italian faded out of the picture when he heard rumors that the brig had been raised.

Cutting winter wind scoured down upon Kythera. Hamilton, who had not brought his winter wardrobe, fired the stand-by divers and went to Constantinople for his ulster and astrakhan. He came back with a band of naked divers from Samos. In one winter month they enlarged the hatches in the wreck and hoisted out several cases.

As the Elgin marbles were raised, they were landed on the beach at Aulemono, covered with mounds of seaweed and guarded by watchmen. The Samiotes continued for two years. The *Times* of London stated that, "The lovers of the Arts, and the admirers of Classical Antiquity, will be exceedingly rejoiced to hear of this fortunate preservation of a collection made with so much care and judgment. It would have been indeed lamenta-ble if, after they had escaped for so many years the ignorance and prejudice of the stupid Turks, they should have been lost on another element, just as they were on their way to a civilized country, able and ready to appre-ciate their excellencies, and whose artists are eager to ascend, by studying them, that height of refinement and perfection in sculpture, which so eminently characterized the efforts of the chisel in ancient Greece." Elgin put it in another way to Henry Bankes: "This operation, with the purchase of the *Mentor*, and her necessary expense, I have valued at five thousand pounds." In 1816, he sold the sculptures to the British Museum for £35,000.

Adventurous young Britons eagerly took up the Aqualung when it was manufactured there in 1950. A rise in the money allowance for foreign travel, a racial urge for the sun and school-day yearnings for Greece sent them diving in the Aegean. Such was the Undersea Archeological Reconnaissance of the island of Chios in 1954, led by Richard Garnett, son of the novelist, David Garnett. The trip was reported by the cinema critic, Dilys Powell, a trim, white-haired lady who had accompanied land digs in the Middle East. She found herself in a tent on a windy beach at Imperio, a bleak *oppidum* with but one *taverna*. She was surrounded by "active young men or good-looking young women. To some of them the simplest archeological classification was a mystery." They had been attracted by "nothing more than a liking for adventure and a desire to dive," she stated. The explorers snorkeled up and down the coastline. When they saw a group of amphora shards on the slope, the leader was summoned. He shouldered air bottles and plunged to outline the area with white tapes. Above him, Alison Marsh, the winsome expeditionary artist, gazed down through her mask and sketched the layout on a plastic tablet. Garnett thought he located twenty classic wrecks, although, said Miss Powell, "The divers are disappointed at finding no remains of the wrecked ships themselves; no wood, nothing save once, a stone fragment believed to be part of an anchor."

On Cyprus a diving club arose among the British garrison, with sergeants, lieutenants, red tabs and privates joined together in a bare-shouldered brigade led by Sergeant W. Jackson, of the Royal Army Service Corps. The Cyprus Club, encouraged by the command and by A. H. S. Megaw, the island's Director of Antiquities, formed an archeological team. Off Salamis the divers found a large terra cotta woman's head, dating from the sixth century B.C. They fetched up many amphoras and potteries and inspected the bases of ancient jetties. Lieutenants E. T. Bolt and J. Crawford found a sixteenth-century bronze cannon, probably from a Venetian or Turkish ship.

In 1955 the Cyprus Sub-Aqua Club was joined by an archeological expedition from the London Underwater Explorers Club, led by H. Penman. The aim was to "explore the sunken portion of the city of Salamis." That suggests that the Club started out with the old handicap—the belief that the Mediterranean rose and drowned cities. The idea is a variant of "Atlantis" and "Lemuria" lost-continent superstitions which have no scientific support.

The American version is the sunken pirate city of Port Royal, supposed to have slid into the Caribbean when an earthquake and fire struck the wicked down. Diving expeditions to walk the streets of Port Royal are a traditional hot-weather newspaper item in the United States.

There are architectural remains in the Mediterranean, but serious scholars deny that the sea drowned them. They fell off ships, they are parts of buildings that crumbled and fell in or people pushed them in. There are many ancient harbor works, which were built in the water, subsided and were ruined by want of repair. The sea-date mussel has feasted on granite and marble jetties since the Phoenicians first put them down. Still another kind of building is found in shallows, the ruins of ancient sea-bathing establishments, where masonry baths were built in the sea in the first place. Erosion of the shore and subsidence of buildings erected on sinking sand spits account for shallow-water finds, such as those of the remarkable ten-year-old excavation at Fos-sur-Mer, near Marseille.

The final act of the American Revolution, Lord Cornwallis' surrender at Yorktown, left a large ship deposit in the York River, Virginia. In the summer of 1781, Cornwallis' ships arrived in Chesapeake Bay to join the British land forces. The Comte de Grasse, commander of the French fleet allied with the Americans, arrived from the West Indies and bottled them up in the river. Admiral Thomas Graves, R.N., tried to break out with an inferior force. He was thrown back into the trap after the Battle of the Capes. Washington and Lafayette were marching on Yorktown. The end was near. Admiral Graves sent the fireship H.M.S. *Vulcan* against the French blockade but the *Vulcan* burned without harming de Grasse. French shore batteries, shooting red-hot cannon balls, set fire to the British flagship H.M.S. *Charon* and burned three transports with her. Cornwallis sank a string of lesser ships as a barricade against the French, and finally scuttled his last two big frigates, H.M.S. *Guadaloupe* and H.M.S. *Fowey*.

Afterward the hulks were forgotten, save by oystermen tonging the excellent York River bivalve. They complained for generations about fouling their anchors and long-handled rakes on wrecks in the river. In the 1930's the Mariners' Museum was founded in near-by Newport News on the tidewater estate of Collis P. Huntington with an endowment of royalties from Huntington's coal mines in West Virginia. (Falling coal production in the mid-fifties hampered marine research.) This museum and library, located in a deep wood, is a joy to students of the sea. Once a professor from the University of North Carolina stopped in for an afternoon and stayed eighteen months.

Joseph Holtzbach, superintendent of the Museum, heard the oystermen growling, and guessed that their trouble was Lord Cornwallis' fleet. He talked about it with Floyd Flickinger, superintendent of the National Park

Bureau's reconstruction of Colonial Yorktown, and the two agreed to try salvage. The Museum agreed to furnish floating derrick, riggers and divers, and the Park Bureau supplied labor and boats. They surveyed the river by dragging in 1934 and mapping obstructions.

The first dive on a promising contact was in forty feet of dirty water. The diver groped around extensively and came up with nothing to report. After some hours they were near to abandoning the idea, when a crew man picked up a leaden musket ball from the deck where the diver had been undressed. This minute and valueless trophy, accidentally lodged in the suit, turned the day bright. The next day the diver sent up two pieces of ship's timber, planks, barrel staves, mast wedges and an old rum bottle. He continued to sling finds from two wrecks which lay close together, decayed and buried in the mud. They seemed vessels about seventy-five feet long. The diver washed away mud with a high-pressure fire hose, which blotted out what little visibility he had.

The York River divers worked two seasons on three wrecks, sending up breakables in wire baskets and guiding a clamshell grab into other material. They got ten iron cannons, a lot of shot, two iron anchors, an unmarked bell, much hardware, crockery and glass, many liquor bottles and a pewter chamber pot. There were hundreds of wood fragments and hemp line, which, when dried and dipped in wax, remained firm.

There was no evidence to identify the wrecks. The only marked finds were a bottle engraved "Edward New," a musket stock initialed "V. R.," a barrel head inscribed "Watson & Co.," and, as the nearest to proof that the ships were Cornwallis', a barrelhead with "Shaw. June 22, '80, S(alt) P.(ork) 154 lbs." The green rum bottles had turned to rainbows; when they were shelved the salvors noticed the bottles changed colors in different degrees of humidity. The main archeological importance of York River was not so much the finds as what had happened to the materials in 150 years' immersion. The observations of the salvors need to be set down as annoying facts you can use when treasure promoters wave their charts and stock certificates:

"The iron cannon in some instances crumbled to pieces right away, the metal having been converted by slow chemical action to pure graphite. The application of preservatives to the surfaces did not materially check disintegration and they continued to sweat and scale off. Only those objects which retained a sufficient amount of the original iron core from which the scale could be sand-blasted, have been saved from further immediate breaking up.

"Wrought Iron had practically disappeared, leaving only a disintegrated mass.

"Pewter and lead articles stood up extremely well.

"Copper survived well, thoroughly encrusted with patina.

"Wooden articles, buried below the mud, were in a splendid state of preservation. Wood not protected in mud was badly decayed and worm eaten.

"Pottery and earthenware have survived well, despite encrustation with oyster shells."

The divers of York River found no gold or silver, bronze or brass.

There is another famous warship that excites ideas of salvage: the U.S.S. *Monitor*. One hot spring morning in Washington I got a call at my hotel from a soft-voiced young man. "I understand you are a friend of Captain Cousteau." I said I was. "Well," said my caller, "do you think he would like to dive for the *Monitor*?" I said, "Sure. We talked about it a couple of years ago when the Navy said they picked up the wreck on sonar." We made a date for lunch. My caller was Stanfield McClure, a pleasant low-powered publicity man, and with him to lunch came a straight, white-haired individual with a weathered brown face, Raynor T. McMullen, president of the Monitor Historical Society. McMullen was the spit of an old sea dog, and I gave a cue to learn his naval background. He said mildly, "I am a retired rural mail carrier from Michigan. All my life I have been interested in the *Monitor*. When I retired I came down here to see if I could find her." My tablemates were the might of the Monitor Historical Society, save for several avuncular retired admirals on their letterhead.

They thought the *Monitor* still existed. The previous summer, 1954, they had taken volunteer free divers to search for the wreck off Cape Hatteras. They did not find her. The fact is, nobody knows where she is, nor did Commander J. P. Bankhead, master of U.S.S. *Monitor*, or the captain of the sidewheeler *Rhode Island*, which was towing the "Yankee Cheesebox on a Raft," know where she was when she swamped and sank in the early night of December 31, 1862, drowning sixteen of her crew.

Commander Bankhead reported, "As near as I could judge, making allowances for current, drift and sea, we were about twenty-five miles south of Cape Hatteras, say in Latitude 34° 50′ N., Longitude 75° 30′ W., depth of water 30 fathoms." Such a fix would trouble an air search for a floating derelict, let alone diving for one that sank ninety-four years ago in the turbid, racing Hatteras Bank, the "Graveyard of Ships." Another important factor is not known: has the *Monitor* disappeared from corrosion? Observation of dated iron wrecks in the Mediterranean gives them about man's three score and ten. However, the *Monitor* was built of one-inch plates of fine charcoal iron, of which nine thicknesses were used in the turret. Her deck plates were two inches thick. She may have outlived later iron steamers. In 1947 a Navy subchaser out of Charleston, South Carolina picked up a sonar trace of a wreck with the dimensions of the *Monitor*.

gh the Navy did not reveal position or depth, the Navy was "willing
elieve the wreck was the *Monitor.*" The announcement touched off a
nging editorial in the Harvard *Crimson*, calling for raising the ironclad
as a national shrine. The Cambridge City Council resolved likewise. Bringing her up will take more than resolutions; McMullen and McClure have
set about raising money and skills for the job. McMullen has put his life
savings into the kitty.

The first diving search for *Monitor* was unsuccessful. McMullen realized
it would take money and organization to carry out an effective hunt. He
passed up diving in 1955 to build for '56. The Society offered a $1,000,
reward for the wreck location. Soon afterward a U.S. Marine corporal
named Robert F. Marx, aged twenty-two, gave an interview in Norfolk in
which he claimed to have spotted the wreck from an airplane. He said it
was in fifty feet of water many miles from the area McMullen had been
working in. Marx said he was a diver of nine years' experience, which
would place his entry into the profession at the age of thirteen. He said
that he and a Marine buddy were going to photograph the wreck underwater and that he was not interested in the reward.

Other prospects of American ship archeology center in warmer, clearer
water. The Caribbean has been a sea of glittering treasure myths ever since
Sir William Phips salvaged the plate ship. Recently a new type of treasure hunter came to the American Mediterranean, Edwin Link, who made
no noise about gold, but energetically began to search for history in the
wrecks. He made a fortune manufacturing a curious device, a sort of collision between the minds of Heath Robinson and Walt Disney, the Link
aviation trainers. In the machine pilot cadets sat in a similated cockpit
which faked the dilemmas of flight and battle. Link sold his company in
1950 and fitted out a sixty-five-ton Diesel trawler, the *Sea-Diver*, as a diving
tender. She carried metal-detecting apparatus and two window-bottomed
launches, in which Link and his wife scrutinized the floor. They recovered
several antique cannons in the Florida Straits, the homeward passage of sixteenth-century Spanish ships. The searches were expertised by Mendel
Peterson, of the Smithsonian Institution. Last year the *Sea-Diver* moved to
the north of Haiti, the old Hispaniola, where Admiral Samuel Eliot Mori-
son, the marine historian, believes Christopher Columbus' flagship, the
Santa Maria, was wrecked. She worked to pieces on a coral reef in 1492.
Columbus salvaged enough timber to build a fort on a near-by island, transferred to the *Nina* and sailed home.

Link felt that metal parts of the *Santa Maria* might be found. He began
reconnoitering the supposed area of the disaster. Mrs. Marion Link was
swimming off Point Picolet, scanning the shallow floor through a mask,
when she saw a ten-foot anchor twelve feet down. Link dived with a wreck-

ing bar and freed the anchor. Peterson stated, "On the basis of the physical condition of the anchor and its shape and workmanship, it could have come from the *Santa Maria*." It was not possible, however, to span the distance between "could have" and *did*. Link set an example for Caribbean antiquarians by turning the anchor over to the Republic of Haiti.

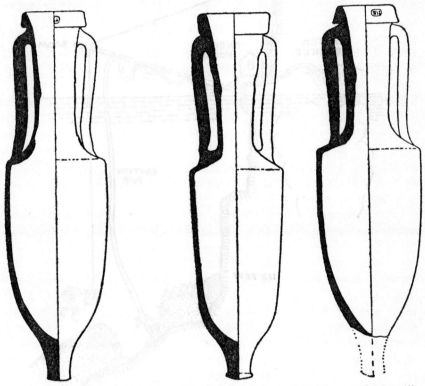

Amphoras from the wreck of the Greek wine ship sunk 205 B.C. off Marseille, salved by *Calypso* Expeditions, 1952. (Institut International d'Études Ligures)

The cleverest method for recovering sunken art objects was invented by the Japanese a hundred years ago. An open boat loaded with Imperial vases went down in the Japan Sea and the Emperor dispatched divers to recover his baubles. The naked divers found the wreck beyond their range. They had no breathing equipment. Not wishing to offend the Son of Heaven, they did some high-pressure thinking and came up with the solution. They captured live octopuses, tied lines on them and lowered the animals into the wreck. The cephalopods, which are as fond of confined spaces as cats, wriggled into the jars. The salvors hauled on the lines and

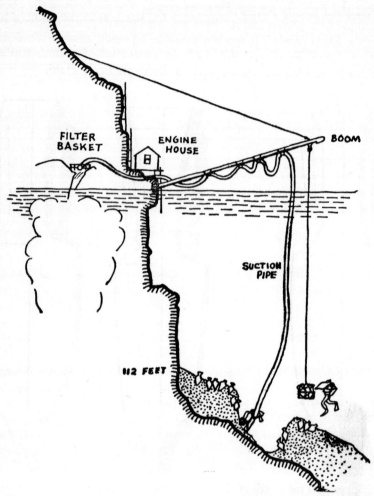

Profile of the *Calypso* excavation of the 205 B.C. Greek wine ship at Grand Congloué island off Marseille.

the octopuses braced themselves in their new apartments. Up came vases and tenants.

The greatest underwater archeological project yet undertaken is that of Captain Cousteau at Grand Congloué, a small white limestone rock ten miles east of Marseille in a chain of treacherous uninhabited islands lying off the forbidding cliffs of the Marseilleveyre. I first saw the operation in 1953, a year after it began. Coming out of the clamor and color of Marseille on the *Calypso*, you enter a desolate passage which seems as remote as Tierra del Fuego. Grand Congloué is the last islet in the chain, a high, sheer, naked place, 450 feet long and 150 wide, without a landing. High on a slanting shelf stands a yellow tin house, flying a green and white flag of conquest: naked Calypso swimming with a porpoise under the legend "Port Calypso." When the ship comes the house pours out yelling men and a dog. An air compressor pounds away in an engine house stuck in the cliff face. One of the islanders runs out on a boom hung a hundred feet over the water, and jumps down on the ship. She moors to the island and a big cruiser buoy. Up a ladder from the sea come two divers in rubber suits. They have heard the *Calypso's* engines from afar, and have seen her slender hull from their job site 140 feet down.

They are excavating a thousand-ton sailing freighter, owned by Marcus Sestius, of the Greek Island of Delos, a ten-thousand amphora ship, laden with Greek and Italian wine and a huge cargo of black dinnerware, which sank about the year 205 B.C. They have been excavating since August, 1952, and they will probably continue until 1958 before they raise the last vestige of the mighty ship. It is the oldest seagoing vessel ever found; the only older vessels in existence are Egyptian tomb boats and prehistoric canoes dug out of Irish peat bogs. The leviathan herself exists in the fossil mound below the engine house, at the foot of one of the most beautiful coral walls in the Mediterranean. Port Calypso is a Homeric evocation and a living epic of men struggling with the sea. The men in the tin house rebuilt it after a complete blowdown in a mistral. They have lost one of their comrades and they live in a lunar solitude. They dive every day, come mistral or winter water, straddling a powerful suction pipe, carving history from the floor. They have lifted five thousand Greek and Italian wine jars and ten thousand pieces of blackware. They have been televised from the excavation, and they are furnishing evidence for archeological deductions more thrilling than a detective novel. But that is Cousteau's story to tell.

11

The Wet Saboteur

ITALY was the only belligerent which entered the Second World War with underwater infantry and cavalry trained and ready. The beginning of submerged "chariot" attacks went back to the end of the First War. In 1918 the Allies in Italy had opened the final Piave offensive and were uneasy about an uncommitted enemy force which might intervene, the Austrian fleet holed up in the Adriatic port of Pola. Three dreadnoughts and a battleship squadron had lurked there since the beginning, doing nothing, but threatening to come out. The French submarine *Curie* had been lost, trying to break into Pola in 1914. Two ingenious Italian officers proposed to try again, Major Raffaele Rossetti and Surgeon Lieutenant Raffaele Paolucci.

They constructed a 23-foot chariot, capable of cruising at two knots on a compressed-air engine. It carried two detachable warheads with 350-pound charges of TNT. Straddling this machine, the two Raffaeles planned to ride into Pola with only their heads out of water, steer it through the antitorpedo nets and stick the explosives beneath the waterline of the Austrian ships. Before their mission was over, Rossetti and Paolucci were very much submariners.

A torpedo boat put them into the water a quarter mile off the Pola breakwater on a moonless late October night. They wore waterproof suits with built-in buoyancy chambers. They wrapped their heads in shiny cloths, which they hoped the defenders would mistake for discarded chianti bottles. As it turned out, it was a big night for empty chianti bottles in the sea. The Austrian-Hungarian Empire had just collapsed, quite unknown to the two Italians. A few hours before, the warships had been

seized by revolutionary Yugoslav seamen. Rossetti and Paolucci were unwittingly caught in a mockery of fate—if their audacious venture succeeded, they would be destroying ships already seized.

Major Rossetti steered from the rear saddle, while Dr. Paolucci navigated
from the forward seat. They chugged off with their heads wreathed in
phosphorescence. They dragged the chariot over the steel outer net,
mounted and made for the harbor gate. A dark vessel came out toward
them. Rossetti put his hand on the mine detonator to destroy themselves,
rather than have the machine captured; Italians in amphibians with tractor treads had once jumped the nets trying to torpedo the twenty thousand-
ton dreadnought *Szent Istvan*, and Rossetti wished to preserve the surprise of
the new weapon. But the black mass passed without seeing them.

They reached the breakwater, which they planned to skirt toward the
harbor gate. There were sentries walking it whom they might pass safely
if they hugged the wall below. The doctor swam over and ducked under
to see if the wall was sheer, or if it had a dump rock foundation, which
would impede the chariot. The wall was vertical. They proceeded and
passed a guard. Rossetti rolled his head to suggest a bobbing bottle, and
was not challenged. A rude surprise waited at the gate. Since the amphibious tractor attack, the Austrians had reinforced it with a 180-foot timber
boom bristling with three-foot steel spikes. The two adventurers paused
and hung on to the boom, discussing what to do. It was 1 A.M. At 3, they
were scheduled to cross the last defense. Dawn was due at 5:15. The tide
pouring out of Pola carried the chariot out of their grasp.

Dr. Paolucci swam after it, forgetting the phosphorescence he kicked
up. He dived and caught the gadget and they drove back to the boom. A
light rain began to fall. Taking a chance that the guards would take shelter
from the shower, they got up on the boom and lifted the ponderous torpedo over the spikes. In the water again, they came upon three lines of
torpedo nets. It was now raining heavily, a comfort to their secrecy, but
disquieting because they could no longer see the ships. They worked the
chariot over the nets. A bit further on they struck three more nets. The
doctor thought they had gotten turned around somehow and were back at
the first nets. But the Major was confident they were on course. The tide
was now running heavily against them and they were nearly exhausted.
The current carried the chariot sideways and they had another fight to trim
it and get back to the nets. Rossetti tied a line to the torpedo's nose and
swam under water to the sixth net. Bracing himself on it, he pulled Paolucci and the chariot through. The torpedo capsized. They dived and recovered it.

They had passed eight barriers to Pola. They recalled their orders,
"Whatever force you may meet, however important, attack!" By now they

should have done so and been outside rejoining the torpedo boat. Half the air pressure in the engine had been used. They knew it would never carry them out, whatever happened. In the two hours of darkness left, they resolved to attack the biggest target, the superdreadnought *Viribus Unitis*. Their latest aerial photos had shown that she was sixth in the shipline; they would have to pass five capital ships to reach her. At this point the rain turned to hail.

They crept past five ships and found the *Viribus Unitis* ablaze with lights, a most disheartening sight after their epic struggle to reach her. There would be no cover for the attack. They vaguely wondered why the ship was lighted, but could not know that the revolutionists were celebrating. They pressed on. The chariot suddenly sank by the stern, carrying Rossetti under. Paolucci secured his ballast tanks and turned to help his companion. The machine sank from under them both. "Of all the trying moments we had spent, this was the most painful," the doctor said later. Then it bobbed back to the surface and they mounted again. They went a hundred yards past the target in order to get into the tide, cut their motor and drift silently on the *Viribus Unitis*. The first drifting run carried them away off from the ship. They rode back for another pass.

The young doctor was to have the honor of affixing the warhead. But Rossetti said he'd dive too. Paolucci said, "It was just as well. Under the bows we met unexpected difficulties which he overcame with admirable firmness and with his greater experience, both of which I do not possess." Dr. Paolucci seemed to regard himself as a man along for the ride. He held the horse while the major fixed the dynamite. Again the tide carried off Paolucci and the chariot. He fought twenty-five minutes to return for Rossetti. When he got back, it was dawn, 5:15. Reveille sounded in the fleet; revolution or no revolution, the wake-up men do not forget. The warhead was timed to explode at 6:30. They armed the other warhead, left it on the torpedo and set it adrift in the tide, aimed at a group of battleships.

A liberty boat, lying at the accommodation ladder of the dreadnought, at last spotted the attackers. A searchlight picked them out. "*Wer da?*" came the challenge. They answered in German, "Italian officers." Rossetti and Paolucci were taken aboard the ship that was going to explode in thirty-five minutes. They were astonished to see YUGOSLAVIA on the sailor's hatbands. An officer told them the Austrian admiral had been sent ashore and the flagship was now commanded by Captain Vukovitch, of the Yugoslav National Council. Rossetti demanded an immediate private interview with Vukovitch, and told him, "Your ship is in great immediate danger. I urge you to abandon with all hands." The captain asked why. "I cannot tell you," said the Italian, "but she will sink very soon." Vukovitch guessed.

He issued orders, "Abandon ship. Italian mine fastened to the bottom."
He told the Italians, "You may save yourselves." The weary and distraught
charioteers jumped into the water. The doctor nearly drowned. Rossetti
helped him and they swam for shore. They were overtaken by a boatload
of furious sailors, who suspected the Italians had tricked them in order to
escape. Back to the doomed ship they took the pair. Paolucci saw a clock
reading 6:27. Three minutes to go. The sailors cut off their rubber suits,
looking for clues. A bar of chocolate fell out of Rossetti's suit. The sailors
studied it. A sailor yelled, "Down in the bilge with them, if they're going
to blow us up!" The ship's bells struck 6:30.

The bomb did not go off. At the end of their string of torment, Rossetti
and Paolucci felt joy and bitterness; joy that men were not to die and
bitterness that they had failed as soldiers. Fourteen minutes later Paolucci
heard "a dull noise, a deep roaring, not loud but rather soft. A high column
of water soared over the side. Underfoot the deck shook and trembled. We
were alone. Every man was saving himself." Rossetti picked up the chocolate bar. He was very hungry. He bit into the chocolate.

Captain Vukovitch came by, strapping on a life jacket. He shook hands
with them and pointed to a line hanging over the side. The Italians slid
down into the water and swam to a boat. The *Viribus Unitis* sank bow
first, heeling increasingly and then turned turtle. The doctor saw the "big
turret guns broken like toys, an instant before they vanished, and I saw the
green keel shining. I saw a man climbing up the keel toward the stern."
It was Captain Vukovitch. "He reached the propeller cage," said Paolucci,
"as she slowly sank, he stood straight up. He was carried down in the
whirlpool and came out of it swimming. A big beam, swirling in the
foam, struck his head and killed him."

Four days later Rossetti and Paolucci went home. The Italian Government awarded them 650,000 lire. They gave it to the widows of the *Viribus
Unitis*. Rossetti said, "While I live the image of that gallant captain will
remain."

In 1935 Mussolini unleashed his legions, tanks and bombers on the naked
Ethiopians. In his marble halls in Rome, he shivered at the prospect of the
British Mediterranean Fleet intervening to chop down his supply lines
to Africa. Lieutenants Teseo Tesei and Elias Toschi, engineering officers
at the Italian submarine base at La Spezia, thought that Italy's best chance,
in this event, would be a devastating initial blow by an unheard-of weapon.
Remembering Pola, they designed an underwater electric torpedo two men
could ride astraddle with oxygen rebreathing lungs. They would be able to
sneak through torpedo nets and booms and fasten explosives under anchored ships.

The Siebe, Gorman Company had recently licensed manufacture of the

Davis oxygen lung in Italy and there were a dozen precedent designs for underwater chariots. Tesei and Toschi were, however, the first to build and successfully test such a vehicle in January, 1936. The Italian Navy ordered several and set up a secret crew training center on a private seaside estate. Britain did not interfere in Ethiopia, so the new weapons were stored and the crews dispersed to regular duties.

When Mussolini hitched on the tailgate of Hitler's bandwagon in June, 1940, the unit was reactivated and named the Tenth Light Flotilla. The first attack was planned for August; four chariots against two British battleships and a carrier in the base at Alexandria, Egypt. The chariots were carried to Tobruk in a surface ship, which put them on the submarine *Iride*. The submarine and a trawler went out to sea for a dive to test the pressure resistance of the "pigs," as they called the secret weapon. Three R.A.F. torpedo planes came along inopportunely, skimming in a V, two hundred feet above the water. They machine-gunned the *Iride* and skipped a torpedo which blew off her bows. The charioteers were unhurt on the trawler, but the *Iride* sank with her crew, the chariots and the breathing gear.

The divers went down naked and found the submarine lying on her side in the clear green water fifty feet deep. They radioed Tobruk for diving lungs and continued to plunge. They located seven men alive in the after torpedo compartment. When the oxygen lungs arrived, the men who had come to sink ships tried to rescue men sunk in one of their own. There was an escape lock with inner and outer hatches to the torpedo room. The outer hatch was jammed shut in the explosion. They got a line on it and the trawler heaved the hatch off. There were two dead men huddled in the lock—and the inner hatch was also jammed.

The men inside were sliding into imbecility from mounting carbon dioxide and poisonous gases from the flooded accumulator batteries. The divers signaled the prisoners their last hope: they must open the watertight bulkhead door and flood the compartment. Then swim under water through the door and make their way out of the broken midships section. The trapped men refused. The divers returned to the sailing trawler which hung over the wreck, exposed to return R.A.F. sweeps. A half hour later, white water boiled from the green sea. The divers harnessed up and swam down to help the escapees.

The first escapee arrived on the surface. Toschi said, "After twenty-four hours in a steel tomb, in complete darkness, on the verge of insanity, stifled by poison-laden air, a fugitive from excruciating agony, this man, at the sight of the sunlit sea, of the world, and of nature, screams out his enormous shout in assertion of his right to live. It is the wail of a newborn child magnified a hundred times by the force of his twenty years." The seventh man had to be dragged out by a diver. Two of the rescued men died of lung hemorrhages, from failure to exhale as they soared to the surface.

The next Italian attempt on Alexandria, by the submarine *Gondar* with two chariots, was turned back by a twelve-hour depth-bombing by Royal Navy vessels, which forced the *Gondar* to surface from a depth of 510 feet. Toschi was among those captured. The British had not yet been attacked by chariots and had no hint of their existence. The co-inventor did not tell them.

There remained the submarine *Scirè*, equipped with pressureproof deck hangers to accommodate three chariots. Her commander was a skilled underwater operator, Prince Valerio Borghese. In October, 1940, he sailed to attack Gibraltar itself. He dived past the mouth of Algeciras Bay against ocean currents pouring at one and a half knots over the Gibraltar sill, then turned back and the *Scirè* bumped along the rocks of Spain, 230 feet down, using the current to work into the bay. The Rock of Gibraltar is the eastern point of the bay entrance, and shelters the fleet anchorage inside. All the rest of the bay is Spain, and the Franco regime was neutral in favor of the Axis powers. Prince Borghese had commanded an Italian submarine in General Franco's service during the Spanish Civil War and had good liaison with the *caudillo*. Lights blazed in the bay towns of La Línea and Algeciras and the Spanish lighthouses sent out bright beams. Gibraltar itself was lighted up; the British saw no point in darkening an area amidst surrounding illumination. The *Scirè* entered at periscope depth, steering by the Spanish lights and passed the Rock. At 1:30 in the morning the *Scirè* reached a point in the inner bay, blew air ballast and gently settled on the floor fifty feet down. Six charioteers donned their rubber suits and oxygen sets. The radioman brought Borghese a signal from Rome: two British battleships were inside the mole at Gibraltar. This information could not have come from Italian reconnaissance aircraft; it was sent to Rome by Spanish spies. The chariot crews exited from air locks, took their cars out of the garages and drove them to the surface. The *Scirè* climbed and bade her three chariots *arivederci*. She dived and passed out of the bay.

The charioteers did not have to return to the submarine. The Spanish would take care of them. When they had stuck dynamite on the British bottoms, they were to scuttle the chariots and diving gear, swim ashore in Spain and be flown by L.A.T.I. airline to Italy. The first chariot failed and carried its team down to 130 feet. The riders tried to start the motor and blow water ballast. The machine did not respond. They surfaced, sank their diving gear and swam ashore. The second chariot made its way to the north mole of Gibraltar, where both divers' breathing sets failed. They opened the flood tank of the torpedo and set it adrift. They, too, went to the Spanish reception committee.

The third chariot was in charge of Lieutenant Gino Birindelli, who had been with the *Iride* when she sank at Tobruk. His companion was Petty Officer Damos Paccagnini. Their target was H.M. battleship *Barham*. Their mount was also slow and defective. They reached the floating gates of the military harbor and passed them, to within 800 feet of the *Barham*. Birindelli laid his course and submerged to 45 feet for his run. At that point, Paccagnini's breathing set failed. The lieutenant sent him to the surface with orders to float quietly; the water was full of phosphorescent plankton. Birindelli then continued, jolting slowly along the rough rock bottom, until the chariot failed entirely, 225 feet from the battleship. He tried for a half hour to drag it bodily to the target, and was forced to surface due to carbon dioxide narcosis. He set the time-fuse before he departed. He sank his breathing gear, tied his rubber suit along a submerged buoy chain and swam away in his coveralls. His escape was not as easy as that of the others. He was inside the enemy anchorage. At dawn he turned up his sleeves to hide his cuff stripes and walked through dockyard workers and sailors. He saw a little ship called the *Sant'Anna*, which he reckoned might be Spanish and friendly. He went aboard and hid in the fo'c'stle. It was a Spanish ship, but it was not friendly. Her sailors called the dock police. Birindelli and Paccagnini were both taken. At this point, no Italian underwater attack had come off and Britain had captured Toschi, inventor of the chariot, and two crewmen, but still had no notion of the secret weapon.

The warhead of Birindelli's machine exploded harmlessly. The second chariot, which had been flooded to sink, instead drifted ashore in Spanish territory. Spaniards latched on to it and took it to one of Franco's torpedo works. Several Spanish newspapers got their signals crossed and published the news: from *Informaciones*: ITALIAN SUBMARINE NEAR GIBRALTAR?, and Madrid *A.B.C.*: "The apparatus found on the beach at La Línea passed through Algeciras today. It is 5 meters long, shaped like an ordinary torpedo, but new features are a couple of small seats and hand-levers. Nothing is known of the crew, but it is supposed that the apparatus must have been launched from a submarine, a ship or an aircraft. When it was found the propeller was still in motion."

Spies reported to Italy: "During the last few days harbor ships have been dropping depth charges, attributed to nervousness since the piloted torpedo affair." Thus began the slaughter of many fish and underwater men.

In May, 1941, Borghese took three more chariots into Algeciras Bay aboard the *Scirè* and bottomed to receive the Rome radio on what targets there were. This time there were no warships behind the mole. So the pigs were directed against merchant ships. The crews tried hard; when one torpedo refused to start, they removed its warhead and towed it behind another pig. A crewman's breathing set failed and he passed out. While his mate aided him, the torpedo sank too deep to find. All three chariots sank without inflicting damage on the foe. But the crewmen made the 8:15 for Rome. As Borghese says in his memoirs, *Decima Flottiglia "Mas,"* it was "realistic training for the operators." It is not given often in war to send expensively trained cadre with secret weapons deep into an enemy stronghold, have them fail and get them back the next morning by air.

Co-inventor Tesei died heroically in July, 1941, in a combined underwater, surface and air attack on Malta, which failed to combine. Few political nightmares have found such courageous champions as those of the Tenth Light Flotilla. They had awful equipment but they fought bravely in the secret sea.

Despite persistent equipment failures, Gibraltar remained a practical training course. Borghese made another excursion in the *Scirè*, and, while lurking in the Strait, deliberately laid off a passing Allied convoy. He still believed in harbor attacks. The pilot of the first pig breathed wet caustic soda from his oxygen recirculating device. He surfaced and put on a reserve set. He stuck his explosive on the tanker *Fiona Shell*, blew her up and was airmailed home. The second chariot got under an empty tanker, the captured *Pollenzo*, of Genoa, and forbore attack because she had once been an Italian ship! They sank the motorship *Durham*, and made for the Spanish travel agency. The third pig blew up the Royal Navy tanker *Denbydale*, 15,893 tons. The crews all got silver medals. Commendatore Borghese was promoted and said, "King Victor Emmanuel deigned to receive me in audience and accorded me a long gracious interview." The king wanted to know why Borghese got the medal. The Prince explained the Tenth Light Flotilla. He said they had trained near one of the Royal estates. Victor was absolutely astonished and wanted to get in on it. He was allowed to make a visit to the training base in a rowboat loaded with a wild boar which His Majesty brought as a gift to "the splendid fellows."

Then the Tenth made a serious score. By 1941 German submariners had reduced the Royal Navy Mediterranean fleet to two capital ships, H.M.S. *Queen Elizabeth* and the *Valiant*. Mussolini had five battleships against them, but his naval might stayed in port. Borghese wanted to encourage the Italian grand fleet to venture out in Mare Nostrum. He decided to sink the two surviving British battleships at Alexandria.

Borghese loaded the pigs on the *Scirè* and sailed east. He stopped at the Italian base on Leros Island, Greece, and covered the deck hangers with tarpaulins, since "Leros was full of Greeks." They had been around thousands of years before Borghese's crowd grabbed their island and were less than sympathetic. Nor was there going to be Spanish hospitality in Egypt. Borghese had a couple of agents at Alexandria to help, but the charioteers knew they weren't going to get a ride to the airport when they got ashore. It was their most daring venture.

The *Scirè* dived for hours to reach her launching point just off the western light of the harbor and hit it with consummate navigation. She passed through several minefields to get there. The three pigs departed in the clear, starry night of December 18, 1941. Japan had just come into the war and the Allies were perilously near defeat in all theaters. Borghese's expedition might prove the breaking point.

The chariots skirted the outer breakwater and passed a half mile unchallenged to the harbor gate, which was closed by a formidable swinging boom. The Italians were investigating it when three destroyers came in from the sea and blinked their lamps. Guide lights came alight in the channel and the boom swung open. The pigs slid through behind the destroyers. A big blond lieutenant named Luigi Durand de la Penne and Petty Officer Emilio Bianchi drove their chariot through a cold and hostile harbor toward the 32,000-ton *Valiant*. They bumped her bottom and the usual happened. The pig sank in sixty feet of water. De la Penne dived after it and couldn't find his teammate. Bianchi had disappeared. The chariot would not stir. The big man lugged it along the floor, stirring up clouds of silt that obscured his wrist compass. He played it by ear. A pump was pounding in the belly of the great ship. After forty minutes he fixed the warhead on the *Valiant* and set the time detonator for 5 A.M. He ascended, sank his respirator and swam away. A searchlight and then a machine gun played on him. He climbed on a bow anchor buoy of the battleship and there was Bianchi. The usual had happened to him, too. He had passed out on oxygen and awakened floating. The Italians were bagged and taken aboard the *Valiant* at 4 A.M. The story of the *Viribus Unitis* was repeated—Italian underwater attackers being brought aboard the ship they'd doomed. De la Penne and Bianchi refused to talk. They were conducted to the ship's brig. Ten minutes before the explosion was due, de la Penne asked to see the captain, told him the ship was going up and that he should remove his men. Captain Charles Morgan, R.N., asked where the charge was located. De la Penne would not answer. He was taken back to the brig. On the way down he heard hoarse bleats on the tannoy, ordering abandon ship, and people jostled him and his escorts on the stairs. He waited in the cell. The explosion doused the lights and shook down leg irons on de la Penne. The *Valiant* listed on her side. He unbolted his port, but could not squeeze through. He left it open to contribute to the entrance of water. He did not realize the cell door was unlocked.

Morning light came into the cell. De la Penne departed into empty corridors, went up ladders, found an open hatch and walked out on abandoned decks. He walked aft and saw Captain Morgan giving orders to sailors, trying to save the *Valiant*. The Italian demanded what had been done with Bianchi. The master paid no attention. The watch officer said, "Be quiet!"

De la Penne shrugged and proceeded further aft. He joined a group of officers who were studying the battleship H.M.S. *Queen Elizabeth*. She was at anchor some cablelengths behind. Her crew was also up early and gathered on the foredeck. There was a heavy report. The *Queen Elizabeth* fidgeted and a shower of iron and Diesel oil erupted from her mainstack and spattered on de la Penne's study group. The *Scirè's* second chariot team had done her in. These two cavalrymen swam ashore and tried to make the Fascist lines outside Alexandria, but were picked up. The third pig had been sent to mine an aircraft carrier. She was not in port so they dumped a tanker.

Prime Minister Churchill did not report this terrible blow by six men until four months later in a secret session of the House. He unloaded six months of frightful sea news: the loss in the Mediterranean of H.M.S. *Ark Royal* and *Barham* to Nazi submarines, and the "British Pearl Harbor"—the *Repulse* and the *Prince of Wales*, sunk by Japanese surprise dive-bombing off Malaya.

Mr. Churchill said, "A further sinister stroke was to come. On the early morning of December 19, a half dozen Italians in unusual diving suits were captured floundering about in the harbor of Alexandria." They had sunk the *Valiant* and the *Queen Elizabeth* by "extraordinary courage and ingenuity." Said the Prime Minister, "Thus we no longer had any battle squadrons in the Mediterranean." Mussolini warships did not come out, however, and the heroism of the Tenth Light Flotilla went for nothing. After the war de la Penne received the *Medaglia d'Oro*, Italy's highest military honor. At the ceremony an Allied officer impulsively stepped forward and asked to pin the medal on de la Penne. It was Admiral Sir Charles Morgan, the man whose ship he mined.

The *Valiant* and the *Queen Elizabeth* did not disappear in the sea. It was not deep enough. The big ships sat there embarrassed, with their drawers full. Realizing that they would look natural to Axis reconnaissance planes, the British erected awnings, polished the brightwork, and put a jolly bosun's mate by the accommodation ladder to pipe aboard gay parties of visitors, hoping many spies were among them. While the show went on topside, the artificers patched and pumped below. Churchill said in his secret speech, "The enemy was for some time unaware of the success of their attack." He had the entire six chariot men in Britain.

Mr. Churchill sent a note to the chiefs of staff: "Please report what is being done to emulate the exploits of the Italians in Alexandria Harbor . . . One would have thought we should have been in the lead."

At Gibraltar, in the meantime, the Royal Navy was trying to find ways to meet the novel attacks. Depth bombs were dropped periodically in the anchorage to discourage the invisible warriors, but it was also necessary to inspect ship bottoms. This task fell to Lieutenant William Bailey, R.M.S.O. (Render Mines Safe Officer), who knew how to disarm a live floating mine, but had now to cope with mines stuck beneath the ships. He called for volunteers, and was joined by Lieutenant Lionel Crabb, who had volunteered for the Navy in 1939 and could not pass the physical exam. He sailed on merchantmen and slipped into the Navy when the doctors weren't looking. The volunteers used Davis lungs. In the summer of 1942 the Italians introduced individual divers who carried small limpets from Spanish shores. They damaged four ships.

One day Lieutenant Bailey was examining a hull, when he saw out of the corner of his eye a large dark animal approaching. He put his hand on his knife in case it was a shark. It was an Italian diver coming with a load of mischief. Bailey had the initiative. He closed in and stabbed him. The Italian swam away rapidly. Without foot fins, Bailey could not catch up. It may have been the first man-to-man fight under water.

The game of wits went on at Gibraltar. The base had become an undersea war college with students enrolled from both sides. The Italians came up with a dazzling idea. In Algecires Bay lay the scuttled Italian tanker *Olterra*. One day a nondescript party of Italian civilians arrived in Algeciras and announced they were going to repair the tanker to sell to a Spanish steamship company. They were Italian Navy people in mufti. They floated the ship and towed her to the mole in Algeciras Harbor, six miles across the bay from Gibraltar anchorage. The raffish crew equipped the *Olterra* as a launching base for chariots. Below the waterline they cut a large hole leading to a flooded compartment of the hull. When the hole was shut tight the compartment could be pumped out and the pig moved into a well-equipped machine shop. The daring ruse succeeded completely, despite the fact that the *Olterra* was under direct surveillance of the British consulate in Algeciras. The Italians called themselves "the Great Bear Flotilla."

The officer who conceived the idea, Licio Visintini, led the first three chariots out of the *Olterra* on December 8, 1942. All were lost by depth bombing. Only one survivor, Lieutenant Vittorio Cella, regained the *Olterra*. The British communique announced that three chariots had "tried to penetrate the harbor. It is believed that they were brought from Italy by the submarine *Ambra*." The Bear Flotilla's secret was still good. The British buried Commendatore Visintini at sea with military honors. A wreath was dropped in the water by Crabbe and Bailey, who had just finished working all night on a ticklish search for warheads that Visintini might have planted.

The Italians waited five months for new chariots from La Spezia. Their next sortie sank the freighter *Camerata*, and badly damaged the *Mahsud* and the Liberty ship *Pat Harrison*. Spanish friends planted pieces of Italian diving gear on the beach to give the impression they had been left by submarine-launched pig crews who had taken the air for Rome. The crews were safely back in the *Olterra* with their pigs.

The third sally, in August, 1943, was led by Lieutenant Commander Ernesto Notari. He got under the Liberty ship *Harrison Gray Otis*. His rider, Petty Officer Giannoli, was inexperienced and bungled his job. He went up and Notari went down with the torpedo to 112 feet. The goofy device then zoomed to the surface, the motor running at top speed. Notari had to ride it away on the waves, expecting shots any moment. He left a spectacular phosphorescent wake. Then Notari acquired an unexpected and wonderful escort. A school of porpoises swam along with him, splashing and diving with antic humor. Porpoises were so familiar in the bay that no patrol boat would bother looking for a bedraggled charioteer speeding along in their midst. Notari got back to the *Olterra*, undetected.

His companion, Giannoli, ballooned up alongside the Liberty ship. He swam around under the counter, stripped off everything but his underwear and climbed up on the rudder. He clung for two hours to the ship that was going to blow up, until he felt sure his comrades had escaped. Then he swam around to the side and gave himself up. The skipper of the *Harrison Gray Otis* signaled for the mine removal divers. Leading-Seaman Bell, R.N., arrived in a launch and prepared to dive. Giannoli was placed in the launch in the hope that he would give the location of the explosive. The diver had one leg in the water when the five hundred-pound warhead went off under the engine room. A hunk of plate tore up through the decks, passed through the side and struck Horace Webster, a sailor guarding the Italian. (Webster was unconscious for three weeks and awakened with no memory of what had happened. Seven years later he read a newspaper story on the affair and it all came back to him.) The two other pigs sank the big Norwegian tanker *Thorshovdi* and the freighter *Stanridge*. Great Bear Flotilla had now sunk 43,000 tons of shipping without drawing the slightest suspicion to its secret base.

Gibraltar University closed when Rome fell in the autumn. Many Italian underwater operatives joined the Allies. The Spanish governor of Algeciras lasted longer than they did; he rushed aboard the *Olterra* to destroy the equipment and prevent the British from learning the secret. Lieutenant Crabbe was right on his tail. He cannibalized three chariots and reconstructed one for test diving. The Armistice also stopped an Italian scheme to carry a midget submarine across the Atlantic and send her into the Hudson River. The little submarine had been built and tested and was to enter New York in December, 1943.

The final action of the intrepid Tenth Light Flotilla came in 1944, when some of its survivors, including Luigi de la Penne, joined British charioteers in an attack on the harbor of La Spezia, where the pigs were born. The targets were two Italian cruisers taken over by the Nazis. The ten thousand-ton cruiser *Bolzano* was sunk in this strange affair.

In an earlier war over twenty-four hundred years ago, the harbor of Syracuse was prepared for Athenian invaders. Big ancient freighters along the piers and warehouses were protected by a row of pilings driven into the water, and beyond that boom there were sharp stakes driven in completely under water to hole the bottoms of the approaching enemy. The Athenians arrived in a towering 250-ton ship and started shooting into the warehouses. The Syracusans replied with a heavier barrage. Then they saw strange activity on the Greek ship. Men were jumping into the water with saws and swimming to the palisades. They dragged heavy ropes which they tied to the tops of the pilings. They dived under water and sawed off the pilings, and the men on the ship heaved them out of the water.

That is from Thucydides' chronocle of the siege of Syracuse in 414 B.C., an early account of underwater demolition teams leading an invasion from the sea.

Up to 1943, divers and submerged cavalrymen were used against ships as an extension of submarine boat warfare. Then the diver took on a new role as the vanguard of armies in the island invasions of the Pacific.

The United States had no underwater swimmers until the middle of the Second World War. They were created by a terrible island invasion at Tarawa in the Gilberts in 1943. The Second Marine Division's landing craft could not get over the outer reef and Japanese underwater obstacles. The Marines had to wade 500 yards in direct fire of machine guns, mortars and 90-millimeter guns. Over a thousand were killed and 2,557 wounded in three days. Obviously somebody had to go in ahead of the assault and remove such obstructions on the islands to come. The Navy called for volunteers for underwater demolition teams from the men of the construction battalions, the toiling resourceful "Seabees." Seabee service was nominally noncombatant, but the Seabees in the islands knew different. The Navy aimed the call at them to locate men with engineering and explosive-handling experience—which it got, and brave men to boot. The Underwater Demolition man was unarmed, and carried a pack of high explosives on his back. As he waded and swam into Japanese fire, he had no way to reply except by living through it, blowing a channel for the assault boats and swimming away while the Marines answered for him.

The Navy had few accurate large-scale charts of the unknown atolls and volcanic islands in the far Pacific, so the U.D.T.s drew reconnaissance jobs as well. Weeks before an island invasion they would swim in pairs on parallel courses toward the Japanese redoubts, looking down through masks and estimating bottom depths and contours, sounding with small plummets and skirting the fringing reefs to find passages. They wrote data on plastic plaques strapped to their thighs. They took their findings back to the swift destroyer that brought them, where a shelf chart was compiled and sent back to the staff planners.

Then the underwater scouts returned to the island as many days ahead of the assault as was reckoned necessary to remove the obstacles. They first appeared at the invasion of Kwajalein Island in February, 1944.

The U.D.T.s had a glorious week at Guam. The Japanese had lined the three thousand-yard invasion beach with submerged coconut log cribs filled with broken coral and interconnected by heavy wire cables. The fence was behind the fringing reef. The underwater men arrived seven days before the landing in infantry landing craft, and paddled off in rubber rafts loaded with the powerful explosive "tetrytol." The LCI's opened up a racket of curtaining fire over their heads at the Japanese fortifications. The UDT's paddled to the fringing reef at high tide. The coral heads were only eighteen inches deep and the reef was seventy-five feet across. Each man took two or three twenty-pound packs of tetrytol and ran across the reef into deeper water. They swam to the cribs, wired them and blew them up. Some of the men crossed the reef three times a day. Two hundred UDT's worked at Guam and not a man was lost. When the first assault wave hit the beach, they found a sign: U.S. MARINES. WELCOME TO GUAM FROM UDT-4

The underwater demolition teams posed a serious dilemma for the defenders. To shell the pests would reveal Japanese gun positions. Not to shell them would assure a quicker removal of the obstacles. The Japanese commander at Leyte chose to fire. The ships off the beach thereupon knocked out his gun emplacements, one by one. When the UDT's were swimming back to their ships under rifle fire, they would duck under to grab sinking bullets as souvenirs.

The underwater dynamiters were two days ahead of the Marines at Iwo Jima and lost two swimmers in the intense Japanese fire. They returned to the destroyer *Blessman* and were moving off when a Japanese plane dropped a five-hundred-pound bomb into the mess and killed twenty-eight divers.

After Guam the Japanese stopped building cribs. For the expected invasion of the home islands they stationed men under water to meet the landing craft. They were a special volunteer force called the *Fukuryi*, who wore rubber suits and helmets with self-contained oxygen rebreathing systems. They were to patrol the floor from dawn to dark at over a mile an hour. In a test a *Fukuryi* officer walked the bottom twenty-seven feet down for eight hours. They carried thermos bottles of hot soup in their suits and drank through rubber tubes. Their weapon against invasion boats was a contact mine on the end of a long pole. They were human spar torpedoes.

Unlike the *Kamikazi* suicide pilots and the midget submarine crews, the *Fukuryi* had a complicated morale problem. The diver who won immortality by banging his charge on an LCA would surely kill himself, but he would also kill his friends near by, who were still awaiting their transfiguration. The volunteers did not want to depart on another man's glory ticket. The Japanese Admiralty, ever sensitive to fine points of chivalry, actually constructed underwater bomb shelters for the disinterested parties. Japan fell without a battle for the beaches, or there might have been strange battles between underwater demolition teams and the *Fukuryi*.

American and British demolition teams were a proven weapon by the time of the great embarkation in Normandy. Here there were no fringing reefs. The beach obstacles had been mapped by spies and low-flying planes, and to preserve the surprise, the dynamiters did not arrive until the first wave of infantry. At Utah Beach, the U.S. Cotentin Peninsula sector, the underwater teams were made up equally of soldiers and sailors. The Navy trained the Army. The invasion plan provided also a beach obstacle task force of Army engineers to follow the UDT's. They were to remove everything dry after their colleagues removed the wet obstructions. Owing to ship mix-ups and sinkings, all the demolition parties landed at the same time on the wrong beaches and with them came their replacements, who were not due until the fourth and fifth landing waves. For a few minutes there were no riflemen on Utah, only a company of men loaded with dynamite like pack mules.

But it worked out fine. They dropped off the ramps into three feet of water and waded ashore, each man carrying sixty pounds of explosives. All the obstacles were found high and dry. The Army and Navy did not go to war over jurisdiction. The sailors blew up the stuff that *should* have been wet, while the engineers demolished that which was demonstrably dry. They blasted a fifty-yard path through the low tide terrace, scarp, berms and backshore, flinging up steel and concrete pikes, steel tetraheads, hedgehogs and "Belgian gates," a large, expensive steel structure in which the Germans indulged. Then the dynamiters thought they might as well clear the whole sixteen-hundred yard landing sector. That they did in one hour.

It was different at Omaha Beach that morning. The Army-Navy Special Engineer Task Force of sixteen teams reached the beach ten minutes late. Two-thirds of them were on the wrong sectors. Three teams were without infantry or tank protection. They faced greater obstacles than at Utah. For instance, D-3 Draw at Les Moulins had four continuous lines of German obstacles in the water. The first was Element C, a steel gate ten feet high, standing on a braced girder structure. It had waterproof teller mines lashed to the uprights. The second fence was of logs driven obliquely into the sand. They had contact mines on their ends, pointing toward the sea. The third line was built of log ramps, reinforced and mined. On the high-tide line was a palisade of steel hedgehogs, shaped like cruel children's jacks, made of railroad rail and angle steel, planted firmly to stove landing craft.

Eight men of UDT 11 were dragging their rubber boatload of explosives from a landing craft when a German shell burst over them and set off their primacord. One man survived. Team 14 was on an LCM hit directly. There were no survivors. Team 15 was swimming ashore, towing its raft, when a mortar shell fell into the vessel. Three divers were killed and four wounded. Replacement team F followed in. A shell struck its LCT, which lost control. Another shell landed in the ramp, killing fifteen. Nevertheless, the dynamiters went to work wrapping the powder bags on Element C and wiring them to detonators. It took thirty charges, precisely placed in structural joints, to shatter Element C into harmless girders on the floor. Shells exploding in the water jolted the divers, and they had to get out of the water when they blew an obstruction. Infantrymen were also wading ashore and surviving crews of the unfortunate DD amphibious tanks were floating around them, helpless in Mae Wests and rafts. The DD was a land tank with a canvas air pocket wrapped around it. They were supposed to sail right through to the beach in the first assault wave from six thousand yards out. Of the first twenty-nine, two tanks reached the beach. The casualties among demolition men were 41 per cent on D-Day at Omaha Beach.

One of the saddest events of that gray turbulent morning was the fate of A Company, 116th Infantry, on Dog Beach, off Vierville. It arrived on six assault landing craft in a high surf and a rising tide. The boats were still far out when one of the LCA's foundered in ten feet of water. The infantrymen were loaded with about a hundred pounds each. They jumped off the LCA and drowned under their packloads. The other boats of Able Company were hit by artillery and mortars and the men went into the water. All the company officers and most of the NCO's were lost. Only a third of the company reached the beach. The official history states, "The leaderless men gave up any attempt to move forward and confined their efforts to saving the wounded, many of whom were drowned in the rising tide." A small emergency breathing bottle and a diving mask would seem a useful temporary issue to soldiers in beach assaults.

First ashore that morning at Sword Beach, the landing of the Second British Army, were men of "Locku"—Landing Craft Obstruction Clearance Parties. Under their slick suits they wore kapok vests to protect their rib cages from underwater explosions. Like the American UDT's, they were volunteers, "hostilities only" men, from prosaic callings—carpenters, costing clerks, lorry drivers, divinity students. As they swam in the heaving surf in the predawn, they saw a phenomenal sight against the black silence of Europe. Two bright lights beckoned to the correct landing sectors. These came from the British midget, submarines X-20 and X-23, which had been lying off the beach for two days. Their skippers, Lieutenants G. R. Honour and R. R. Hudspeth, had started for Sword Beach two days before the original invasion date of June 5. Weather omens had held up their guests for twenty-four hours, but the midgets held station with weak engines against cross-tidal currents of the River Orne and were there to guide the first wave of the Second Army when it approached.

One spring day in 1944 in Scapa Flow the British Home Fleet lay at anchor behind booms and nets that had been strengthened and restrengthened after German submarines had penetrated Scapa and sunk ships in both world wars. Now there was a new little nuisance about, the X-boat, or midget submarine, pioneered by the Japanese at Pearl Harbor and adopted by the Royal Navy. Six months before, four British X-boats had penetrated far into Norwegian fiords, through minefields and nets, and knocked the forty thousand-ton battle cruiser *Tirpitz* out of the war. The British admitted the possibility that the Germans had raised one of the scuttled midgets and might try her on Scapa Flow. H.M.S. *X-24* was sent to Scapa clandestinely to make dummy runs and see if the nets were tight and the hydrophone operators on their toes.

The little sub kept out of the fleet anchorage during her probes, returning by a circuitous route to her tender H.M.S. *Bonaventure*. On this last day of the trials, however, the saucy reservists of the *X-24* prevailed on their regular navy skipper to come in right through the big ships. Sailors around the fleet sighted the cocky fifty-footer and men lined the rails to see her. On the shelterless deck of the *X-24* lounged two bearded disreputable types, soaked in spray. They came alongside the mighty battleship *Duke of York*, flagship of Admiral of the Fleet Lord Fraser of North Cape. The two poor examples of officers suddenly stiffened to a fancy salute, and by etiquette a thousand men high above on *Duke of York* drew themselves up and acknowledged it. One of the midget crew drew out an Aldis lamp and winked a message: W-H-A-T A B-I-G B-A-S-T-A-R-D Y-O-U A-R-E!

That was the midget submariner, laughing at his handful of low cards, wearing a funny hat, and dying often and suddenly in his war on the giants.

The submariner moves with every ship against him, his own and the enemy's. Destroyers and planes bomb first and ask questions afterward. The gigantic French submarine *Surcouf*, 4,330 tons submerged, which carried 120 men and a seaplane, was sunk by an American freighter in the Pacific in 1942. The roll of submarines sunk by friends is a long dirge. They have gone down by the scores in night convoy collisions and inexplicable mechanical failures both in war and peace.

British X-boats went to the Pacific after the European victory. There they fell under the command of Vice Admiral James Fife, U.S.N., for a mission against the Japanese heavy cruisers, the *Nachi* and the *Takao*, which were at anchor in the Johore Strait, off Singapore's northern dockyard. Admiral Fife delivered a rousing send-off speech, "a cause of much embarrassment to all concerned, except the Admiral himself," said C. E. T. Warren and James Benson, the historians of the X-boat war, in *Above Us the Waves*. The midgets were used to British admirals giving them a slight nod as they slipped out, and if they succeeded in demolishing the combined German and Japanese grand fleets, they might expect the admiral to remove his pipe and murmur, "Well done." Admiral Fife's peroration was, "You're the little guys with a lotta guts. Good luck!"

The *XE-1* and *XE-3* left Borneo under tow of big submarines and were cast loose forty miles from the Japanese cruisers. The *XE-1* was not able to make the *Nachi* and had to turn back due to no fault of herself or her men. The *XE-3* was commanded by Lieutenant Ian Fraser, a small, dark, deep-eyed volunteer from big submarines, who was a sharp student of the little ones. It was his first mission in X-boats. He sailed awash up to the Strait entrance at night, seated outside on the casing with a pair of glasses. He decided that there was less danger of detection if he got out of the main channel, so he passed through the minefields. He sighted a tanker coming with gunboat escort and dived. The *XE-3* bottomed for a half hour on top of a mine, as Fraser discovered when he got up to periscope depth.

He continued thirty feet under water in the Strait itself, probing ahead with Asdic and changing course in the bending channel. He made about six miles in three hours, and figured he was a half mile from the harbor boom, which had to be tackled in daylight. He settled on the bottom and the four-man crew took benzedrine pills to keep awake. The little sub stirred up at dawn. Fraser peeped at the trawler which opened and closed the boom. The gate was open. The *XE-3* slipped through. The water was calm and slick. Fraser ran his periscope up and down very quickly to avoid leaving a noticeable wake. Normally the inner roads would be full of traffic, but the Japanese Empire was at sunset and gloom. Few boats were about. Fraser pressed on at higher speed against a flow tide, still undetected. At noon he saw from afar the superstructure with many bridges and the raked clipper bow of the *Takao*. He pulled the eye piece down and commenced his target run. At 2 o'clock he upped his spy and jerked it back instantly. A populated Japanese liberty boat was less than a hundred feet off.

He went on blind toward the forward gun turret of the *Takao*. The bottom sloped up sharply and he hugged it. It was apparent now that the big cruiser was practically touching bottom herself. That was the best defense of all against underwater attackers; good earth right underneath. The *XE-3* hit something with a loud reverberation and stopped in a depth of fifteen feet. Fraser was on target with a bang and the *XE-3* was in transparent green water. There was no disturbance from the cruiser. Fraser reversed his screws and backed out. For forty minutes he nuzzled along the flanks like a piglet rooting for dinner and found a deeper place amidships. There was very little space, but he got the submarine under the cruiser.

The job of going out and sticking the limpets on the *Takao* was up to the *XE-3*'s diver, Leading Seaman J. J. Magennis, a slender green-eyed individual with long, thick, curly hair and a spreading smile. Magennis snapped on his face mask, strapped the oxygen rebreathing bag on his chest and shinnied up into the air lock. They closed the hatch and Magennis flooded the lock. He opened the outside hatch and heaved it with his back. The hatch touched the bottom of the *Takao*. It would open only one quarter of the way. Magennis pressed the oxygen out of his bag, deflated his own lungs and squeezed himself out.

The hull surprised him. He had been used to flat-bottomed ships. The Japanese cruiser had a deep cutter keel and the vast expanse was fouled with years of barnacles and waving weeds. Magennis opened the chest of explosives carried on the *XE-3*'s port flank and took out six magnetic limpet bombs. He noticed tiny bubbles streaming across his mask; he had scraped a hole in his oxygen bag getting out the hatch. It would not endanger his breathing if he kept the bag fully inflated, but the bubbles might be seen on the surface, and if he lost pressure water would flood his caustic soda and sear his lungs with burning liquid.

Magennis had put himself in for a lot of trouble already, and so had Ian Fraser, but they were the kind who get on with it. Magennis started scraping barnacles to stick a bomb. The magnet hold was weak on the dirty hull and the limpet skidded up the slope. He caught it and figured he could insure the limpets would stay under the *Takao* if he put two on either end of a line and hung them across the keel, balancing each other. For a half hour, with his oxygen leaking away, the diver cleaned spots on the *Takao* and distributed the limpets forty-five feet apart. The firing pins in three of them jammed, but he placed them anyway for tidiness' sake. His hands were lacerated by the barnacles and he was nearly fainting when he swam back to the *XE-3*, deflated the oxygen bag and snaked into the air lock. It was slow agony to secure the hatch and he had barely enough strength to turn the valve that blew the airlock. His shipmates opened the inner hatch and lifted him down.

Before they departed, Lieutenant Fraser pressed the levers that released two big charges of explosives carried on the outside. They would lie on the floor with time fuses started as a parting gift from the *XE-3*. The port container of explosives slid off, but the starboard carrier would not release. Fraser tried to shake it off by going full astern. The *XE-3* would not move. He put her forward, then astern. They pumped tanks and blew them. The *Takao* sat firmly upon them as their time fuses clicked all around. The crew tried everything to worm loose. All of a sudden the *XE-3* shot out by the stern. They worked swiftly to prevent her from breaking water. Even so, there was a swirl on the mirrored surface before they got to the bottom again. They were only seventeen feet down, an interesting under-sea sight for any idle eye. Fraser said they could not escape with a flooded explosion container on the starboard. The little skipper asked Magennis for his leaking oxygen bag. The diver later reported his reaction to this request: "Lieutenant Fraser immediately volunteered to go out and clear same, but, knowing it was my job, I went out and did same." Magennis took a big monkey wrench and went through the lock the second time. When he opened the outer hatch a boil went to the surface. They had been banging, struggling, scraping and agitating the waters around the *Takao* now for nearly three hours and the Japanese were still dreaming. Magennis swung the spanner in slow motion and pryed at the release pins. The con-tainer slid off seven minutes later. Magennis returned to the submarine.

The *XE-3* started out of the Strait submerged. Depth-keeping was un-predictably tough the whole way, because they were in a mingling of fresh river water and sea water, fluids of different densities. A submerged sub-marine is a precarious bubble whose crew must alertly manipulate many complex buoyancy controls to avoid plunging or surfacing when she is in layers of fresh or salt, hot or cold water. The *XE-3* broke surface in a sudden salt stratum a mile off the *Takao*, but was submerged in five sec-onds. Nearing the boom, a fast motor boat passed over them in the evening water. Ian Fraser said, "We had our fingers in our ears waiting for a bang. Luckily, there was no such thing and the boom was reached and passed at 1949 hours without further incident." Two hours later their stuff blew a hole sixty by thirty feet through the barnacle ranch on the *Takao's* bottom. Fraser and Magennis received the Victoria Cross.

12

The Big Shoot

"W E ARE another bunch of little people from under the sea," announced the secretary of the Santa Cruz, California, Devil Divers. He was reporting the birth of a new amateur diving club to *The Skin Diver*, the lively organ of the most rapidly growing sport in the world. Another club wrote, "After nearly breaking up, the Long Beach Junior Neptunes are back on their feet again and going strong. Past President Bob Evanoff, who got married and is now expecting a junior Junior Neptune, felt that he didn't have enough time to carry on the tasks of President."

Mask, fin and lungs had struck California, where Huckleberry Finn drives a hot rod and movie actors put on lungs to swab out their swimming pools. Kabezone Kelley, historian of the Puget Sound Mudsharks, wrote in *The Skin Diver*, "It is getting so we have to go as far as thirty miles out to find new spearfishing grounds, but I guess everybody is feeling the hard times. Every time a new spot is found, somebody has to go and break the fishing record, requiring the old record holders to call off their sightseeing and frantically call for their gunbearers."

By 1955, 25,000 Aqualungs had been sold throughout the world, eight out of ten in California. A half-dozen variations of the compressed-air lung were on the market. Sales of foot fins, masks and breathing tubes reached the hundreds of thousands. One estimate held that there were three million free divers in the United States. The figure was more probably 300,000, of which possibly 50,000 used breathing gear with some frequency. The sport was spreading fantastically each year, however, and the end was not in sight. Diving had about as many followers as skiing had twenty years before. There were about 200 U.S. diving societies by 1955.

The affiliative urge produced some strutty club names: Hell Divers (Norwalk, California), Dixie Divers (New Orleans), Davey Jones' Raiders (Long Beach, California), Jax Jetty Jumpers (Jacksonville, Florida), Sea Spooks (Chula Vista, California), Long Beach Sea Barons (California), Kelptomaniacs (Los Angeles), and Tigers of the Sea, 750 miles from the nearest brine in Park Ridge, Illinois. There were founded the Coast of Maine Neptunes; The Creatures, of San Marcos, Texas; the Diving Jets, of Passaic, New Jersey; the Long Island Sand Fleas; the Portland (Oregon) Puddle Pilers, and the Bottom Scratchers of San Diego, California. They named themselves Arizona Desert Divers, of Phoenix; Inland Aqua Fools of Clarkdale, Michigan; and Undersea Maniacs, of Garden City, New York. There were a few restrained groups such as the Sunday Skin Divers of Culver City, California, and the Anthropo-Piscatorial Society of Connecticut, seated at New Haven. La Jolla, California, girls started one called the Sea Nymphs, which was fortunately not proximate to the Long Beach theater of the Sons-of-the-Beaches. If they should meet, however, the happy pair may join the Aqua Familias, of Long Beach, a man-and-wife diving club.

Los Angeles policemen formed The Hammerheads Club. Men on active military service founded the Hawaiian Coral Gypsies, the Azorean Pescadores, Honolulu Depth Devils, Jax Navy Sea Searchers (Jacksonville, Florida) and the Hospital Skin Divers in the Panama Canal Zone. The luckiest serviceman's club was the Deep Sea Wanderers, made up of the crew of Tank Landing Ship 529, which plied between California and Japan. The Navy acquired divers without spending a penny on training. The Wanderers were formed by the men themselves, paying for their own equipment. The air lung was magical. Commander F. D. Fane, of the Underwater Demolition Team, at San Diego, shrewdly offered to lend his men Aqualungs on their free days. He found them holding diving parties with wives and kiddies. On one outing they nearly lost a Marine colonel. He was found unconscious a few feet down entangled in kelp, but came around under artificial respiration. Commander Fane said, "We sure sweated him out. Imagine going on the carpet to explain how we'd drowned a Marine colonel on a picnic."

Many diving clubs saw their unique value in police and rescue work and volunteered as civil defense units. By 1955 it was getting tough for robbers on the lam to toss the evidence in the water. Members of the La Jolla Skinsters, Richard Ridenour, Robert Wedgewood and Daniel Stevens, plunged in for money and watches thrown into the Pacific by burglars who were being arrested. The divers fetched up the exhibits in fast order. The amateurs were on call to recover drowned bodies. The Alameda County, California, Underwater Rescue Unit dived fifteen hours for a child in a lake. The Fitchburg, Massachusetts, Sharkmen joined the civil defense in a truck with blinking red lights and a siren. On a test alert they drove a mile and got a dummy body from a sunken automobile in ten minutes. Charles Stanley, of the Mid-West Amphibians was diving in a quarry near Racine, Wisconsin, when he discovered a new convertible car at a depth of forty feet. There were no bodies. It seemed a stolen machine. Stanley swam around behind to make a note of the license number for the police. The license plate read MEOW. He foresaw the sheriff's reaction to a man in duck feet and a black rubber suit coming in to report finding a car in forty feet of water with the license plate, MEOW. Stanley twisted off the plate and took it to the law.

Inevitably, crime also went under water. In Florida hundreds of outboard motors were missing from boats in a marina. Suspicion attached to a lone diver who prowled the waters near by. The police watched him from jetties and saw a hand reach from the water over a boat transom and loosen a motor. They closed in, but did not have lungs to continue the game of cops and robber under water. The finny burglar retreated under a pier and plastered his head with floating garbage as a disguise. The police waited. The diver lasted twenty-three hours before he crawled out. The police said, "He looked like a prune."

The Skin Diver appeared in Lynwood, California, in 1951. It was edited by two divers, James Auxier and Charles Blakeslee. They ran chatty club news, memoirs of divers and many photographs of people holding up fish they had pierced. The big shoot was on. Anglers and commercial trawlermen resented the apparent ease with which the divers caught big fish and soon inspired legislation against underwater hunting. It was the Mediterranean counterrevolution of the thirties transplanted to California and Florida. The hunters were slow to defend themselves. A minority slaughtered fish with the avidity of nineteenth-century commercial hunters shooting the bison, the fur seal and the passenger pigeon.

In Florida, twenty coastal counties prohibited or heavily restricted undersea hunting. The Overseas Highway, a viaduct road running out to the southern keys, which is the perch of thousands of anglers, was forbidden to fish hunters for a mile on either side. Amphibious feuds broke out between fishing boats and divers; in one case a party boat attempted to ganghook the divers and they fired harpoons through the bottom of the craft. Florida divers were held accountable for shoot-and-run tourists they'd never seen.

California divers rallied to avoid outlawry. They joined fishing organizations and made a pact with the commercial abalone divers to respect each other's territories and quotas. The divers formed the Ocean Fish Protective Association and began to regulate their kills, forestalling legislation. By far the most positive development came when diving clubs took up photography and underwater nature study, the stage reached earlier in the Mediterranean. The Club Alpin Sous-Marin of Cannes set its program in 1946 as "Excursions, explorations and submarine archeology, swimming, nautical sports and undersea hunting." Three years later it dropped "hunting" and substituted "ichthyology." French diving clubs endorsed a proposal to forbid hunting with breathing devices. The law was enacted. Some persons thought lung divers should have regulations similar to those of motorists—the lung should be inspected and certified as safe and the diver should be required to pass a proficiency test and be issued a license before he could dive. U.S. commercial helmet divers were already licensed, after passing Navy tests, but the explosion of free divers in the fifties got little informed attention from legislators.

The French Government has placed diving-law enforcement on the clubs. Today in France a hunter must belong to a recognized club, which issues his license and sees that he does not chase fish with a lung. Club members are commissioned as *gardes-pêches*, or fish wardens, to keep an eye on hunters. As a result, those who simply must slaughter animals for pleasure are traveling to Brazil and remote coasts which do not yet have underwater laws. The others are contributing to our knowledge of the sea by photography and observation. Underwater archeology grows almost entirely at the initiative of these amateurs. In California the Scripps Institution of Oceanography at La Jolla enlists skilled amateurs to work with its free diving team on submarine research, and its veteran chief diver, Conrad Limbaugh, journeys far to talk to club meetings.

In Wisconsin the Mid-West Amphibians volunteered to aid the State Conservation Department in finding why lake trout were not reproducing in Green Lake. The Amphibians knew that the final beneficiary of this project could only be their rivals, the anglers. That was one reason why they went to Green Lake. They set an example for other clubs at odds with fishermen. The Green Lake survey was well planned and equipped. Ten divers participated with a state conservation team, using outboard motor boats and a barge equipped with an echo-sounder. It was November, a time to sharpen iceboat skates in Wisconsin. The party slept in arctic tents and jumped into the frosty water from a pitching barge, without ladders, overloaded with 150 pounds of rubber suit, diving lung, speargun and camera. The echo-sounder registered several big trout below but only one was sighted by divers. The Amphibians swam to the mud bottom, to depths of 120 feet, in two days of severe, icy dives. They photographed sculpins, an ocean fish which was "a complete surprise to the conservation men," said Lee Gleason, the club reporter. Green Lake is fresh water, eight hundred miles from the sea. In the gumbo on the floor the free divers

speared or grabbed in their hands mud puppies, a species of water salaman-
der. When the salamanders were dissected, the conservation men found
trout eggs in their stomachs; in one there were seventy-two undigested eggs.

One of the leading Atlantic coast clubs, the Long Island Dolphins,
sought out the New York Conservation Department and asked what it
could do to aid fish research. The delighted bureau gave the divers forms
to report their observations. The divers installed permanent camera tripods
on coastal and bay floors to make time-lapse films. The Cleveland (Ohio)
Skin Divers undertook a rugged chore for the Cleveland Museum of Natural History by diving under the ice in Lake Erie to study the "life pyramid"
in winter. The pyramid, also called "the chain of life," is simply the underwater economy—what fish eats what other fish or plants, and so through
the nutritive cycle. The Danish biologist, C. G. J. Petersen, once followed
the pyramid of ocean cod, through intervening predators, to the nutritional
base, eelgrass. He showed that ten tons of weed produced one ton of plant-
eating fish, which nourished a tenth of a ton of carnivorous cod. The University of New Hampshire zoologists, Lorus J. and Margery Milne, found
that the same ten tons of eelgrass fed two tons of ducks, brant and geese.
A plague on New England eelgrass in 1931 spread enormous devastation
among fish and birds. The imaginative amateur divers who volunteered to
study the life pyramid had ventured into a very useful field.

Such researches were offset, however, by the main trend of killing fish.
In 1954 the U.S. Amateur Athletic Union recognized underwater hunting
as a competitive sport. People wearing official badges could run about in
white pants, shooting off starting guns and hand out trophies. Hunting was
changing from the queer doings of hungry persons in tire-patch suits,
flailing themselves alive on rocks, to groups in spacemen uniforms lining
up to receive trophies for stabbing the most fish.

I was in France as American waters filled up with guns and flying spears.
I said to Cousteau, "Any day now some guy will shoot another and come
up and say, 'I thought he was a grouper.' " Cousteau said, "What do you
mean, *any* day now? In 1940 I was diving at Dakar and a type ran his
spear through the calf of my leg." Several children have been injured by
loaded spearguns on shore, but at this writing no hunter has been killed by
another under water. Give it time.

Some American diving sportsmen regret that the first formal notice of
the undersea adventure was the recognition of fish-sticking as a competitive
sport by the A.A.U. One veteran told me, "This will make a lot of trouble
and lead the enthusiasm of the youngsters the wrong way. I would like to
see conservation organizations and marine research people get together
and show the kids the wonderful things they could study under water. Phil
Wylie, the writer, was a big fish killer until just recently. He got converted

by a look-box and says he's a fish-watcher from now on in. You have thousands of youngsters beginning to live in the sea. They could discover great things if there were less of this spear business."

Henry del Guidice of the Long Beach Neptunes, denounced newcomers who were sacking the lobster and abalone beds. "I have six kids," said del Guidice. "If we want abalone I find that three seven-inchers are more than enough for my family and I leave two abalone behind. How in the name of all that is good and decent can the Ocean Fish Protective Association prevail on our legislators to enact laws to limit the commercial fishermen's depredation of our ocean wildlife while some of our so-called sportsmen are just as guilty?" Kabezone Kelley, the Pepys of Puget Sound, wrote in *The Skin Diver:* "The octopus hunters are increasing in numbers and enthusiasm so I guess I'll have to go on record as beginning some legislation for octopus protection to prevent complete extinction. No more than two men to any single octopus and none to be taken while mating." The Newbury, California, Men-o-Mar club decided their hunting championship would be confined to inedible fish.

In 1954 eight California divers founded The Orcas, named after the killer whale, which you might think a most rapacious band. Instead, as founder James Crank reported, "It is devoted one hundred per cent to underwater photography and its various problems. Many of us are more interested in bringing back photographs instead of fish, and that is how we came together." There appeared at Fort MacArthur, California, the 554th AAA Missile Mariners, members of a Nike rocket battery. They started out with a "few abalone and a case of pleurisy," and "just when we schedule a meeting one of the Nike batteries goes on a training phase," lamented their correspondent, Sergeant Ronald Polk. A new club weighed in called the H^2O K9s, nothing more sinister than Water Dogs, and one called the Grouper Gropers of La Jolla, whose reporter, William Light, wrote to *The Skin Diver:* "Despite the name, we are not devoted to the art of spearing Grouper. We believe these magnificent creatures should be protected, as the spearing of them has increased to the point where they are quite depleted in La Jolla and the Coronado Islands. We feel that line and spearfishermen alike should cooperate in protecting these fish."

Undoubtedly what Mr. Light meant by "line" fishermen is what the dictionary calls an angler. What he meant by "spearfishermen" was undersea hunters. The American sport was entangled in a kelp jungle of jargon. The term "skin diver" lost any meaning it may have had. Originally it described one of the hardy California pioneers of the thirties who plunged without breathing apparatus and wore nothing but bathing trunks. Today most divers wear a warm rubberized garment or long woolen underwear, especially in the chilly waters of California. Skin is just about the last thing you can see on a well-equipped Californian. Robert Dill, the diving geologist of San Diego, insists he is not a "skin diver," he is a free diver. This simple, correct term covers naked diving and all the various independent breathing devices that divers now use.

The worst term was "frogman." It was coined by someone who had seen a diver waddling around on deck in his foot fins, but had never seen him swimming gracefully under the sea. A Washington research group contributed another clinker—"Scuba"—for Self-Contained Underwater Breathing Apparatus. It was thought up by "Pousnrcs," or members of the Panel on Underwater Swimmers of the National Research Council. "Spearfisherman" was another misnomer. A man standing in a boat can be a spearfisherman. Divers with spears or spear guns are underwater hunters, from the clear French term *chasseur sous-marin*. There is confusion about the various breathing devices used by free divers. "Aqualung" is used in newspaper stories to cover any kind of lung, including the homemade devices that people kill themselves with. "Aqualung" is the registered trade mark of the United States and British-licensed *scaphandre-autonome* of Cousteau and Gagnan. It is a compressed-air lung. The name was coined by Henri Dolisie, of Montreal, Canada.

There are other compressed-air lungs, such as the Divair and the Hydropak. Why can't they all be called "air lungs"? There are several makes of oxygen lungs such as the Davis, the Momsen, the Draeger and the Lambertsen. They share the same principle, that of purifying the exhalations in a container of caustic soda. They should be referred to as oxygen lungs, because they have quite different characteristics than air lungs. Oxygen lungs are limited to a depth of thirty-three feet and they do not release bubbles like the air lungs. We are already getting into helium-oxygen breathing mixtures used in air lungs. It is important for the safety of novices to tag this as "helium diving," because helium mixtures will take a man safely past the fatal zone of air diving—three hundred feet. If it is not clearly stated in the first paragraph of newspaper accounts that the deep dive was made with helium, some venturesome reader may try to beat the record with compressed air and kill himself. People do not refer to airplanes as bicycles, and the differences in diving gear are just as great.

By the mid-fifties, individuals were coming forth to lionize themselves by breaking "depth records." They were not content with the unanimous findings of diving physiologists that 300 feet was the limit of survival for compressed-air diving. A Florida lawyer named Hope Root added affirmative evidence in an Aqualung dive from a boat equipped with echo-sound. The graph traced him to a depth of 500 feet. Root was never seen again. A fifty-two-year-old Parisian dentist, Henri Chenevée, a skilled free diver, but unable to resist reporting bizarre undersea exploits, signed a gripping article in the weekly *Radar*, which usually occupies itself with multiple murders and flying saucers. Dr. Chenevée stated that during the summer of 1954 off Corsica, he had swum to a depth of 430 feet, breathing compressed air. His feat had been witnessed by Corsican officials, who attested that he had surfaced holding in his hand a tag marked 130 meters (430 feet), which had been hung at that depth on a weighted line.

The story was a sensation. Chenevée's claimed accomplishment was like running a three-minute mile. The French National Federation of Undersea Studies and Sports issued a communiqué to France's diving clubs, saying it had the duty to inform them that:

"1. All test dives which have been attempted to date under unimpeachable technical control, have resulted in death beyond a depth of 100 meters (330 feet).

"2. All physicians and research specialists studying deep diving, estimate that diving beyond sixty meters (200 feet) with air is dangerous, and at more than 100 meters survival is a gamble."

The Federation was concerned that Chenevée's "dramatic account and the mania for breaking records, so contrary to the spirit of underwater exploration, will provoke new attempts, certainly dangerous and perhaps fatal, and without usefulness."

Frédéric Dumas, who once swam down to 307 feet, seconded the Federation's communiqué and added that depth records were "imbecilic." He described his 307-foot dive as a chore undertaken to find out what had fouled the dragline of a minesweeper. "Afterward my only impression was that the dive had been stupid and reckless. It never entered my mind that it was a world record, and nobody else gave a damn either. We didn't tell any newspapers.

"Six years later," said Dumas, "Cousteau and I were discussing the limits of Aqualung diving to define them for *The Silent World* and we put in the minesweeper dive as an extreme example of the depth range, because it happened to be accurately fixed by the sounding line and echo-sound and a bit of seaweed I picked off the bottom. I deeply regret having mentioned the dive. The dreadful fact is that any bold and ignorant novice can swim down to 1,000 feet if he pleases. *The sea gives no warning and no resistance to such attempts.* The record mania is a grave danger to novices and can set diving back if it results in deaths due to ignorance and bravado. Depth records are the enemy of our sport and science."

The Club de la Mer of Juan-les-Pins, decided to do something about Dr. Chenevée's claim. This group, the second diving club of the Côte d'Azur, numbers veteran underwater personalities, such as Louis Lehoux, the famous "Lou-Lou"; tall, tough André Portelatine; Henri Maleville, a phenomenal naked diver; the racing driver, Pierre Laporte; and Jean Delmas, who has dived in the Mediterranean, Red Sea, Persian Gulf and Indian Ocean. The Club announced that it would send a diver to 495 feet, using exactly the same equipment and controls as Chenevée had: a line weighted with twenty pounds and bearing depth markers each ten meters, or 33 feet.

At sea off Cannes, a boatload of reporters and local officials solemnly measured the line and hung it straight. Portelatine and Laporte plunged. Ten minutes later they surfaced. Laporte's nose was bleeding, but Portelatine held in his hand the last six markers, including the incredible 495-foot sign. The witnesses signed affidavits and placed them in a sealed envelope. The Club also placed a secret letter in the envelope. The documents were read at a press conference the next day in the Antibes Town Hall.

Dr. Chenevée appeared at the conference and protested that the Club de la Mer had "committed an unsporting and inelegant gesture to cast doubt on the French diving record and affront the proofs I have sincerely given." There was a rumble of laughter at this, since the proofs were the same in each case. Portelatine then read the sealed letter. It described how he and Laporte had gone down a hundred feet, where Laporte put an arm through a turn in the rope and proceeded to haul up everything so Portelatine could pluck the depth markers. Laporte had bloodied his own nose on the way up to add a touch of color. The Club had deliberately pulled off the stunt to arouse public opinion against deep-diving claims, which youngsters might try to emulate and lose their lives.

Chenevée arose and said he would repeat his 430-foot dive with unimpeachable controls. Portelatine asked, "With a 200-pound weight?" That would weigh about 125 pounds under water and be virtually impossible for a man to haul up. Chenevée said his vacation was over but he would try next year. He changed his mind a day or so later and gathered witnesses and reporters for an attempt off Cannes, without informing the Club de la Mer. As he was about to dive, a speedboat arrived, carrying Portelatine and a Club de la Mer delegation. They had been tipped off by a reporter. Portelatine addressed Chenevée very earnestly, "If you go to 330 feet, you are defying physical laws and gambling your life." He offered to dive to 200 feet with Chenevée to act as safety man. The Doctor played it to the end. He dived alone. Thirteen minutes later he surfaced in distress. He was pale, gasping and spitting blood. "I nearly died," he said. He had no depth markers at all, although the highest one was at 265 feet.

California got in the act with a girl champion, a handsome young lady named Zale Parry, who wisely did not exceed 209 feet. She was chaperoned by her fiancé, a skilled diver named Parry Bivens. Florida was stung into action and struck back with a miss who swam seven miles horizontally under water and a young man who submerged in an air lung for 24 hours.

He was soon rendered ex-champion of submarine tree-sitting by New York and Ontario rivals. In the meantime, a French expedition permanently dislocated the free depth record by sending divers 1,350 feet below sea level, in the Dead Sea, which was already 1,300 feet below sea level. André Galerne, a Parisian professional, made the world's highest dive in a hydroelectric dam in the Alps. California gave an encore in a 350-foot free dive by Jean Clarke-Samazan. He was breathing a mixture of helium and oxygen, but some newspaper reports did not point this out. Samazan published an article entitled, "I Survived the Deepest Dive." It was somewhat inaccurate. At least five thousand men have dived deeper in chambers and vehicles, armored suits, helium helmet suits and submarines.

The glacier coast of New England would seem an unlikely diving ground —Mediterranean divers are amazed that anyone plunges for fun in those murky depths, where 50° F. is a tropical miracle on a day in August. Under Folly Cove and Town Landing there is no color but brown eelgrass and carragheen and pale fish hurrying swiftly by in the gloom. The waves beating on the rocks have knocked divers senseless and drowned them. In Boston, I met one of New England's human icebergs, a mild, handsome twenty-six-year-old named William Westell, who is a bit deaf—from diving, he believes. He went into the surly winter surf as a child and used to swim out a thousand yards and peer into the vague shoals off Rockport and Squantum. He said, "When I was about sixteen I swam away out and saw a lobster about eight feet down on the bottom. I did not have goggles, never heard of them. I went ashore and hung a net in a barrel hoop and went back and got the lobster. I saw in an old mechanic's magazine how to make underwater goggles out of inner tube, two jar caps and isinglass. A poor idea, but it was the best I'd heard of. You can't keep two lenses in a plane. I thought I was grabbing two lobsters. I made me a spear to go after lobsters in rock crevices. The spear broke them up, so I borrowed my mother's kitchen tongs. They worked fine. I always carry them on a cord on my wrist. I got a diving mask from California as soon as I heard about them."

Westell never dives from a boat, but swims out, towing a net on cork floats, in which he amasses his lobster catch. Lobster diving paid his way through college and a graduate engineering course at M.I.T. Sometimes he would tong three netloads a day and make fifty dollars. Westell has closely observed lobster life. "The best catch is in the late summer," he explained. "On the north shore of Cape Cod the lobsters come in to ten-foot depths at that time. They like certain holes and dislike others. You never know why, but you can be certain that they will be crowded into the same special holes year after year. You clean out a hole and two days later it will be full up again with lobsters that know the right hole."

On busy days Westell swam four miles, dragging his net from hole to hole. He could snap over in the *coup de reins,* or lightning surface dive, and drive straight down to seventy-five feet. With the onset of deafness, he limits his dives to forty feet. His friend, Henry Kendall, the diving authority, is also a touch deaf. Both have dived mostly in New England. Diver's deafness has been reported many times by doctors. It does not occur at all among veteran Mediterranean divers I know who have been plunging twice as long as Westell and Kendall. The two admit that their ailment may have nothing to do with diving. Deafness is one of the myriad problems of diving physiology which has received little attention from medicine.

New England's northernmost divers are the hardy souls of the Coast of Maine Neptunes. Recently they lent their skill to fish and game authorities, who were concerned about the pollution of oysters in the Piscataqua River. The Neptunes offered to dive for oysters in a polluted area and transplant them experimentally to another place. They went into the river in two launches in November. The coffee-colored stream and its swift current had defeated previous attempts to tong the oysters from boats. A diver dropped in with a basket and a line on his waist and went slanting down in the cold racing murk. They hauled him in. He had one oyster and a ripped, waterlogged suit. They persisted in rotation, picking an oyster or two on each pass, until they had enough to satisfy the experts.

A Fort Bragg, California, club had the pleasure of saving a commercial trawler, the fifty-foot *Northern Light,* which was stoved on a rock in the Noyo River and cast upon a shoal, where she pounded in the breakers. A Coast Guard vessel and two bulldozers failed to pull her off. The divers fastened hundreds of empty oil drums on the waterlogged boat. She floated at high tide and was towed in. The club covered a man-sized hole in her bottom with plywood and canvas and the *Northern Light* was pumped out. It was a neat California demonstration of how divers can disarm antagonistic commercial fishermen. The Club de la Mer has been helping French fishermen for years. They will go out any time and dive for snagged nets, with no charge.

A decade ago underwater tourism appeared on the Côte d'Azur. Air lung instruction and diving picnics became the biggest thing since water skiing. The chic resort, Eden Roc, which once maintained croquet and bicycling professionals, now has a diving pro, the inimitable Louis Lehoux. "Loulou" has led hundreds of students down in the beautiful Eden Roc reef at Cap d'Antibes, the place where it all began with Guy Gilpatric. Loulou carries a rusty pair of scissors to cut open spiny urchins. He scoops out the meat, puts it in the pupil's hand, and gestures for him to offer it to the fish on the reef wall. The little *saupes* and *pëi-quas* eat right out of the hand. Loulou breaks off a branch of red coral as a souvenir of the first glorious dive.

The Club de la Mer runs air excursions out of Nice for hunting in the Balearics, Corsica and Djerba, the lotus eaters' island off Tunisia. Undersea picnicking extends throughout the French Union. Last year I went ashore at Grand Comore Island in the Indian Ocean. As the launch approached the snowy beach, I saw an open palm-thatched structure which I thought was a boatshed. It turned out to be the cocktail bar of the Comorienne diving club.

An ex-newspaperman named Park Breck and his wife, Jeanne, lay on air lung instruction and underwater excursions in Bermuda. They have a brightly painted truck with an air compressor and diving gear. Last year they handled a thousand people. Breck wrote me, "I imagine I have had more experience with diving psychology than almost anyone else. We are dealing with secretaries on vacation, doctors, housewives, children over fifteen, honeymooners, ex-paratroopers, etc. The other day we had a lady of sixty who was celebrating her birthday. We have had nervous tourists, who panic in three feet of water, scream at the sight of small fish, or pant their way through a bottle of air quickly through sheer insecurity. They have taught us how to teach diving." The Brecks manage your first dive in a memorable fashion, pointing out urchins, anemones, octopuses, sponges, gorgonians and brain coral. While you are feeding fish from your hand, Breck snaps a color photograph and later presents it to you.

Despite the inhospitality of her coastal waters, Britain has thousands of diving enthusiasts, who are encouraged by the Admiralty and members of Parliament. The British Sub-Aqua Club, founded in London in 1953, by N. O. Gugen and P. Small, had two thousand members by 1955, when it started a monthly paper, *Neptune*. There were seventeen branches around the British Isles. Gugen said, "Science and exploration are our main themes. It's not that we don't hold with 'messing about' underwater: let's get all the fun we can out of it. To us the real excitement lies in the opening of the undersea frontiers." In the winter the Club runs weekly training sessions in indoor swimming pools. The Club rules forbid oxygen lungs and air lungs may not be used in hunting. Sub-Aqua teams help the police in body searches. The Brighton branch has carried out a survey on seaweed for the town. In Cornwall members collected jellyfish tentacles for medical research. The Underwater Explorers Club is Britain's other large group. They are actually national federations with branches of club size.

The Union of South Africa had several thousand amateur divers by 1955, Cedric Wright reported in *The Skin Diver*. In the postwar period, when the Japanese and Mexican abalone fishery was not yet reorganized, there was a mad abalone boom in Capetown. Eighty helmet professionals harvested the monovalve in winter temperatures of 45° F. and could not supply the demand. Diving novices deserted their jobs in Capetown and ran off to sea. Five of them drowned in kelp tangles and three more were lost on a boat swamped in a storm. The abalone bubble burst inside of two years.

Bondi Beach at Sydney teems with water-loving Australians, great swimmers who are not discouraged by a dozen fatal shark attacks each year. Oddly enough, free diving in the pellucid, Australian waters did not begin until the mid-thirties when Japanese goggles led some adventurers under water. One of them was a lean, big-boned man named Donald Linklater. He got a free diving tour of the world in the Australian Army during World War II. Early in the war he was in Greece and Syria, where he went out with sponge divers. Returning home, he saw free divers in Java. The army sent him on dangerous island patrols in the islands north of Torres Strait as the Japanese invasion pressed toward Australia. Linklater and his small parties were hungry most of the time on these forays. He suggested that the army furnish goggles and spears so they could live off the sea. This seemed a bit radical, but it did give the army an idea. It gave him a new command, the Torres Strait Light Infantry Battalion. Major Linklater found it was composed of powerful, smiling Negroes. He was puzzled. Then he found out that most of them were pearl shell divers.

On an island Linklater captured some Japanese helmet diving equipment, and decided to go pearling. He put the handpump in a flat-bottomed dinghy, manned by several of his brawniest men, and jumped into sixty feet of water, wearing the helmet but not the diving suit. The tide changed and the pump began sliding back and forth. The tenders were knocked down. The pump teetered over the side and sank into the sea. Linklater was wandering a hundred yards from the boat when his air ceased abruptly. He said, "Tagai, the tender, simply hauled me hand over hand and ultimately dragged me headlong from the water. It was quite a strain on all my nose and neck bones."

As the Japanese were driven back island by island, Linklater dived close behind them. "I was an underwater fanatic," he said, "making goggles from jeep tubes and PX mirrors which had been scraped clean. On my return to Australia I was amazed to see an aquatic-minded continent with every city on the seaboard ignorant of the underwater scene. I decided to manufacture underwater masks and organize spear-fishing."

Linklater's urge was shared by many returning servicemen, who had seen their first native divers in the Pacific islands and the Mediterranean. "My cobber, Wally Gibbins," said Linklater, "is completely obsessed with the sea. Off the Great Barrier Reef, he swam almost to the limits of the Aqualung into the blue depths—for no reason except to suspend himself in the blue nothingness, by himself—and I'll drink with him anytime."

13

Twenty Thousand Years
in a Cave

T HE MOST dreadful journey for a diver is the
watery cave, where he swims blind in fear and
cold. A handful of divers have plunged through submerged doors into
rooms inside the earth and there are several diving clubs dedicated to cave
exploration. Four lives have been lost in cave dives in Britain, France and
the United States. No venture beneath the surface requires more planning,
teamwork and self-mastery.

The first cave dive on record was a *tentative* in 1773 by a naked nameless
Englishman into a siphon of Buxton Water which rises inside Peak Cavern
in Derbyshire. William Bray described it. "At a distance of about seventy-
five yards from the entrance, the rock came down so close to the water
that it precluded further passage; but as there was reason to believe from
the sound that there was a cavern beyond, a gentleman determined to try
if he could not dive under the rock and rise in the cavern beyond. He
plunged in, but, as was expected, struck his head against the rock, fell motionless to the bottom and was dragged out with difficulty."

A watery curtain barred the inner cave world until a scholarly young
French caver named Norbert Casteret pulled off a coup unique in the history
of exploration. His act of premeditated courage took place in the Grotto
of Montespan in the foothills of the French Pyrénées in 1922.

As a boy, before the First World War, Casteret had been interested only
in climbing the Pyrénées. He often passed caves without curiosity. One day

he was climbing alone above St. Gaudens when a torrential rain drove him
to cover. He ducked into a cave. "It was the first time I had entered a
grotto," he recalled, "but this one was huge enough and rugged enough to
satisfy the longings of an alpinist." The dark place inside the earth won him
away from sunlight and high snows. The war interrupted Casteret's obses-
sion; he served three years in the infantry and returned alive. He fell in
with a spelunking group in Toulouse, who were seeking in caves the secrets
of man's unwritten past.

The caves of the Pyrénées and the Dordogne, taken with several Spanish
ones, have told what we know of the early human story before land excavation and radio-carbon dating of organic materials were developed. French
caves hold a profound spell because many were inhabited and contain the
first art. At Lascaux in the Dordogne, in 1940, four boys hunting their lost
dog, tumbled into the Sistine Chapel of prehistory, dry sandstone galleries
with murals of bulls, deer, ponies and reindeer.

The first caveman statues in the round were found in the dry cave of Tuc
d'Audoubert by a professor of prehistory of the Toulouse caving group,
M. le Comte Bégouen. The Count inspired Casteret to seek further. In
August, 1922, Casteret heard of an unexplored cave at Montespan, on the
River Garonne above Toulouse. The noted cave paleontologist, Professor
Jeannel, had looked into Montespan Grotto in 1914. Casteret mounted his
bike and pedaled to Montespan. Villagers conducted him to a thickly grown
hillside, from which a small stream flowed. He could not squeeze through
the creek opening. The villagers showed him where Jeannel had entered, a
narrow dry shaft further up the slope. The professor had found a long
gallery twelve feet high, terminating in a pool of water and an impassable
wall. He had found no signs of human habitation and had written off the
cave as of no further interest. Not even a village lad had been through the
hole since. The villagers showed no interest in learning whether their
ancestors had lived there or not.

Casteret stripped to his bathing trunks, took a candle and slid down the
hole. He walked along the stream bed as the roof slanted down toward
his head. He crouched and continued in deepening water. About 185 feet
from the cave mouth he came upon the pool and saw the roof disappearing
into the water, just as Jeannel had said.

"On arriving at this discouraging spot," said Casteret, "memories of my
former explorations caused me to decide that instead of immediately leaving
the cave, as was natural under the circumstances, I would give myself over
to reflection." He got up on a rock in the posture of Rodin's thinker. "The
geologic nature of the rock led me to suppose that the stream had, perhaps,
forced itself through the limestone foundation of the hill forming an underground stream," he said. "The tiny corridor I was in was maybe the only

outlet." There might be chambers beyond. Perhaps there was a room beyond the cul-de-sac. He thought about the end of the glacial epoch, when man first appeared in the Pyrénées. The climate of that time was quite different, "a sharp, dry cold like that of modern Lapland." If the underground stream had already carved out the cave system during the rumble of glaciers, it had been dry in the time of the cavemen. He "resolved to venture further into the vitals of the mountain and into the unknown reaches of the subterranean stream."

There were problems not exactly prehistorical about it. After he ducked under the water, the submerged shaft could be endless. He might come into a dead pocket when his staying power under water was nearly gone. He might come up on the other side in time (if there was another side) and find himself in a bottomless lake in total darkness. He might come up in a vault full of poisonous air. Or perhaps he would surface in a trap of tangled branches washed into the cave.

Casteret was an extraordinary swimmer; he could stay under water holding his breath for two minutes. It was a lonely decision. There was no one outside the cave who would or could come to his aid. He dripped candle grease on a projecting rock and stood his candle. He would go without light.

He took a great breath and plunged with one hand held ahead and the other reaching up for the rock ceiling. In an instant he popped into sweet air in absolute darkness. It had only been a siphon. There was a room inside. His fears flew away, but a new anxiety seized him, that of losing his direction in the dark. He took a breath and ducked back under the transom. He picked up the candle and left the cave.

The next afternoon Casteret went alone to the manhole, undressed and hid his clothes in the bushes. He wore bathing trunks and clutched in his hand exploration equipment he had bought in the village—a rubber bathing cap, sealing-off matches and a half dozen candles. He had rejected a flashlight because he knew from experience how dry-cell batteries will suddenly conk out. It was after 4 P.M. when he left the smiling sun and heat of day, the nineteenth of August, 1922.

Again he dived under the barrier, and treaded water while lighting the candle. As far as he could see there were only black water and slimy walls. The ceiling was close to the water. Holding up his dab of flame, he swam into the dark. Four hundred feet further on his toes touched slippery clay and he clambered upon a secret shore. He was very cold, but landing eased his anxiety.

He saw the entrance of a large room, with a roof about thirty feet high. The creek was nearly lost in big rocks fallen from the roof, but fresh air played over his goose flesh. There was an air shaft somewhere. He looked around the hall and saw stalagmites growing underfoot and heard the petty chimes of waterdrops upon them. He wrote, "Never had I experienced to such a degree the feelings of isolation, of oppression, and fear such subterranean surroundings inspire, where the most banal accident, such as getting my matches wet might prove fatal." He was six hundred feet inside the grotto, known to none.

At the end of the hall he saw a thick rock pillar rising from the stream. Beside the pillar there was a deep pool and the ceiling sloped into the water. "I faced a new siphon of depressing aspect," Casteret reported. "The water was deep and the vault bristled with black and pointed stalactites." He was obsessed with siphons. Without reconnoitering the area, he filled his lungs, clutched his capful of candles and dived into the second siphon. He did not see a smaller dry gallery branching off on the other side of the pillar. "The excitement and lure of the unknown drove me on up the course of the Stygian stream," said Casteret.

The second siphon was longer than the first. At last he crawled out on a pebbly clay shingle and lighted his candle. Ahead was a cramped tunnel through which ran a watercourse. He crawled on his belly in "a gallery like a rolling mill," in a rain of drippings that several times snuffed his candle. He reached a second hall, larger than the first. Behind him through two siphons, it was a thousand feet to the manhole. The great hall was "a chaos of huge rocks," fallen from the roof. The adventurer danced to restore his circulation. He reverted to the mountaineer, scaling the boulders with slippery feet, seeking the end of the interminable great hall. Sometimes he thought he had reached the limit but "always my feeble candle lighted up Dantesque regions hitherto hidden from human eyes."

Casteret lost sense of time. He skidded ahead and came to a small gap, too small to pass him. He got his head and arm through and let out a triumphant howl. There were floating branches in the water beyond. Shoals of tadpoles exploded off his slapping hand. He knew that tadpoles do not go far into subterranean water. There had to be a sinkhole near, where air was drawn into the cave of Montespan.

Casteret could not break through to the tadpoles and he was far from the entrance. On the way back, dousing candles and relighting them, he had minutes of "agonizing uncertainty" as to the direction he should take. He stumbled out into the creek in Jeannel Hall and had trouble finding the manhole. It was night outside on the world; he had been inside the cave five hours. Casteret had covered two miles inside the earth.

The single evidence he had obtained that the cave was once probably human-inhabited was an animal tooth he had picked up. He took it to Count Bégouin, who thought it was from the prehistoric bison, *Bos primigenus*. Cattle do not frequent caves; this animal must have been slain and dragged to a cookfire in the grotto.

The next summer Casteret went back to Montespan with a caving pal named Henri Godin. The water level was so low that they swam through the first siphon holding lighted candles above water. The second siphon was still under water. But now they saw the dry gallery on the other side of the pillar. They stood in a "fairylike" foyer beneath glistening stalactites and walls shining with trickling water, on a floor of slabs with scalloped edges. And before them was a bright yellow upheaval formed into a grand stairway, patterned with watery honeycombs. They climbed barefooted into the darkness, into a curving tunnel 650 feet long, 16 feet high and 13 feet wide, paved with soft clay. They slithered on their bellies through a long low passage and entered a room where they could again stand. Casteret dug and clawed up earth, seeking a sign of humans. His hand closed on a hard object. "Even before I saw it," he said, "I knew it was a carved flint, a priceless clue for an archeologist. This simple bit of flint was incontestably fashioned and used by a human being. It proved beyond doubt that primitive man had once frequented this deep cavern."

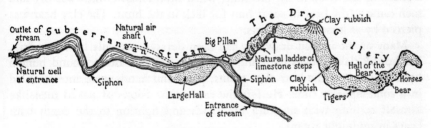

The cave of Norbert Casteret's epic adventure: Montespan Grotto, France. (Charles E. Riddiford)

Casteret took the candle to scrutinize the walls. "It was then," said Casteret, "that I stopped suddenly in front of a clay statue of a bear." It was an effigy of a crouching bear nearly four feet long and two feet high with forepaws extended in the posture of the great Sphinx of Egypt. The sculpture was encrusted with a scaling of drip water, an armor of calcite which proved its great antiquity, and between the forepaws was the skull of a bear. The statute was probably twenty thousand years old. He moved his candle and "one after another, as fast as I discovered them, I pointed out to Godin some horses molded in relief, two large lions or tigers modelled in clay and various (incised) sketches." Casteret said, "On all sides carvings of animals, sketches and mystic signs sprang to our gaze." There were fifty intaglios cut with flint tools of animals either extinct or long gone from the Pyrénées: wild horses, bison, stags, reindeer, hinds, wild asses, hyenas and the Pyrénéean chamois and ibex. One of the horses was a pregnant mare with a sign on its flank that flashed over the millennia, a human hand—Casteret thought it was Magdalenian man saying he had enslaved the horse. There was a cartoon of a mammoth, and of many animals that had been partly obliterated by the drip of water in seven million days. They found a human elbow bone in the floor and tool flints, one incorporated in a stalagmite. Deep in the last tunnel, as in the cave of Lascaux, was the only human representation of Montespan, the profile of a man with a domed head, broken nose, round lidless eye and short beard. There were thirty clay sculptures in the Hall of the Bear and a polished bone spatula, such as sculptors use. In the floor there were pits with human finger strokes where the artists had got clay. Two feline figures, nearly life size, stood in that hidden room—whether lions or tigers Casteret could not tell. The effigies were pierced and dismembered by spear thrusts. Their strongly modeled paws and claws were intact. They found no evidence of cook fires. Evidently the cave people did not live in the inner place. The clay bear and the bear skull between its paws suggested to Casteret that the statue had been covered by a bearskin and head in the old time, when Montespan Grotto was dry and men came to the bear to spear him for luck in the hunt. The clay bear was pierced by at least thirty thrusts.

Many of the incised drawings had been defaced not only by water drip, but by the claw strokes of living cave bears. Then Casteret found human hand prints over the bear claw prints; paws and hands were intermingled in a contemporary time. He left the cave with visions of naked men like himself coming with smoking firebrands and fighting to the death with bears in midnight rooms.

Casteret continued to search the caves. Just before the Second World War he attempted the subterranean river Labouiche which flows into the Ariège above Foix. In 1938 Casteret waded into the cave under low vaulting until he was stopped by rock barring the way. He could not go farther without breathing equipment. He and his comrade, Joseph Delteil, a carpenter of Foix, then roamed up country to a sinkhole at Terrefort, five miles from the impassable siphon. They lowered themselves into a narrow hole and, 130 feet down, found flowing water. They put fluoroscine dye in the stream which later came out bright green from the terminal siphon of Labouiche. Then another war interrupted Casteret's cave explorations.

The sinkhole was assaulted in 1954 by Professor Robert E. Davies, the British cave diver and a party. They went down the shaft with equipment to set up base on the streambed and inspected the downstream tunnel for the possibilities of enlarging it with dynamite. Suddenly they heard yells from the surface. "The hole is caving in!" The pair quickly got aboard ropes and were hauled out past crumbling walls. The slide blocked the shaft and buried the equipment. They cleared the hole before the main effort of the season, a joint project with the Lyon Tritons and the Pierre-St.-Martin speleological group, which included dry cavers who had descended 1,660 feet in Pierre-St.-Martin cave in the Pyrénées in 1952, the deepest cave descent ever made. That was the venture in which Marcel Loubens was killed in a fall when the cable of the electric lift parted while he was ascending.

The Anglo-French attempt in the lower cave at the first siphon was led by Casteret himself, bespectacled and graying, but as wiry and bold as the naked young man who thirty-three years before had dived into the Hall of the Bears. His deputy was Joseph Delteil, the cave-diving carpenter of Foix. Casteret, who described the expedition in a letter to the author, did not count himself among the twelve divers, perhaps because he used no breathing equipment. He dived through a siphon without it.

The international caving party gathered under a curtain of stalactites near the first siphon. The Bishop of Pamiers said a mass for the speleologists.

Five Aqualungers, led by Michel Letrône, sank into the black water, turned up their flukes and swooped under the hanging rock into the siphon. They slanted 220 feet into the gallery to a real depth of 65 feet. "But the passage became too narrow and Letrône had to turn around," Casteret said. "Our English friends, wearing closed circuit oxygen bottles which can go no lower than twelve metres were unable to dive in this siphon."

The expedition was defeated at the mouth of the underground river. They went to the Terrefort sink.

Casteret, Delteil and Davies and four English divers bent their backs under the ceiling and reached the siphon. Davies went under with a line on his waist. He came back and reported the passage was short and shallow and had brought him up in a gallery. He and the black-clad English divers went under the vault and Casteret and Delteil followed without breathing apparatus. They surfaced in a labyrinthine room and pursued the main stream for 700 feet. Casteret told me, "We came to a second siphon that could not be crossed. In short, the Labouiche Expedition ended in failure, which is often the case with siphons. And there you have what we did, or at least what we could not do, at Labouiche."

Graham Balcombe and J. A. Sheppard were Britain's first modern cave divers. In 1934 Balcombe built a "crazy" respirator out of an old bicycle frame and forty feet of garden hose and plunged into a scummy pool two thousand feet inside Swildon's Hole in Somersetshire. He wore a nose clip, goggles and a flashlight strapped on his forehead. The water was very cold with a few feet of visibility and bubbles of marsh gas rising to the surface. Suddenly his light went out. He started up and the light came on again. Then he discovered he had been immersed in mud. "Cold water and my nervy condition quickly reduced me to a state of uncontrollable shivering," he said. He surfaced and ran out of the cave, trying to get warm. Sheppard reassembled the apparatus and went down into a constricted passage. His air pipe jerked free and he barely got out with his life.

The next year the pair took helmet diving suits and a pump and attempted Wookey Hole cavern in Somersetshire, from which arises the River Axe. The first two dry rooms had yielded Iron Age and Romano-British pottery fragments, indicating that it had been inhabited for centuries well into the Christian era. The third chamber, a wet one, is five hundred feet from the cave mouth. Six divers, including Penelope Powell, the pioneer cave diver of the sex, made a base in the Third Chamber and passed into Chamber Five. They got through a short passage sixteen feet down into room six, and penetrated a seventh room. The sensation of these dives was described by Miss Powell: "Leaving the surface and the dazzling glare of the powerful lights and slipping down from the enveloping brown atmosphere, we suddenly entered an utterly different world, a world of green, where the water was as clear as crystal. Imagine a green jelly, where even the shadows cast by the pale green boulders are green but of a deeper hue; as we advanced, light green mud rose knee-high and fell softly and gently into the profound greenness behind. So still, so silent, unmarked by the foot of man since the river came into being, awe-inspiring though not terrifying, it was like being in some mighty and invisible presence, whose only indication was this saturating greenness."

The British Cave Diving Group, founded in 1946, is the world's best trained, although it has clung to oxygen lungs, which limit its depth to thirty feet. The members prefer oxygen gear because it is less bulky than the compressed-air lung. The Group consists of amateurs who dive on week ends and vacations. They have invented a wonderful all-out comfort for the cave diver, called the Aflo. It is a portable assembly of an electric light and battery, windlass, compass, depth meter, watch, plastic writing pad, signaling horn, thermometer, spare light bulbs and a phone connection. Everything but a beer pull. Wookey Hole has been their academy of wet speleology. It is a tourist cave whose proprietor has enthusiastically fostered the dives. There is no sight quite like a hooded man disappearing into a Stygian pool, and no movie suspense like waiting for his reappearance.

The Cave Diving Group includes Somerset and Derbyshire sections. In 1947 they pushed the conquest of the Wookey Hole cavern to the deep Eighth Chamber and emerged in a large room. There they set up an advanced base with emergency food and oxygen supplies for six divers. They found that the cave system turned back on itself in a wishbone shape, so that the ninth room was near the first, although a thousand feet by galleries from the cave mouth. At this writing Wookey Hole exploration has come to a serious impasse in the Eleventh Chamber, which is entirely under water with no shores on which to set up an advanced base. This room is walled in limestone, below the level of the later Triassic Conglomerate rocks of the first ten chambers.

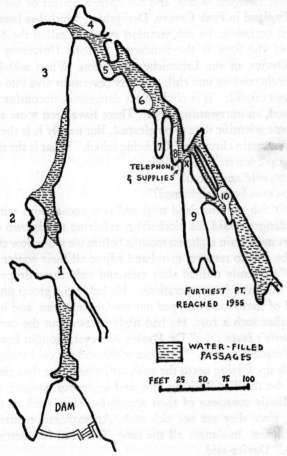

Plan of the ten rooms reached in Wookey Hole cave, Somersetshire. (Cave Diving Group)

The Somerset Section has concentrated on the archeology of Wookey Hole, scouring the river bottom between the mouth and the Third Chamber and excavating the sand banks with water jets. They have found Romano-British pots, lead ewers, fourteen human skulls and assorted bones, and two seventeenth-century glass bottles. If this adventure is interrupted by an atom war, we may expect that insect archeologists of the future will find some lime juice bottles left by the divers and conclude that the extinct species lived in caves throughout its rise, flourish and fall.

The Group has attacked a dozen grottoes, including Carlswark Cave, Bagshawe Cavern, Black Keld, Malham Cove and Giant's Hole and Ffynnon Ddu, Swansea, Wales, and has opened up one of the biggest cave systems in England in Peak Cavern, Derbyshire, which has been penetrated through nine entrances. Its subterranean stream is called the Styx. One of the divers of the Styx is the handsome Oxford University biochemist, Robert E. Davies, of the Labouiche expedition. When asked the reason people lower themselves into chill, slippery caverns to dive into dark waters, Dr. Davis was candid: "It is obviously a dangerous, uncomfortable and, to the uninitiated, an unrewarding sport. There have been some archeological finds and some scientific data to be gleaned. But mostly it is the exploratory urge—like mountain climbing." On being asked, "What is the most striking thing about cave water?" he replied:

"It is silent, cold and green."

"Have you ever been frightened?"

"You can't fish out one dead man and two unconscious without appreciating the danger," said the biochemist, referring to his own experiences. "Newcomers must train eighteen months before we will allow them to dive. They must be able to remove, mend and adjust all their equipment in total darkness. We recently trained sixty men and only three dropped out. But they fall by the wayside on operations." He held up a group photograph of divers. "All of these have dropped out now, except him, and he will soon. His wife makes such a fuss. He had nightmares about the caves. And, of course, the wife's fears . . ." Dr. Davies, however, thought feminine cavers were just as capable as men. "They can withstand the cold water. You can't divide people up. Diving needs the analytical type rather than the emotional.

"Part of the thrill is devising new and ingenious gadgets. Cave divers are tremendously conscious of their apparatus. They work to make things at low cost, since they are not rich men. An exploration may go on for twenty-four hours. In danger all the time. The need for alertness goes on all the time," Davies said.

Cousteau, Tailliez and Dumas have graphically reported their famous 1947 dives into the Fountain of Vaucluse in *The Silent World* and *To Hidden Depths*. They inspired a series of wet cave explorations, despite the weird accident that nearly finished the divers. The compressor used to fill their air bottles sucked in its own exhaust fumes and stupefied them with carbon monoxide hundreds of feet down the slanting water-filled tunnel. Dumas was brought up unconscious by Cousteau, who was himself almost gone. While still under water, Cousteau could not avoid vomiting. He retained a firm bite on his mouthpiece and the contents of his stomach

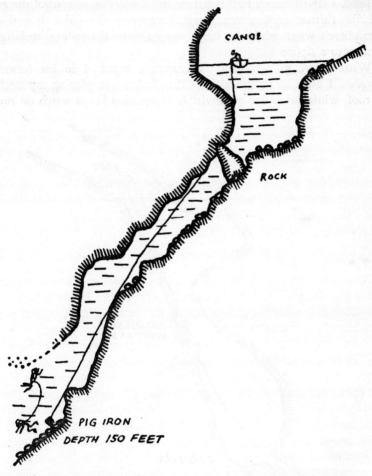

Profile of Cousteau and Dumas' dive in the Fountain of Vaucluse, France, 1947.

passed out through an air vent the size of a paper clip and through the demand regulator without blocking it. Such unforeseen factors as the treacherous compressor add to the cave diver's "heightened subjectivity," as one of them has defined fright. Few of them will bother denying that they are thoroughly scared most of the time.

After Vaucluse, Maurice Fargues led an expedition to the fountain of Chartreux near Cahors with Lieutenant Guy Morandière and Guy de Lavaur, president of the Spéléo-Club de Paris. One hundred and twenty feet down they established an underwater station. They took down an elec-

tric light, a signal buzzer to the surface and a windlass to control the guide
rope for further explorations. Fargues unreeled the guide line tied to
Morandière's waist, while the latter swam around the ceiling, seeking the
entrance to a siphon.

"What a strange sensation," Morandière reported in his *carnet de
plongée*. "I glide on my back above the black abyss, playing my torch on
the roof, while below me my invisible companion keeps watch on my se-

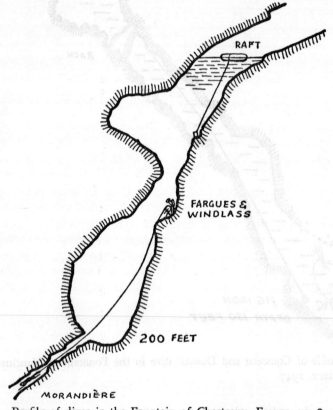

Profile of dives in the Fountain of Chartreux, France, 1948.

curity. In the chaos of the immense vault I hope at any moment to pop into
the air of an unexplored room. Sometimes I am held back by the traction on
my belt. My line gets snagged on rock needles, sharp as sabers. Once my
light outlines the silhouette of a twenty-inch fish. So I am not alone in the
kingdom of gloom. The thought is not comforting. In the blackness there
might be unknown, invisible bodies. I prefer total solitude.

"At one point I feel a strong fear that stops my progress. Near me I see a long silvery snake, wriggling across the ceiling and vanishing into a crevice. I admit that at that moment I am not proud to be facing the unknown fauna of the caves. I swim on a few yards and see another reptile rushing toward me, a ghastly transparent form wriggling across the ceiling. I inspect it with my lamp and laugh at myself. The snake is a stream of my own exhaust bubbles, overflowing from a pocket in the roof, and seeking another hole."

Morandière could not find a passage through the roof, but on a subsequent dive he located a gallery behind a huge hanging rock near the floor. With Fargues feeding him line from the windlass, Morandière passed behind the rock and followed a tunnel sloping sharply down. The water was muddy and the rock wall seemed loose. Morandière was afraid to kick his fins for fear he would start a cave-in. He proceeded down on a slow glide, sinking by his ballast. "I deeply feel that I am acting foolishly in dropping into the immense black throat," he reported. "Dull teeth seem to be waiting for the slightest misstep that will make a mouthful out of me, to be slowly digested by the monster cave. But how can I surface if I had found nothing to report? Rapture of the deep overtakes me. I can feel with my body that I am away below two hundred feet. My breathing is easy, slow and complete. I keep the precious air in my lungs fully ten seconds before exhaling, in order to get the best out of my cylinders, I wonder how long it has been since I entered the phantom glide. I do not know.

"I am shaken out of my revery when the guide rope tightens behind me. It is fouled on something. I turn around with extreme care and reel it in over my elbow until I have retraced five meters. The rope is wedged in a rock fissure. Slowly and gently I free the line. Instantly it is jerked from above. Fargues is giving the emergency signal.

"I climb up the rocky throat hand over hand, and risk kicking my fins to get more speed. I swim across the cavern floor and see that a cloud of dust obscures Fargues and the windlass. I swim into the dust and dimly behold Fargues. He touches the emergency valve on his Aqualung to tell me that his air is almost gone. My own inhalations are becoming difficult. We conduct a confused battle to recover our equipment, jettison our ballast, and turn on the emergency air supply. We ascend as swiftly as possible. When we break water there are only a few breaths in the cylinders."

In 1948 French wet cavers mounted the biggest of cave expeditions in the subterranean spring of Viterelles, near Gramat, led by three members of the Navy Undersea Group (G.E.R.S.) with a section of army engineers. They lowered base camping gear nearly four hundred feet in a vertical dry hole, and carried it sixteen hundred feet through a semiflooded gallery, before they reached the pool in which they dived. Lieutenant Jean Alinat, in charge of diving, sent the underwater explorers in a series of mapping

dives in a long gallery filled with water, each man on a safety line of progressively greater length. Alinat himself made the tenth and ultimate dive
on a 400-foot line and passed up a cramped inclined tunnel into the air
of an enormous clay room, where he found still another siphon at the far
end. To press further meant lugging the base camp underwater to the room
2,550 feet from the earth's surface. Alinat called it a day.

The great city of Lyon on the rushing Rhone has developed a cave diving
group called the Tritons who have, since 1952, systematically explored a
subterranean river in the La Balme Grotto, on the left bank of the river.

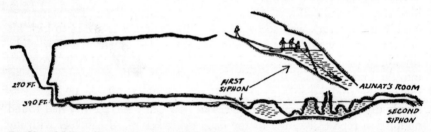

Profile of Vitarelles cave, scene of the largest wet cave expedition, 1948. Note
detail of first siphon showing diving base with rubber rafts and ladder. Beyond
the siphon is last room attained by Lt. Jean Alinat.

They first penetrated a dangerous siphon and came upon a big hidden lake
inside the earth. Working with the city fire department the Tritons developed and tested waterproof lighting and telephonic equipment, which
was set up in the inner room. In 1955, Messrs. Lêtrone, Cachet and Bonne-
valle plunged 265 feet through the second siphon to a room, which they
named the Hall of Hope. At its deepest end there were two galleries, one
dry and the other leading to a third siphon. They have since packed their
base under water to the Hall of Hope over six hundred feet from the cave
mouth and are training divers for the next assault.

A twenty-year-old marine biology student of Stanford University named
Jon Lindbergh made the first U.S. cave dive in 1953. The place was Bower
Cave in the Mother Lode country of northern California, a commercial
resort since gold-mining days. In the cool depths of the huge foyer an
early proprietor erected a dance platform on the edge of a pool. Across
the pool were mysterious fretted niches shadowing the water, but there was
no sight of the siphon which let water into the limestone pool. A San Fran-
cisco speleologist, Raymond de Saussure, was convinced there was a hidden
chamber beyond, and organized an expedition. Lindbergh volunteered as
diver and went alone.

In March Lindbergh reconnoitered the pool and found an underwater entrance to an inner cavern. This was kept out of the papers, no doubt because it would have fetched a tumbling band of reporters, cameramen and announcers. The diver's father is well known and the son was doing this seriously on his own. In May, Lindbergh prepared to enter the inner cavern. He wore a hooded rubber suit for warmth, a single-bottle Aqualung, two emergency oxygen bottles and a small rubber packet which inflates with compressed carbon dioxide to buoy up a diver in distress. He carried a six-inch trench knife and a submersible flashlight. The plan called for two dives. On the first he was to swim into the cave with a collapsed rubber boat and inflate it as a photographic perch for the second dive.

"I entered the water and went down to look around," he said. "I found a big chamber that apparently became larger. With a flashlight I can see between 25 and 50 feet, depending on how clear the water is. I swam about 150 feet under the limestone wall blocking the cave entrance at the surface and came up in the middle of the cavern's air chamber. You can tell if there is air over you if the bubbles from your exhaust cause ripples on the surface when they break out of the water or you can tell by simply following the wall up to the air pocket. It has a distinctive sheen inside the cave."

The explorer found that dim sunlight was reflected into the inner chamber through the underwater entrance. He surfaced in a large room hung with brilliant stalactites and crystalline drapery, then sank to inflate his raft. He released the carbon dioxide and the raft swelled so big he thought it was going to explode. He quickly valved off pressure. The carbon dioxide bottle was too large for the one-man raft. He said, "If the raft had exploded it wouldn't have been serious but would have interfered with our plans."

With his raft afloat, he turned up his flukes and slid down through the clear water toward the cave entrance, which was about thirty feet high and festooned with sharp pendants. Lindbergh had a light nylon safety line around his waist, extending to his companions outside. He snagged the line several times, but cleared it and broke up through the pool safely.

The next day he put a small camera and flash reflector in plastic bags, tied them to his flashlight and plunged into the pool to photograph the inner hall. He passed the bristling door and swam down in the hidden lake to a depth of 120 feet, without sighting bottom. He said, "I found I had difficulty concentrating on more than one thing. I looked at the depth gauge and would forget about the rope. I would remember the rope with something of a shock. As soon as I went to a depth of 60 feet, there was no trouble at all." He may have had a touch of nitrogen narcosis.

Above him was the pale oval of the raft, easily sighted. He surfaced and got his leg over the side of the raft. It filled with water. He towed the flooded raft to the cave wall and moored it on a stalagmite so that it would

not drift while he attempted to bail it out. He removed some of his encumbrances to do the job, his belt weights, which he put in the bottom
of the raft, and his Aqualung, which he tied alongside. The only bailing
implement he had was his mask. He removed it and started scooping out
water. While bailing he smashed the glass in his mask.

He would be partially blind on the exit, with his precious underwater
optical system broken. He sat in the raft and considered his situation.
"Then I discovered that I had a hole about the size of a playing card in
the bottom of my suit. I put everything in my lap and unpacked the camera
gear and got ready for the picture. I didn't notice the boat rocking much
but I took some pictures at 1/25th of a second and this probably accounts
for the fuzziness."

He methodically shot a roll of film and repacked his photographic equipment. Holding his nose he left the raft and dived for the blurred door
and its menacing spurs. "I could see only moderately well without the face
plate but had no trouble finding the entrance," he reported. "The hole in
the seat was an inconvenience but no great problem. I shipped a bit of
water in the suit and was pretty well soaked."

With a tire patch on his bottom, Lindbergh strapped on another mask
and fresh air bottle and swam three hundred feet inside the cave. He felt
dizzy and got out of the cave. He says he would like to go back sometime
and get the raft.

Jon Lindbergh's *sang-froid* overcame the dangers of Bower Cave, but
two young naval reservists of Macon, Georgia, were not so lucky. Lieutenant Murray Anderson and electronics man Donald Gerue began free diving in 1954. By this time the do-it-yourself craze had reached diving apparatus and Anderson built his own fifty dollar lung from a surplus Air
Force oxygen demand regulator. The aviation regulator was designed for
breathing in very low pressures of the substratosphere, not in the rapidly
increasing pressures of the water. Nonetheless, hundreds of these regulators
were built into diving lungs from plans in home workshop magazines.
Several died wearing them. Gerue used a manufactured compressed-air
lung, which provided a breathing supply for a half hour in shallow water.

The two had a fine initiation in the sea at St. Mark's Light off the Florida
coast, and had built up a team experience of four months, when Anderson's
wife, Betty, said she had heard of inner caverns under Radium Springs,
near Albany, Georgia, the papershell pecan and peanut capital of the
world. The Creek Indians had called it Blue Springs, but when, some years
ago, the papers came out with the news of Madame Curie's elixir, local
land agents decided what they had in the springs was radium. A hotel and
bathing beach give on a circular pond which has an islet in the middle. A
tributary of the Flint River rises out of Radium Springs. "A fashionable

resort has grown up around the entire area and so there was a great deal of interest in our diving there." Gerue told the story of Radium Springs to his friend, Professor Delvin Covey, of Wesleyan College, Macon, for this book.

"We made our first trip to the springs during March, 1955," Gerue began. "Between then and May 14 we made seven trips. On our first dive we went only as far as the end of the first corridor. The first part of the descent is made through a boil in the pool, about twenty-eight feet deep.

"The boil is all rock with about four feet of silt on the floor. The silt looked hard packed and sandy but changed and became cloudy at the slightest movement. As we swam, our fins stirred up clouds so that we could not see what was behind, but the visibility ahead was good. The rocks are very sharp and light brown in color.

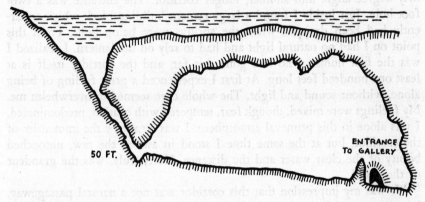

50 FT.

ENTRANCE TO GALLERY

Profile of underwater cavern at Radium Springs, Georgia, where Donald Gerue and Murray Hamilton dived.

"We saw only rock bass and some small, fresh water eels in the way of animal life. As far as we could tell there was no vegetation, but there must have been some sort of fungus growth on the rocks; for any abrasions made by hitting them began to swell almost immediately and soon became infected.

"At the bottom of the boil there is the entrance of a passage which declines at about a forty-five degree angle. This passage-way is about thirty feet long and six feet in diameter. It reaches, at the end of the decline, a depth of fifty feet. We had to stop at the end of the passage on our first dive, because we had no lights; and all natural light stops at that point. In all we made about sixty dives and always went down together. Each time we explored slightly farther than we had gone on previous dives.

"When we went for our last dive Murray and I were using the same equipment we had used from the first. His homemade open circuit breathing apparatus holds forty-four cubic feet of air, which is a sufficient supply for about twelve or fifteen minutes at the depth to which he had gone. However, it has no air reserve, and this flaw may have been the cause of his death.

"Our additional equipment consisted of Navy battle lanterns, a depth gauge, divers' knives and weighted belts. We were using a Cornelius three-stage compressor and had also three hundred-cubic-feet tanks of compressed air. I was wearing a Pirelli short rubber suit and fins, but Murray wore only swimming trunks and fins.

"I made the first dive that day and can report only my own impressions and observations, since Murray's dives cost him his life.

"When I reached the lowest point in the passage, I turned left at a fifty degree angle into another, longer corridor. The entrance was a two-foot hole. Just inside I found a large cement building block which apparently had been dropped when the springs were being built. From this point on I had no natural light and had to rely on my lantern. I realized I was the first human who had gone this far, and the corridor itself is at least one hundred feet long. At first I experienced a great feeling of being alone, without sound and light. The whole cave seemed to overwhelm me. My feelings were mixed, though fear, tempered with caution, predominated. I was alone in this primeval atmosphere. I was struck by the immensity of the corridor, but at the same time I stood in awe at the raw, untouched beauty of the clear water and the distance. Here, truly, was the grandeur of the deep!

"It was my impression that this corridor was not a natural passageway, but was caused by some cataclysmic action many hundreds of years ago. The rocks are generally of the same composition as those on the first passage and are extremely jagged. As much as I could tell by artificial light they are light brown in color, flecked with white and black. They are quite porous and absorbed all air bubbles almost immediately. The roof in this passage is about forty feet high.

"The depth at the end of the corridor is seventy feet, and it appeared to me that this is the deepest spot in the whole cave. At this point there is a large, egg-shaped chamber on the left. Just at the left side of the entrance I found a large, jagged rock. I tied off my rope here and went back to tell Murray what I had found. To this point I had used about one hundred and seventy feet of the rope. I had been down in the cave about twenty minutes.

"On shore I sat talking with Murray for about a half hour while I rested and had my air supply replenished. Again I decided to go ahead and told Murray to follow when my silt had settled enough for him to see. I waited at the tie-off for about fifteen minutes, but he didn't come down to me. I saw his light at the end of the corridor, however. When I went back up for more air, he told me the silt hadn't cleared enough and so he had gone back. By this time the sun was about ready to set. I went back into the cave to untie the rope so we could go home.

"Along the passageways the water seemed to be flowing at the rate of one knot. In the small passage openings and in the chamber the flow got up to about four knots, and I had to pull myself along on the rocks. After about twenty-five minutes of looking around, I turned to go out, taking the rope with me. Just then I saw a light coming into the corridor and waited at the rock. Though I didn't know why Murray had changed his mind about coming into the cave, I was not concerned about it. He looked around at me as he swam past, and I made some remark about the size of the cave. He nodded assent and swam on into the chamber at the left. By this time I had had to turn on my reserve supply of air, so I flashed my light to signal that I was leaving. I cannot be sure he was aware I was leaving. However, he must have known that it was time for my air to be running out. I lay the rope down inside the chamber and followed it back out.

"I waited outside for about two minutes and said to some of the boys there that Murray should be coming out. Already I had a premonition of something wrong. Within another five minutes I went back. In the long corridor the water was very cloudy with silt, and I could see no more than six inches ahead. I followed the rope along the corridor, calling, but Murray did not answer. My air gave out and I had to hurry back to the surface again. It took about five minutes to refill the lung, and I went back down to the rock where I had made my tie-off.

"I held onto the rope, swimming in every direction and calling for Murray. Again my air was giving out, and I had to get out. The boys on the bank had felt my tug at the rope and thought I wanted more slack, so they fed it to me. Then I knew that I, too, stood every chance of being lost. I had to fight down a growing fear and panic. I finally had to sit on the floor, taking in a bit of rope at a time until I found out which way it led. When I came out I had spent a total of two and a half hours at a depth of seventy feet in 68° water and could not go down again. I was cold, tired, and frightened; and I knew that Murray was dead.

"We called two Navy divers from Charleston, South Carolina, and they found Murray at about 6:30 the next morning, on their first dive, about six feet from the end of the rope and in approximately the place where I had last seen him. I must have gone past him several times, but could not see him because the water was so cloudy from the silt he had kicked up."

14

Senses of the Deep

NINETEENTH-CENTURY depth explorers, such as Sir John "Challenger" Murray, Professor Wyville Thomson, Louis Agassiz and Albert of Monaco used specimen nets and sampling and measuring instruments lowered patiently from ships. These devices were fingers of the blind. Today electronic ears and eyes are scouting ahead of man's actual advent in the deep. The first of the new ideas was seeing with sound.

The 1914 graduating class of the Friends' School in Washington, D.C., was gathered on a May day to hear the commencement address. The speaker was a tall old man with a sunburned face, a grand white beard and a shock of white hair. He did not inflict upon the boys and girls a homily on Youth's Need for Spiritual Rebirth. He started right out, "Did you ever put your head underwater and chuck two stones together to see what the sound is like?" The Class of '14 sat forward to hear this novel approach by the distinguished guest, Alexander Graham Bell.

Dr. Bell said as a boy he had clicked stones under water and was startled at the loud report. He sent another boy up the beach a piece to smack pebbles under water and found that he could hear them clearly with his ear submerged. He sent another boy a half mile across the bay and distinctly heard his stones. In fact, said the inventor of the telephone, with slow emphasis: "*There is a whole world of sound beneath the waves waiting to be explored. I have often thought I should like to go on the banks of New-foundland and fish with a telephone. If you were to send a transmitter down among the codfish with bait, perhaps you would find something there to hear. I have never tried it. I leave that to you.*

"Three quarters of the earth's surface is underwater and has not been explored to any great degree. The only way we have of reaching the mountains and valleys at the bottom of the sea is by sending down a sounding line and bringing up a specimen of the bottom attached to the sinker. It is no joke, however, to reach the bottom of the deep blue sea through one mile or even two miles of water and it takes several hours to make a single sounding.

"Why should we not send down a sound instead and listen for an echo from the bottom? Knowing the velocity of sound in water [averages 4,920 feet a second—J.D.] and the time taken for the echo to reach the ear, we should be able to ascertain the depth of the deepest part of the ocean in seconds instead of hours. Here is something worth doing. It has never been tried."

Unknown to Dr. Bell, it had already been accomplished. In 1911 the French physicist Paul Langevin and his Russian colleague, Chilovsky, built an electric ultrasound detector with which they tracked a submarine cruising beneath Brest harbor. Chilovsky had found the principle years earlier, but could not interest the Russian Government. Indeed, just a month before the Friends' School commencement, a brilliant, red-headed giant with a spiky beard and powerful spectacles, Reginald A. Fessenden, had detected submerged icebergs and made acoustic soundings to eight thousand feet in the very Grand Banks Dr. Bell talked about.

Fessenden was a fighting bull. Son of a Canadian country rector, he bucked through heavy lines of business men with his ideas. He was so nearsighted his naked eyes were microscopic. Behind deep lenses they swept the world like lighthouse beacons. He started out as chief chemist for Thomas A. Edison in the 1880's and in 1900 invented a radio receiver. In 1906 he built a radio station at Brant Rock, near Plymouth, Massachusetts, and talked by radio telephone with a Plymouth trawler at sea. Her skipper did not give a history book utterance. He asked Fessenden the price for cod on the Boston Fish Pier.

The first year Fessenden broadcast a Christmas concert, he himself rendering "Silent Night" on the fiddle. It was heard on ships in the West Indies. Brant Rock was financed by Pittsburgh money men, who decided to lose Fessenden. They tricked him away on a business call and sent a gang to seize the radio station. Mrs. Fessenden barricaded the place and summoned a posse which ran the Pittsburgh delegation off the rock. The ensuing lawsuit ran twenty years, with Fessenden taking on all comers. Company after company folded or merged as the radio industry grew. Finally Fessenden was in court against the titans. He won three million dollars from them.

Back when the *Titanic* crashed the iceberg, Fessenden was one of the engineers who sprang forward with iceberg detectors. The situation was a typical one in the history of safety at sea. Existing protective devices were ignored by steamship companies until they struck disaster. Before the *Titanic* sinking in 1912, Fessenden had allied himself with a farsighted engineer and business man, Harold Fay, of the Submarine Signal Company in Boston. They built an oscillator which fanned out underwater code signals in a radius of fifty miles from lightships. They envisioned a "wall of sound" to warn ships off shoals and rocks. Fessenden converted the oscillator to bounce sound off an iceberg into a receiver on the sending ship. He called it a "singing sounder" and tested it on the U.S. Coast Guard cutter *Miami*. He detected icebergs two miles away. Captain J. H. Quinan, of *Miami*, said, "The echoes were not only heard through the receivers in the wireless room, but were plainly heard in a storeroom below the waterline." The device was more effective as a bottom sounder, however. Fessenden demonstrated the singing sounder in Boston Harbor to the press, and parties of Japanese and Argentinians. He installed one in a submarine and it worked beneath the surface. When World War I came, he hurried to England and demonstrated the "wall of sound" on H.M.S. *Vernon* in October, 1914. For an unknown reason he was not permitted to show the iceberg detector. He protested that it was equally useful for locating German submarines. Winston Churchill, then First Lord of the Admiralty, seems not to have known of the affair, for he was exactly the type to grab it. Fessenden's detector lay untouched at Portsmouth until January, 1917, while U-boats almost strangled England, sinking up to £1 million in shipping each day. To cap this weird incident, a submarine signal delegation sold Fessenden's invention to the Germans in 1914. Fessenden was not with the party. The Germans standardized all detection equipment on poor frequency and it never worked.

Back home, with United States at war, Fessenden collided with a phalanx of dollar-a-year men, the Special Navy Board on Submarine Devices. They excluded him from the committee on underwater sound and issued a directive that no information was to be given him. He received a consolatory note:

"You are not the only one who is being turned down. Up to date everything I have done has been turned down and I think this is true of all the others. [Signed] Edison."

The combat navy was desperate for U-boat hunting devices. One device used by destroyers escorting convoys was the "binaural," or two-ear listening set. Hydrophones in the water on either side of the ship's bows were wired back to two trombones in the chart room. An operater stuck the trombone mouthpieces in either ear. When he picked up U-boat noises, he pushed and pulled the trombone slides to speed up or retard the reception of the sound. The rate at which it arrived in either ear indicated the direction of the submarine. Fessenden said this sort of thing was gorgeous nonsense; his automatic detector gave continuous signals and revealed each move of the invisible U-boat.

Fessenden bellowed at the Navy Sound Committee, but they had their ear sets tuned out. He went to an embattled admiral and offered a free demonstration. The admiral let him install equipment in the U.S.S. *Aylwin* in Boston in November, 1917. The Sound Committee heard about it and forbade the test. The admiral said, "Hell, Doc, go ahead anyway." The professor agreed to the toughest test the admiral could think of. Fessenden and his operators were closeted with the sounder in a windowless room on the *Aylwin*. They could not see the water or the compass, and could not hear orders. A submarine was to run a prescribed course, known to the *Aylwin* but not to Fessenden. Afterward his detector log had to check with the submarine's course.

The game of blind man's bluff started. Fessenden called out the submarine's whereabouts for hours. Then he said to the skipper, "The submarine is in position to be depth-bombed." The captain replied, "Doc, her course is a half mile off to port." Fessenden said, "I beg your pardon. She is now directly beneath us." The echo-sound operator yelled, "Quiet! Listen to this!" They heard five strokes of a bell, the submarine's signal to surface. The ringing was right underneath the *Aylwin*. The submarine was rising straight for them. The skipper pelted to the bridge and eased off. The submarine surfaced close alongside. She had been unwittingly carried under the *Aylwin* in a current. Despite this spectacular show, the detector was not taken up by the Navy, although it was installed in the S.S. *Leviathan* in 1928.

Fessenden was a convivial soul. During prohibition he studied brewing, chemically analyzed his water and turned out the nearest thing to beer in Boston. In 1921 he was awarded the gold medal of the Radio Institute, which pleased him mightily, since Guglielmo Marconi had received it only the year before. Fessenden thought the medal looked funny. He suspected that Marconi's medal was solid gold and his was dross. He sent his prize to the Government Assay Office which confirmed his suspicion. Fessenden hurled the medal all the way to Philadelphia with a letter demanding the Institute purge his name from its rolls. The radio engineers knew their fighting Fessenden. They called in the previous medals, had them assayed and showed the professor they were all equally cheap. Fessenden rejoined the Institute. His last invention was microfilm photography for preserving books and documents. He retired to Bermuda and spent his last years promulgating cockeyed ideas on ancient civilizations.

As far back as the 1850's that strange and tragic genius, Lieutenant Matthew Fontaine Maury, U.S.N. tried to determine the depths of the ocean with echo-sound. Maury was the first Navy hydrographer, a cripple who compiled the first charts of the North Atlantic from thousands of random hempline soundings by ships of many countries. He went over to the Confederacy during the Civil War and invented electrical mines to use against Union blockaders. His defection removed him from further influence on ocean science. Maury attempted echo-sounding by exploding dynamite under water and listening for the echo. William Ryan, one of the designers of the first cathode-ray tube sounder in 1946 which brought echo gear within range of the private boatman's pocketbook, said, "Although Maury didn't hear the echo, he had the right answer. He had everything but the vacuum tube. His signal was too weak. Today we have to amplify the sound over a million times to receive echoes."

In 1919, Britain brought Professor Paul Langevin and his assistant, Dr. Charles Florisson, from France to join experiments on the first Royal Navy "Asdic" submarine detectors. The name comes from the Anti-Submarine Detection Investigation Committee for which the French scientists worked. The American counterpart is "sonar" for Sound Navigation and Ranging. The first practical sea-going echo-sounder was the work of a delightful and diminutive senior scientist of the U.S. Coast and Geodetic Survey, Herbert Grove Dorsey. In the early twenties Dr. Dorsey built what he called a "fathometer," which gave depths by translating the echoes visually to a rotating flashing neon light. Dr. Dorsey took ship hundreds of times to test the device, despite his total proneness to seasickness. During a voyage, he would lie down on the chart-room floor under the sounder, and watch the neon light in a shaving mirror.

The greatest increment of fish since the miracle at Cana came about *anno domini* 1933, when Captain Ronald Balls, of Great Yarmouth, Norfolk, installed Dorsey's fathometer in his trawler. He bought the bottom detector as a navigational aid. Balls watched the neon whirligig constantly to compile of mental profile of bottom. Many times he noticed that blips flared in midwater. Something interfered with the sound waves between the boat and the bottom. Was it fish? Balls consulted Dr. W. C. Hodgson, of the Lowestoft Fisheries Laboratory, who believed that fish might reflect sound and suggested that the skipper drop a trawl net when he saw the mysterious blips. Captain Balls was already an expert at a form of sound detection used by the Norwegians. The master seiner of a fishing boat went out in a dory and lowered a plummet on piano wire. He placed his ear against the wire and felt it for the vibrations of crowded fish striking the wire. Balls had the imagination to go further, and try to detect fish on an echo-sounder.

The result was sensational. In the same period off North Shields that Balls' crew hauled 2,000 pounds of herring in 400 net shots *without* echo-sounder, they took 4,400 pounds in 70 shots with the sounder. Echo-sound brought up twelve times as many fish as random casts.

A Norwegian biologist, Oscar Sund, thought that fish shoals would also show up on a recording echo-sounder, one that translated the stream of pings to a continuous drawing of floor contours and intervening objects. Professor Sund promoted money to buy a Marconi sounder and put it on the oceanographic vessel, the *Johan Hjort*. In the Lofoten grounds, he obtained the earliest fish trace, a level stratum of spawning cod. He showed the picture to the commercial fishermen. They did not believe a machine could locate fish. Sund convinced several masters to give it a try. They came home with vast hauls and the others hastened to get echo-sounders.

Aboard the *Johan Hjort*, Gunnar Rollefsen worked out a clever way to locate rich prawn beds. Prawns and other bottom dwellers could not be detected by sonar, but Dr. Rollefsen discovered they gave themselves away just the same. He noticed that the sound impulse sometimes pictured the floor and also penetrated further and drew a line of bedrock as well. He found this always meant a soft clay bed. Prawns live on clay beds. Rollefsen suggested to the fishermen that when the sounder showed double bottom, they lower prawn trawls. It brought about a new multimillion dollar prawn fishery in south Norway.

New England fishermen were the last to adopt echo-sounding. Some masters privately acknowledged the effectiveness of sonar, but publicly opposed it on the argument that the gadget would demean a fisherman's secret handed down for generations of *how to smell invisible shoals of fish*! Roy Wittick, a big buyer on the Boston Fish Pier, pestered the skippers for years to install Ryan's "fishscope." Not until 1954 did one give in. His trawler came in days early from Brown's Bank, after the first cruise with the suspicious gadget. Fish bulged from the iceholds. The other skippers sliced open their mattresses for money to buy the new fish smeller. Even more responsive were "Newfy John" from Newfoundland and the masters of the Nova Scotian fishery.

British and Norwegian scientists and fishermen carried echo-fishing to the ultimate refinement: they learned how to recognize the exact species showing on the graph. In January, North Sea sprats gave a comet-shaped trace. Herrings off Fraserburgh formed plumed silhouettes. Mackerel registered a thin character with striated marks. The identifications were checked by sampling nets and jerking a "ripper," a cluster of hooks, through the shoal. California salmon trollers learned from the research vessel, the *Scofield*, that salmon made small pips on the fathometer, while sardines showed a solid wide flash. These identifications were made by vertical sounders. The ship had to be directly over the fish to pick up a trace. Japanese and Norwegian experimenters then detected fish in a much greater area with oblique sounders, which picked them up nearly a mile away.

Today the Norwegian fleet follows a tactical plan. Charts of the fishing grounds are overlaid with numbered squares. A fast sounding boat sails across the squares, radioing to the other boats the numbers which show promising fish traces. Each trawler makes for her allotted grid, stops down and sends the master seiner out in a motor launch with a small hypersensitive detector, which he lowers in the water to find the *thickest* part of the shoal. Only then do the trawlers cast their nets. The Norwegians now catch three times their prewar tonnage and the crews get home more often.

Echo-fishing brought a paradox. It was easy to catch too many fish and rupture the net under their weight. Captain Saunderson, of the Hull steam trawler, the *Cape Duner*, met this hazard off Cape Farewell, Greenland, in May, 1952. His sounder showed a gray mountain of fish from the six hundred-foot floor to the surface. He annotated the graph, "Sheer wall of fish," and shot a trawl, ordering the winchman to haul as soon as the net hit the floor. The winch groaned and the *Cape Duner* careened with the load coming up. The trawl was near to bursting when they boarded the silvery, wriggling mass. Captain Saunderson hauled nine trawls in ten minutes and steamed off for Hull with 31,500 pounds of fish. The United Nations Food and Agricultural Organization, which is laboring in many parts of the world to improve fishing techniques, summarized the import of echo-fishing: "What is taking place in sea fisheries is the conversion from hunting to a kind of animal husbandry." R. E. Craig, of the Aberdeen Marine Laboratory, has said, "In the herring fisheries, echo methods should be seen as a revolution comparable with the introduction of steam, and a swifter one."

The Peterhead trawler, the *Rival*, cleaved the smooth waters of Loch Ness one December morning in 1954, bound for the Caledonian Canal and the western fishing grounds. The skipper and crew were below at elevenses, leaving Peter Anderson, the mate, at the helm. He switched on the fish detector and idly watched it sketching Chinese brush drawings of crags on the floor of the loch. The stylus arm swept across the unreeling graph paper, cartooning a slope going down to 540 feet. Anderson noticed a black form taking shape 180 feet above the floor. He watched it closely for it was too black and sharp to be a fish school. A fairytale presence appeared before his eyes. It was a dragon with a head and an antenna, or horns, then forefeet, the thickened body, then a Jurassic spike from the spine. "I couldn't believe my eyes," said Anderson. "I shouted to the crew and they came crowding up to the wheelhouse." They saw the stylus continue the caricature—two more sets of legs, two more dorsal projections, a long curling tail. The paper calibrations showed it to be fifty feet long.

The stylus drew a blank and scaled another Chinese peak. Peter Anderson turned his helm hard over and ran back on the same course. They watched the sounder. Nothing showed between the two crags.

They tore the trace out of the roll and studied it. The scrap of paper got wrinkled and dirty. In Peterhead, the first people they showed it to said, "It's Nessie! It's the Loch Ness Monster!" Some joked and hinted that the pawed paper was a hoax. The trawlermen bristled and took the document to L. A. Southcott, an echo-sound expert of Kelvin & Hughes, Ltd., manufacturers of their detection set. He examined it under a magnifying glass. "The paper and the ink are definitely genuine," he stated. "I can certify that it hasn't been tampered with in any way. It is a true impression of an object. This is definitely animal matter of some kind, proved by the fact that echoes from the sounding machine have passed right through the object on to the loch bed below. This object certainly isn't a whale or any other kind of fish that has been charted."

There is no known limit to the size of some fish. Apparently they continue to grow until they die. Most are killed early in life by predators. Others die in traffic accidents—on nets and hooks. They are massacred by changes in temperature and chemical composition of sea water, explosions and pollution. Yet lone iconoclasts probably survive their generations and tribes and grow to great size. Perhaps there is a Loch Ness monster, to be proven and give great joy to science, journalism and Scottish tourism. Dr. H. Slack, of Glasgow University, looked at Rival's echogram and said, "It certainly could be an animal of some kind, but its bone structure and general shape are unlike anything of which we have knowledge."

The second eye in the depths was the robot camera. There were several unlucky attempts at deep photography before Newton Harvey and Edward Baylor secured pictures from a depth chamber 4,200 feet down in 1939. An early stimulator of deep pictures was big, boyish-looking Maurice Ewing, Director of the Lamont Geological Observatory at Palisades, New York. Dr. Ewing is a man of long silences—part shyness and part deliberation. He seems the least impulsive of scholars, yet he has been with the vanguard on deep-sea cores, seismic surveys and robot depth cameras. He was lured into the sea by a Princeton professor emeritus, Richard M. Field. Dr. Field is Circe's academic rival. He has submerged two generations of physical scientists. He rides out of retirement to scientific meetings with a wing collar and a red carnation in his lapel and looks around for young fellows who are dry behind the ears and ready for his siren song.

Ewing's depth robot of 1941 was a "pogo-stick" camera with a single photoflash bulb. He dropped it from a ship without a line and the pogo stick sank vertically. When it struck bottom a contact trigger set off the flash and dropped ballast, and the camera returned to the surface on buoyancy. It produced photos of the floor sixteen thousand feet down and was hard to find when it surfaced. Ewing worked at the Woods Hole Oceanographic Institution in Massachusetts. During the war he secured photographs of the wreck of a Nazi submarine over a half mile down. One of his aides, David Owen, carried on and proliferated the technique. Last spring I went out to Woods Hole to see what Owen was doing. He was in his workshop amidst a clutter of Aqualungs, rubber diving suits, depth cameras, pipe structures, vanes, cables, clamps and tackle. He is a modest young man, the author of *A Manual for Free Divers* and the deepest photograph ever made—three and a half miles down on the Western Atlantic floor. It showed a scattering of globular shapes imbedded in sediment which had sifted over some of the balls like first snowflakes. Nobody knows what these shapes are. Owen's cameras are lowered on cables and flash when they touch bottom. He showed me a long pipe carrying a stereoscopic camera, which had taken stereo pairs on the floor of the Hudson Canyon, the submarine ravine off New York City. The pictures showed small starfish on a barren floor full of animal holes. Another shot, made 6,000 feet down off Cape Cod, depicted a sea spider and brittle stars on a similar perforated bottom.

One of Owen's consultants at Woods Hole was a smiling, imperturbable deacon of the Congregationalist Church at Belmont, Massachusetts, Harold E. Edgerton, otherwise Professor of Electrical Measurements at M.I.T. Twenty years ago Dr. Edgerton created the electronic flash photographic system, in order to obtain precise pictures of dynamos and fast-moving parts. It consisted of damming up tremendous electrical energy in a condenser and letting it loose in a gas-filled lamp. Electronic flash produced illumination many times brighter than the sun and vastly more precise than magnesium flash bulbs. Edgerton froze rapid motion into still life at a three-millionth of a second. His flash tube could be used thousands of times.

Edgerton adapted the device for underwater photography and was soon free diving with a hand-held electronic camera. His previous hobby had been photographing humming birds in flight as a member of the five-man American Trocidilagraphers Society (humming bird portrayers). Then fish won out over birds. Captain Cousteau turned up at Edgerton's lab in Cambridge and invited him to work with the Calypso expeditions on the mystery of the Deep Scattering Layer.

The Deep Scattering Layer, sometimes called the Diffusion Layer, is the imponderable of present-day ocean science. It was discovered when World War II vessels spread over the oceans with powerful recording echo-rangers, hunting for submarines. Thousands of echographs from all oceans and seas showed level false bottoms above the real floor. They did not resemble the broken patterns of fish shoals. Many a commander was routed out of bed by an excited sonar man, clutching a graph with a thick floor two hundred feet down when the hydrographic chart said it was ten thousand feet down. The actual bottom always showed on the graphs as well. What was this presence that wrapped the globe? There was no evidence save the stacks of graphs.

As records accumulated, the mysterious layer was discovered to rise toward the surface at night as fast as fifteen feet a minute, and sink at dawn at twelve feet a minute. Some of these vertical migrations ranged from 1,500 feet down to within a hundred feet of the surface. The most sensitive graphs revealed two or three scattering layers on top of each other. The old-fashioned sounding lead passed right through the layer without hindrance. Scientists speculated that the layer might be caused by microbubbles of air, but if so, why did it rise at night and fall in the morning? Others supposed it was a dense stratum of shrimps, which can give a clicking noise that registers on sonar. Or perhaps it was a vast congress of squids inflicted with photophobia which caused them to shrink from the rising sun and return to the surface at sunset.

Edgerton and Cousteau were keenly attracted to the riddle out of plain inquisitiveness. Others were interested for practical reasons. If the globe-girdling layers proved to be edible animals, mankind's food supply would be assured forever. Submarines towing nets through the layer might abolish protein hunger in Islam and the Orient. The military also connected submarines with D.S.L. It had been noticed that you could follow a sounding whale on the echograph, but when it struck the layer, the whale vanished. A submarine diving beneath the layer could not be detected by the echo pings of a destroyer.* All well and good, but how could you compile an instruction manual for submariners on "Layer Evasion Theory and Practice" if you hadn't the faintest idea what the D.S.L. was?

Edgerton built robot electronic flash cameras to send into the D.S.L. They were stop-motion 35-millimeter units housed in pressure-resisting tubes without a shutter. He did not need a shutter in the total darkness of the deep. An accompanying tube, holding the flash unit, flickered four times a minute, exposing the film. The unit made 800 pictures on a single immersion. In three summers, using improved models each year, Edgerton made over 25,000 shots in the D.S.L., so many that experts could not ana-

---

* No military submarine has ever gone deeper than one thousand feet and come up. A dive to three hundred feet in postwar "Guppies" or the atomic *Nautilus* is considered exceptional. Even without D.S.L. cover, there is no known echo-sounding device that could detect a submarine three thousand feet down, and 90 per cent of the oceans are deeper than that. The Navy which builds a combat boat that can dive to three thousand feet will enjoy virtual freedom of the seas, with high immunity to depth bombing, as well.

lyze them in less than ten years. Later the pictures were interpreted in a
brain machine, which counted the organisms in each frame and signaled
when an unusual shot came along.

The total result of human and mechanical ingenuity exerted on the Deep
Scattering Layer by the Calypso expeditions and other scientists is less than
nothing. The mystery, if anything, has increased. The *Calypso's* Mediterranean and Red Sea and Indian Ocean pictures showed billions of tiny
specks, which may be plankton or dead tissue. Clouds of two-inch shrimps
were found in some shots. But in some of the thickest layers there were no
shrimps at all. Many shots show siphonophores—trailing colonies of microorganisms; some portray small jellyfish. There were no large animals in
25,000 shots. The camera generally photographed an area of a square
yard. Edgerton built a microcamera for close-ups of the specks. He secured
exciting shots that showed them with blurred wakes. The specks were
moving during an exposure of 1-3,000th of a second! The velocity was three
to ten feet per second. These seemed valuable clues, but they were all
erased by the fact that the camera sometimes showed thicker population of
small animals above and below the D.S.L. than in the layer itself. Edgerton
and Cousteau dived through the layer in the French Navy bathyscaphe, the
FNRS-3, watching keenly in the zone that confounded cameras. Both got
the impression that tiny animals were thicker below the layer than in it.
Dr. Edgerton continues with infinite patience. His latest camera model
is equipped with its own ultrasound transmitter so that it can be stationed
in the layer within an error of a few feet.

Television first went under water at the Bikini atom bomb tests in 1947,
where two U.S. Navy cameras were lowered as far as 180 feet to examine
the devastation of the bomb. The next year British experts began underwater television experiments to be used in marine biology; the French Navy
undersea research group made a *tentative*; and engineer J. R. R. Harter
resigned a high-paid job in commercial TV to work on scientific television
for the U.S. Navy. The Royal Canadian Navy and Canada's National Research Council built excellent underwater cameras.

The energetic and progressive Scottish Marine Biological Station at
Millport, on the Firth of Clyde, founded by old "Challenger" Murray, was
the first to put television to work for fishermen. Lowered from the research
vessel the *Calanus*, the camera was in a barrel-sized cylinder at the top of
a derrick frame which rested firmly on the floor down to six hundred feet,
the maximum depth of the Firth. The director, Dr. Harold Barnes, and
his experts have concentrated on fixed, finely detailed views of the floor,
which are transmitted by cable to a monitor on the *Calanus*. The biologists
measure and count bottom organisms, and move the rig from one plot to
the next assembling a large chart which shows the relation of animals one

to another and to their environment. In 1953, the Office Française de Recherches Sous-Marine at Marseille built the first undersea television camera to be operated by a diving cameraman. It was used by archeologists to supervise digging of the 205 B.C. Greek wine ship 125 feet down at Grand Congloué Island. The Marseille group has since built several advanced units, including a robot designed to be lowered 3,000 feet.

One of the most spectacular uses of submerged television came in 1954. On a bright January, the world's first jet airliner, the Comet, pride of British civil aviation, rolled on her low tricycle around the perimeter at Rome airport. She was the *Yoke Peter*, one of the first Comets in commerce and she had thirty-five people aboard, including Chester Wilmot, the ex-war correspondent. The machine was Britain's bold venture to regain civil air parity, lost during the war by an Anglo-American agreement that America's huge plant would build the Allied air transports and Britain would build combat planes.

The Comet was the masterwork of a pioneer of flight, thin, courtly, withdrawn Sir Geoffrey de Havilland, who built and flew his first airplane in 1908. After the Second War he decided that Britain could not overtake the Constellations and Stratocruisers, America's gain of war. He must burst past them with a liner five to ten years ahead of development rates. That meant a civil jet craft. Sir Geoffrey did not build a prototype Comet and peddle it around. He sold the first Comet from blueprints, guaranteeing it would serve. I saw the first one flying in 1949 at de Havilland's. She was piloted by Group Captain John Cunningham, a benign ginger-haired citizen in a business suit, who slammed away in the morning for Rome or Benghazi and got back for high tea. He was the leading night fighter ace of World War II.

As the *Yoke Peter* turned on to the runway at Rome, Comets had been carrying passengers for two years. One Comet had dissolved in midair and the type had been psychoanalyzed at the Royal Aircraft Establishment at Farnborough without finding structural faults. On the takeoff, the *Yoke Peter* whined and pitched up to a scream. Quickly the plane caught the air and drove steeply toward the thin substratosphere where kerosene would burn longer. In minutes, the Comet dropped Italy behind and climbed above the sea for her cruising altitude of thirty thousand feet, which would be reached over Elba Island. Below in the ocean of air swam a slow propeller liner, a B.O.A.C. Argonaut, whose radio man took a routine message from the *Yoke Peter*. Halfway through, transmission abruptly ceased.

At about 26,000 feet, the Comet flew into many pieces with a dull report. Sundered parts, spinning collages of aluminum, engines like flaming brands, tailplane, souvenir zipper bags, knee rugs, bottles, copies of *Punch* and people fell five miles to the Ligurian Sea.

There were many witnesses on Elba. Fishing boats chugged toward the downfall. They gathered fifteen floating bodies of people who had died instantly of massive bends when the pressurized cabin burst to flinders in thin air. An R.A.F. Shackleton and a tourist York, bound for Cyprus, flew by and sighted fishing boats gathered in oil slicks and flotsam. They circled low and logged the occurrence, with no idea that a Comet had gone down.

The disappearance of the *Yoke Peter* seemed the end of Sir Geoffrey's calculated audacity. It gave no pleasure to United States aircraft constructors. It was not just a blow to British aviation, but to international air commerce, which de Havilland was leading into the jet epoch. Why did the Comet fall? Mr. Alan Lennox-Boyd, Minister of Transport and Civil Aviation, got on the telephone to Malta and asked Admiral Lord Louis Mountbatten, Commander-in-Chief, N.A.T.O. Mediterranean Fleet, how they could recover the wreckage and find out what had happened.

Mountbatten was no novice of the sea, whether on deck or beneath it. At fifty-three he had become an ardent Aqualung diver and knew the blue vistas of the Mediterranean underworld. He said, "It is bound to be a very sticky and long job on account of the great depths and winter storms. In summer you can go a hundred feet down in this water and see a hundred feet more. But looking for things five hundred feet down in winter? We'll be lucky to see ten feet, even with television. The wreckage is spread far and wide. It will be rather like searching from a helicopter in deep fog for a handful of peas scattered in an acre. We are willing to try." Soon afterward Mountbatten received a signal from the Admiralty: ENDEAVOR TO LOCATE AND SALVE COMET.

To the site came Elba Force—five Royal Navy ships, five Italian draggers and divers from Risdon Beazley, the salvage firm in Southampton. The divers brought a ten-foot grab and two deep-diving units made by Roberto Galeazzi, of La Spezia, Italy's venerable submarine engineer known as "the depth magician." Dr. Galeazzi is a Leonardo-like old man with a vast white beard. He was the first individual to reach seven hundred feet in the sea in his "butoscopic turret" in 1930. The turret is a steel canister with a bulbous top encircled by twelve ports, so that the observer could see completely around himself and a fair area above and below. The diver sat in a saddle, mounted on a rotating frame. All the gadgetry was fixed to the frame—oxygen rebreathing unit, batteries, and ballast controls—so the man could spin around freely without knocking his head on stuff clamped on the walls. The wonder of the electronic age also came to look for the Comet in the shape of three underwater television cameras, referred to as "TV chains," because they were industrial rather than broadcasting units. They send pictures by cable to a screen on the surface. One camera, built by Marconi and Siebe, Gorman, had an extraordinary field of vision, covering a full hemisphere. Inside a domelike lens, there was a periscope lens which could be remotely controlled to scan all of the dome.

The first position, given by trawlermen who had picked up bodies, was twelve miles south by southwest of Point Calamita. Eleven island witnesses went to where they had been at the time and pointed to where the Comet had showered into the sea. Several of these alignments bisected a position six miles nearer to the Point than the trawlermen's location. Captain Croston, of the York aircraft which had circled the flotsam soon after the crash, produced a snapshot of the Italian boats against the peaks of Elba. Air Ministry experts plotted the position of the boats. They were three miles southeast of the main observer bisections. This welter of clues confronted Elba Force with a search area of two hundred square miles.

The frigate H.M.S. *Wrangler* made the first sonar sweep along observer lines A and B, provided by two eyewitnesses who had been near each other and pointed on parallel lines. The *Wrangler* went pinging and pipping south, bouncing acoustic impulses off the sloping mud floor—310 feet . . . 430 feet . . . 1,450 feet deep—until she was fifteen miles out. In the chart room the sparking sonar stylus etched up and down on the unrolling graph paper, drawing a profile of the bottom. The stylus did not prick out a bump of any kind. Behind the *Wrangler* came the antisubmarine frigate, H.M.S. *Sursay*, strewing buoys to mark off the area searched. Two months later, when an Italian dragger struck three of the Comet's jet engines in a cluster, the spot was just a few yards from the *Wrangler's* first unrevealing sweep. The patient searchers theorized as they pipped, swept, laid buoys and took them up. They began to believe that the one indisputable position, the photointerpretation, showed slick and bodies that had already drifted off the crash area in the southwest current. However, they pursued all alignments.

The first piece of wreckage was recovered by the Elba dragger *Favilla*— bits of aluminum and a passenger's zipper bag marked BRITISH OVERSEAS AIRWAYS CORPORATION. It was an omen, nothing more. They could not tell where the dragnet had gathered the bag on its five-mile sweep. The island fishermen continued business as usual in the southern grounds as Elba Force groped for the Comet and their nets brought up bits of airplane from time to time. These scattered recoveries showed that the plane must be strewn far and wide. On the first three weeks, the draggers and the *Wrangler* made only six finds. The *Wrangler* was relieved by H.M.S. *Wakeful*, equipped with a Pye underwater television chain.

The chartered trawlers went "from strength to strength," adopting a method of dragging a loop of wire from two parallel boats, with otter boards as crude hydrofoils to spread an eight-hundred-foot width of chain and wire on the bottom. They snagged nothing but mine sinkers and cables. The *Wakeful* lowered her television camera on sonar contacts established by the *Wrangler*. Contact "Fox" proved to be small modern wreck. Contact "Dog" sent a buzz around the ship and a scramble to look at the sight on the tube. On the floor, six hundred feet below, the camera revealed a mound of amphoras, the remains of a Greek or Roman freighter of perhaps two thousand years before, when Icarus was the only aviator. The camera drifted over the fat-bellied amphoras in a smooth panning shot and from the last amphora came an enormous conger eel, which glared malevolently at its unseen audience. Elba Force did not disturb the amphoras. They were looking for an airplane.

The Italian boats stopped immediately when they fouled a drag and tried to keep fast to the obstacle. They called to the boom defense vessel, H.M.S. *Barhill*. She came up over the contact and circled it with six five-ton anchors on buoys, then moved out for the fleet auxiliary salvage ship, the *Sea Salvor*, which staked out on the buoys, making a very tight station for the descent of observers. The retired Navy divers Bray and Gilpin descended in Galeazzi's turret on a sliding shackle on the dragline. Down below, even with powerful searchlights, they could see only ten feet and phoned constantly to move them a bit this way or that. The seamen then hauled and slackened the moorings to move the ship as precisely as possible. The *Sea Salvor* chewed up her capstan barrels and fairleads as her men toiled. Once they adjusted moorings eighty times on a single contact. The exhausted men had to be reinforced by a working party from a frigate.

Putting television on a contact was even more complicated. The TV outfit was not aboard the *Sea Salvor*, but on the frigate *Wakeful*. The salvage ship had to let go her moorings and make way for the frigate to shackle the TV camera on the dragline. In rough winter seas, the tethered trawler, the salvage ship, the six buoys and the television frigate got into awful bumping snarls trying to fish what might be a meaningless wingtip of the *Yoke Peter* or a portable typewriter. It was important to eliminate every contact.

Their first big contact was "George," 430 feet down. In a week on this site, the grab took fifteen hunks of the *Yoke Peter*, including both starboard and port undercarriages, the main plane elevator, a wingroot still attached to a ripoff of the fuselage, a section of airframe, three radio sets and the navigator's maps and logs. Elba Force was encouraged, but there were so many pieces. The *Yoke Peter* must be scattered in a thousand parts.

The boom ship *Barhill* had to bow out, punished by the great anchors and buoys. Her winch drums were warped and her apron battered. She plodded to Malta for refit. A smaller force persisted. The operation had now been on two months. New finds kept them in heart—a large section of fuselage, ribs of the starboard outer engine, gas tank sheathing, fuselage structure marked by fire, more maps and sad passenger property. They made the greatest single lift, most of the cockpit and the tricycle nose wheel, in one piece. There was part of a human skeleton in the cockpit. Two jet exhaust pipes and skin sections were coming out of the sea in the grabs when heavy news arrived from Naples. The South African Airways Comet, the *Yoke-Yoke*, had leaped from Rome airport and exploded at the same altitude and time after takeoff as the *Yoke Peter*. The wreckage shattered into the sea off Naples, too deep for salvage. All Comets were grounded.

Eight months after the *Yoke Peter* fell, a fishing boat brought up the secret, a section of the cabin top between the forward wing spars. This bent souvenir contained the two glass ports for the radio direction-finding aerials. Ninety per cent of the plane had been recovered before this talisman came up and ended the search. In England, the assessors of the Royal Aircraft Establishment brought the cabin top before the Court of Inquiry under Lord Cohen. They laid it down and arrayed around it the pieces exploded away from it.

The chief assessor called attention to a corner of the R.D.F. window. In the reinforcing plate there was a crack less than one quarter of an inch long. It occurred during manufacture, one of the many slight imperfections in aircraft building. De Havilland had a strict procedure on flaws of this sort. The worker reported each one to the inspector. He referred it to the technical office. An expert looked at the flaw and ordered a remedy in writing, in what is called a "concession note." The concession note covering the tiny crack was found in de Havilland's files. It was approved by the design department which had ordered the crack to be stopped by drilling a sixteenth-of-an-inch hole at the end to prevent it from spreading. It was a standard procedure, approved to bring the part to full strength. Apparently, however, this area of the cabin was under heavier stress in flight than the designers could know.

The separation of pieces radiated from the little crack. On the top skin of the wings they found paint scratches from cabin parts, exploding from the R.D.F. window. There was no fire at the time of explosion. As the engines fell, fire broke out around them.

Elba Force saved the future of jet liners. Comet II is now flying, strengthened by knowledge hard won from the sea.

Last year I met the Royal Navy officer who found a sunken submarine with television. He is a weathered blue-eyed, companionable Hampshireman named William O. Shelford, retired Navy Diving Superintendent, the organizer of the great helium dive in Loch Fyne. Captain Shelford directs technical development at Siebe, Gorman, the ancient firm which renews itself generation after generation with submarine engineering brains. Captain Shelford lacks senior service starch. He does not commit that besetting sin of navy anecdotage, understatement. He tells the tale straight, relishing the action, comedy and characters. He told it to me in several public houses in London and the country.

The lost submarine, H.M.S. *Affray*, a new snort type, left Portsmouth for Start Point on a training cruise in April, 1951. The submarine disappeared without signal or trace, which set off the first operational test of a rescue and salvage plan of the North Atlantic Treaty Pact powers, known as Subsmash. Shelford was one of those who planned Subsmash.

"There are two stages in the scheme," he said. "Submiss One is a signal that goes out immediately when a submarine is one hour overdue." It rallies neighboring ships and aircraft to the presumed last position of the submarine. "Subsunk Two," said Shelford, "goes out an hour later or when a submarine is known to be in trouble. It brings maximum rescue effort—salvage ships, diving tenders, hospital ships, fast Asdic vessels to sweep with echo-sound. A lot of people arrive, deep-sea divers and blokes who designed that particular submarine, for example. When the *Affray* was lost, I was in Malta. They gave me fifteen minutes to leave my wife and son and take off from Valetta airport. When I got to Portsmouth, there was still no trace of the *Affray*. We did not know if she had been cruising on the surface or submerged. There were no escapees and no sounds of men hammering on the hull, which would have been picked up easily by Asdic. All we had was her presumed course, which meant a search area of about two thousand square miles."

The charts indicated flat bottom ranging from 180 to 222 feet deep, as Subsmash Two brought search vessels in force. There were a score of ships, including H.M.S. *Reclaim*, the deep-diving tender, under Lieutenant Commander J. N. Bathurst. A corvette and a destroyer dashed about, bouncing Asdic pings off the floor, recording all protuberances on the bottom which might be the *Affray*. "We had everything to work with," said Captain Shelford. "Risdon Beazley was standing by with all his men and equipment, and we were forty deep in divers, Navy and civilian, arriving in the Portsmouth to volunteer. When the Asdic sweep would pick up an interesting contact, the corvettes would crisscross it from every angle to build up a contour feeling of the thing on the floor. If there was any chance it was a submarine, we would stake off the *Reclaim* over it and dive on the contact.

"Working the contacts with divers was hard going. We had about five days a fortnight of favorable tides, and often the weather scrubbed the days when the tide was right. When you are lowering divers you must keep the tender in place, which meant six anchors well laid and several cruiser-buoy moorings every time we sent a man down, and at just the right tidal condition. It was a job of eliminating probables. The Asdic ships recorded thousands of raised objects on the floor. Many a ship had gone down thereabouts.

But echo-sound was sensitive enough to write off the great majority of the contacts. We went on monotonously sweeping and staking off on possibles, for the divers to have a look. We got no *Affray*, but we discovered some strange facts about this nice flat floor on the charts. At one place marked as a slight variation of 180 to 200 feet in the floor, we found a submerged ridge a mile long which rose fifty feet from the seabed. Asdic survey of the ridge showed no submarines, no *Affray*. At another spot the chart marked a sunken Liberty ship, safely out of the way on a 200-foot floor. We found the ship standing 68 feet high on a 180 foot floor; it was where many a submarine had cruised blissfully underwater. We went down and saw that the hatches had been torn off the Liberty ship when she sank. We looked down and sighted layers of lorries, jeeps and tires, still neatly guyed off in the holds. This wreck could have fouled a submarine, but the *Affray* was not there.

"After some weeks, Jack Bathurst and I got a call from the Navy research lab at Teddington. It was Buster Crabbe (Commander L. P. K. Crabbe, the bold man of the underwater war at Gibraltar). Buster said, 'Why don't you use underwater television on the *Affray*?' I said, 'When do the dancing girls come on?' He said, 'Look here, this is serious. We have an underwater TV camera and I think you could use it.' We didn't see much in Buster's box of tricks, but we went up to see him and brought the apparatus back to the *Reclaim*.

"Television was surprisingly successful," said Shelford. "It had a finer definition of underwater objects than the human eye and it could be lowered in tides that were not safe for an observer. Bathurst and I decided that we could make use of television, if we were able to sell the Portsmouth command and the Admiralty on it. We laid on an underwater demonstration for a party of high officers. They sat nice and comfy in the wardroom while we put a diver down 150 feet to pose for the camera. The image was quite clear. I handed the diver's phone to an admiral and said, 'Like to speak to the diver, sir?' He said, 'Hullo, Diver, do you hear me?' The diver said, 'Yes, sir.' The admiral was pleased as punch with this TV phone call. He said, 'Diver, please write something on your blackboard.' The diver bent over and chalked away. Then he held it up to the camera. He had written, WHAT ABOUT A RISE IN PAY FOR DIVERS?"

After we had downed a toast to the opportunistic diver, Shelford continued: "The television was a fine new tool for the search, but weeks went on without a trace of the *Affray*. We'd all been at sea, working straight through, and I was getting tired and a bit suspicious of the presumed course we'd been working on. Also my poor wife had been left with all the family problems in Malta, such as selling the house, and had finally returned to London with our son. I asked for a week end to see them. Before I left the *Reclaim* I took a last look at the search chart which was covered with a transparent overlay for people to scribble on with crayon. My parting shot was to draw a blue line on the overlay and write, 'More probable course of the *Affray*.' " Shelford is a former officer in submarines and had had many experiences with the wide variety of courses people took to Start Point.

Ashore, a group of journalists surrounded him. The press had been having a vigil. The peacetime sinking of a submarine is the sort of prolonged, suspenseful human interest story newspapers like and it is good for their circulation. To a search officer, as Shelford explained, "it is difficult because men have been lost without trace and you think about their families and don't want to give any hint that might hurt anyone. The relatives, after all hope is gone, as it had been for over a month, still have feelings that you must be very careful about. Some say, 'We want our boy's body for decent burial,' and others say, 'Our boy would wish to sleep there with his comrades.' What makes it a very knotty proposition is that the Admiralty wanted to bring that submarine up and find out what happened to it. That is the most important thing, and it cannot be influenced by where you want bodies buried. This you can never explain to reporters who want something hot for the evening edition. I gave the press a bad time and went home. I was even very guarded with my wife and son about how the search was getting on."

Captain Shelford's family reunion dinner was disturbed by a call to report back to the *Reclaim* immediately. "That really seemed like enough," Shelford said with a smile. "I gave a short comeback, 'Why?' The voice said, 'I can say nothing, sir, except that it concerns the blue line.' I rushed back aboard. Everybody was gathered around the chart studying my blue line. Right on the blue line was Contact Jig, which had been turned up by Asdic on the second day of Subsmash and had been put aside because it was outside the official crash area. While I was ashore, they had staked off on Jig and sent down a man in a Galeazzi observation chamber." Risdon Beazley had lent the chamber to the *Reclaim* to speed up the search, since the Galeazzi diver required no decompression. Contact Jig was 276 feet down.

The man in the bottle had ten-foot visibility. He phoned, "I see brightwork. It is a fresh wreck. I think it is a submarine." No ships had been sunk in these parts since the war; shining metal promised to be the *Affray*. The *Reclaim's* sorely tried sailors had staked out and hauled anchor and big cruiser buoys for months, but it was never possible to hold such a precise station as the one dictated by the ten-foot visibility on the bottom. All they could do was try.

Shelford said, "We sent down Buster's television. We trimmed the camera twenty feet from the floor. The first thing we saw was the empty forward gun turret of a submarine. The submarine was standing upright with no weed growing on it. A current tugged at the *Reclaim* and the camera was swept slowly aft on the starboard side. The lens passed the conning tower and we read the letters, one by one, **Y-A-R-F-F-A**

The crew jostled each other to look at the monitor, shouting over the magical sight. The *Reclaim* took courage for the hard task that remained—to find out what happened to the *Affray* and lift her, if possible. To survey the submarine they had to swing the TV camera and the bottled man, foot by foot, down one side and up the other, by precisely moving the tender in running seas, winching the ship to and fro on her anchor cables and mooring wires. They completed the tour of the submarine's sides and found no collision hole in the hull. Then they juggled diver Albert Middleton atop the wreck and inched him from the bow down the starboard length of the *Affray*. He phoned, "I think the snort mast is fallen down, but I can't be sure."

"We put a diver right on the snort," said Shelford. "He reported, 'It's broken off like a carrot.' A clean break almost. The snort was nearly broken off at the base and was lying over the side at a right angle. We didn't know what to think. We felt certain it was material failure and it seemed vital to recover that snort. We concentrated on it the rest of the good tides. We sent the TV camera down and made cracking good photos of the break. Bringing up the snort was not easy at 276 feet. We had to lift without destroying evidence of the accident. Already we had accidentally made the job tougher by fouling an anchor on the submarine's jump line, which runs from the conning tower to the stern. The jump wire was tangled over the broken snort. Getting a diver into this maze was the next trick. Television helped considerably. We put TV into the site and then lowered an extra-heavy diver's shot painted white. By watching the screen we were able to position the shot. Then the diver and camera could be sent to the same spot by lowering them on sliding shackles on the same wire. This sounds simple, but it took days to get right on the snort head. The *Reclaim* moving about, jiggled the camera here and there, and we watched many oddments on the floor, dropped grapnel wires, empty tins and bottles thrown over our sides. I said to Bathurst, 'Have your steward number his empty gin bottles so we can get some landmarks down there.' "

Making cables fast to the snort could not be done by men in the Galeazzi bottle—here was very deep and dangerous work for men in flexible dresses with their hands free. They estimated the situation in a final television survey, and helmet men went down with wire straps to clasp on the snort mast. They were going into the zone where compressed-air divers are subject to drunkenness that cheats a man of responsibility. "One of the divers was working on the snort," said Shelford, "when he suddenly phoned, 'This thing is so huge I can hardly get my arms around it!' The mast was actually less than a foot in diameter. We knew the man had been hit with narcosis and hauled him up."

It took four days to strap the snort mast and heave it up gently. The broken end showed clear signs of material failure, no signs of collision. They scanned all the hatches with television and took photos from the monitor. All hatches were closed tight. The Admiralty wanted to know the position of the engine room telegraphs. Shelford said, "We got the camera right into the 'bathtub' of the conning tower and had a close look at the bridge telegraph. It showed that the *Affray* was stopped when she sank. The affair was as mysterious as ever." The problem narrowed down to the question of whether the mushroom valve, which admits the snort to the engine room, was open or closed. This fourteen-inch valve is recessed in the hull plating so that there was no way to get grabs on it and try to wrench it free. To try to blow it out with dynamite would certainly destroy the clues.

"Some brilliant scientists," said Shelford, "devised an underwater X-ray camera to examine the valve. We got one poor X-ray which indicated the valve was open, but it was not conclusive. The only thing left was to rip off the casings to get at the valve. The constructors of the submarine warned us that she might roll over on her side under this attack. We thought of an answer for that; we put down two huge anchors astraddle the submarine and tried to pull her upright by the crossbar. Mind you, a two-thousand-ton submarine.

"Risdon Beazley made a special grab we dreamed up, a two-and-a-half-ton scissors grab with colossal vice heads welded to the scissors tips. It was the biggest pair of pliers ever made. We got a purchase on that submarine and ripped off plating by the mile. Then, suddenly, the Admiralty called off the operation. I believe the accident was officially laid to a battery explosion. But, before we touched the sub, I saw something on television that convinced me the snort valve *was* open and that's where the water got in that swamped the *Affray*. I *know* that valve was open."

Captain Shelford's flat assurance led me to ask, "Why are you so sure?" He said, "When we found her, the wreck had been down only two months. No marine growths had had time to form on the hull. Consequently there was nothing for fish to feed on. There were no fish around the wreck, except for one spot. Time after time I watched little fish hovering there on television. They were right above the snort valve. It proved to me that something nutritious was coming up through that hole."

15

The Last Frontier

THE UNDERSEA moviemaker, John D. Craig, was working off Lower California twenty-five years ago, when he heard of mysterious Japanese diving activities at Cedros Island. Captain Craig sailed to the island to have a look and found the usually friendly Japanese silent and inhospitable. Around the island there was a forest of long bladder kelp, whose foliage spread in a thick tangle on the surface. Craig's plummet showed the depth to be forty-two feet. He decided to go down and see what interested the Japanese. He could not get through the weeds in his helmet suit, so his crew cut a hole in the fronds. Craig did not notice that his boat had drifted. With his suit inflated for forty-two feet, he sank seventy-two feet into a submarine canyon.

He passed out from the squeeze and recovered half-consciousness rolling on the bottom, entangled in the tenacious weeds. He said, "There appeared before me, out of nowhere, a large white form. It had arms and legs, heavy and puffed like pillows. It had a dome-shaped head and a white eye. The strange bulbous thing disappeared. In a minute it ran into my line of vision again. Suddenly my wits returned. It was a Japanese diver, wearing white burlap coveralls over his diving dress to offer a less attractive surface to octopi. In his hand he carried a common garden rake. I couldn't figure that out.

"He stood there for fully two minutes, watching my lines strain as the boys pulled and I tried to get to my feet. Then he disappeared again. Suddenly I got sick. He was going off to let me die, fouled in kelp. I was hopelessly lost.

"This was the first time my position really impressed itself on me. More air was coming into the dress and my head was clearing. With a tremendous

277

effort I got myself turned halfway around. There, right behind me, with a knife in his hand, was the Jap diver. He was cutting my lines!" He cut Craig's lifeline and held him tethered as he hacked a path through the kelp toward the helpless diver. Craig struggled to his feet and began to run. He tripped and the Japanese came relentlessly on, cutting through the seaweed jungle. Craig said, "Just at the point where he had a free swing at me, he sheathed his knife, seized the other end of my life line, tied its cut ends together, and motioned me to my feet. He motioned me to follow him and I meekly walked behind him out of the valley and into the purple fields."

The Japanese diver was a sargasso farmer who planted, nursed and harvested the high stand of kelp. Bales of kelp in Japan sold for $420 a ton, where it was used in food, candy and woven stuffs, as an ingredient of drugs and plastic buttons and for agar-agar oil. A band of Japanese had been nine years cultivating this underwater kelp farm in Mexico. The crop was perennial, ready for harvest the year round. A diver earned up to $300 a day.

The daily menu in Japan includes many seaweed dishes: *dashi konbu*, for soup stock; flavored rolled kelp, *konbu maki; nori tsukudani*, seaweed cooked with sugar and soy sauce; sea lettuce; and *oboro konbu*, powdered kelp for instant soups. The Atlantic French, Scandinavians and British islanders have long gathered seaweed as fertilizers and food. In the west of Ireland people eat carragheen moss and bladderwrack for the gripe. The ancient Greeks ate seaplants as a laxative.

Carragheen, a brownish-red slippery, gummy weed that grows on rocks or any firm object in the intertidal zone, is the most utilized seaweed. It is the correct construction material for a Rhode Island clambake. It occurs in several varieties in the northern seas. Carragheen has been harvested as a food ingredient for centuries in western Europe, North America, China and Japan. It takes different folk names in each country such as "laver" in England and "slack" in Scotland. Very few of the three thousand species of seaweeds are recognized by common names. Carragheen contains re- markable colloids or algins which are soluble in water. They have found their way into practically every homogenous food manufactured today. The extract carrageenin is used to clear ale and beer during worting. It is the custardizer in cheese spreads and ice cream. The reason why ice cream is no longer lumpy and thick with ice crystals is due to the smoothing effect of the seaweed extract. It goes into chocolate syrup, bottled salad dressing, pumpkin pie mix, canned whipped cream, cake icing and dog food. Dr. Leonard Stoloff, of New Bedford, Massachusetts, who found many of its commercial uses, works for the Seaplant Chemical Corporation, which ad- vertises carrageenin products as "improving mouth-feel." It is the subtlety of skin balms and cough medicines.

The Scots and Irish used the weed in pudding and jelly long before contemporary food factories started to blend it with everything. It was a family industry in the British Isles and was brought to New England and Nova Scotia by immigrants, who handed down the processing art. The first physician to catch up the peasant tradition was an Irish locum tenens named Todhunter who declared its benefits to a Dublin medical meeting in 1831.

All attempts at artificial cultivation of the prodigal weed have failed. It is gathered in New England by boatmen with eighteen-foot rakes, who get two cents a pound, wet, from avid buyers on the beach. Divers have found it growing forty feet down. Five booming plants extract carrageenin for U.S. food factories and cannot meet the demand. It has virtually eliminated from usage the slogan, "Shake well before using."

Seaweed algin was discovered in 1883 by the English biochemist E. C. C. Stanford. It is a complex organic compound, tasteless, odorless and almost transparent, which has come into an extraordinary variety of uses. It softens textiles, gives them a high sheen and adds to the strength of the fibers. It is used as filler in paper and cardboard, and as a binder in coal briquettes. It serves to waterproof tents and is nearly noninflammable. In Ireland it is turned into wallboard; in the United States to producing humus; in Japan, to glue and the pigments of decorated porcelain.

A team of pharmacists from the University of California has rolled up its pants to pull two dozen different weeds from the Pacific shore line, quick-freeze them and test the extracts in the laboratory. One green weed, *Ulva linza*, found from Alaska to Mexico, proved to kill several types of microbes infecting the human system. The scientists found that weeds gathered in winter had no power over bacteria, while those taken in the autumn and spring were active. It seemed like a discovery until a team member, Dr. Yi-Hsien Sha, brought forth a Chinese pharmacopoeia published in 1598, which instructed druggists to beware of winter seaweeds.

Thirty years ago an American cattle feed manufacturer named Philip Park took a postman's holiday to look at European cows and what they ate and he saw a curious sight in the Channel Islands. Purebred Guernseys of the most aristocratic lineage were plodding away from their fat grass pastures and promenading on the beach at low tide, gobbling up stranded seaweeds. Park took weed samples home with him and had them analyzed. The laboratory showed how smart the beasts were. Park began harvesting the kelp beds off the California coast between San Pedro and Santa Barbara with an ingenious marine reaper. The reaper extends a row of knives three feet under water, which mows kelp fronds, and an endless belt carries the weed into a well deck of the barge. The state government exacted a lease on Park's wet acreage, but he prospered in the miracle cropping. Park found that topping the high weeds encouraged their growth and he could take several harvests a year. He chopped and dried the weed in his plant and it came out in dark green flakes with a pleasant, tart taste. Mixed with other dry fodder, Park's sea food had spectacular results. A kelp-eating Jersey cow from Ferndale, California, "Silken Lady's Ruby," was the first to produce over ten thousand pounds of butter fat, an international mark for bovine philanthropy. "Swaps," the noted California race horse, was a kelp muncher. Rocky Marciano, the pugilist, used seaweed extract to stop nosebleed and cuts between rounds.

The finest cattle in France and much of her incomparable garden produce come from a thin coastal belt in Brittany and Normandy known as the *ceinture dorée*, which is manured with kelp. In Jersey and Guernsey there is a proverb, "No seaweed, no wheatfield." Seaweed is a very old, important matter with the French. King Louis XIV once gave all seaweed harvesting rights to the Royal Company of Glass Manufacturers, who used kelp ashes in glazing. The peasants fought for their manure and the edict was revoked.

A half century ago scientists were already discovering medical applications of marine research. Albert I of Monaco, Prince of Oceanographers, gave them an opportunity aboard his research ships to widen knowledge of the oceans. The Prince blew the house take of the Monte Carlo casino on the sea, established two great marine research centers and the famous oceanographic museum of Monaco. It wasn't even a tax writeoff, since Albert was the tax collector. He was a real deepwater sailor. Aboard his yacht the *Princesse-Alice*, in 1901, there came the discovery of allergies, a gift from the sea to the zoologist Paul Portier.

Professor Portier, at ninety, was still working at the Institut Océanographique in Paris, when he told how it happened. The old savant had a ruddy face, splendid white hair falling to his collar and a Louis-Napoleon mustache and goatee. He was blind in one eye from looking through microscopes, and had to refrain from looking into them with the other eye, a considerable hardship for a working experimenter. However, he was able to take his customary eight-mile walk every day. He was a great friend of Louis Boutan's.

"In the seas around the Azores and the Cape Verde Islands," Professor Portier began, "where the Prince conducted us that year, there were an abundance of *Physalia* [Portuguese Men-of-War]. Under a vividly colored float they dangle tentacles that can inject powerful poison. These fragile beings can paralyze all kinds of huge prey. Indeed, when we injected the animals we had on board, pigeons and frogs, with macerations of these filaments, they died rapidly. It was most striking how the poison brought paralysis. We called it the effect 'hypnotoxine.'

"Back in Paris, I suggested to my master, Charles Richet, that we try to develop immunization for this poison of jellyfish. My proposition did not arouse much enthusiasm on his part, and I myself considered it more or less the ritual complement to our experiments. One would have thought that we would be getting back to the classic, even banal, phenomenon of Pasteur. It was then that with stupefaction we saw that the result was not at all what we had counted on."

The experiments consisted of giving dogs injections of tiny doses of jellyfish poison, the usual method for building up immunization, which would permit them to receive safely progressively larger doses until a serum culture could be developed. The contradictory results were typified by the case of the dog Neptune.

"He receives a feeble dose of poison.

"An hour later, he is alertly walking around the lab.

"Three days later, another injection, with double the amount, but still not much. Very little reaction. The next day he is in perfect health.

"Twenty-seven days after the first shot, the dog is gay and alert. We give him an injection only a fraction stronger than the second one. This is not a mortal dosage.

And yet immediately we see something dramatic. The dog falls on one side, loses consciousness. A half hour later he is dead. The dog had died from an injection which would have caused a new dog only to sneeze or to have itches!"

Said Portier, "Dr. Richet asked me if I had not mixed up the vaccinated dogs and those not. No, it was not that. We were faced with a new, unheard-of phenomenon.

"Once the phenomenon was firmly established, Richet proposed that we baptize it," the Professor continued. "I admit I did not see the use of doing so. To create still another neologism! There were already too many, much too many, particularly since people no longer knew Greek. 'Of course,' said Richet, 'you are right, if what we have just discovered is merely a curiosity. But if it has generality, we must have a name for it.' We drew up to a small blackboard under a staircase. He asked me if I knew the Greek for immunity, protection. 'It's *phylaxis*,' he said. I said, 'Well, then, how about *anaphylaxis*?'"

The old researcher paused and struck out on his peroration, as though he were once again in the lecture theater. His audience was the reporter and two of his feminine assistants. "Mesdames, Messieurs, in a general sort of way, there are two kinds of scientific discovery," he began.

"When Mr. Dale [Sir Henry Hallet Dale] was led to conceiving of a chemical substance that should be secreted under the influence of emotion on certain nerves, he eventually found the illustrious chemical mediators, adrenalin and acetylcholin.

"When Pasteur, looking at the culture of chicken cholera after his vacation, found it strangely developed, that was pure accident, a truth found without seeking. But the famous creator of bacteriology seized its significance immediately and, under the impulsion of his genius, laid down the principle of vaccination.

"Anaphylaxis is in this latter category of discoveries in which pure chance has a principal role; on condition, of course, that the phenomenon is produced before eyes capable of analyzing and understanding it. And now, you have the circumstances of our discovery of anaphylaxis."

The work won a Nobel Prize, which was given to Professor Richet, but not to Paul Portier. In late years the scientific world has come to recognize Portier's prime part in the discovery of anaphylaxis. On the semicentennial of the event, Portier, Richet and Prince Albert were portrayed together on a Monocan commemorative postage stamp.

A writer is sometimes cautioned about mentioning experiments on animals out of respect for antivivisectionists. If any such offended by this report is undergoing treatment for allergies, he should further brandish his integrity by resigning either from the antivivisection society or the treatment, for Portier's use of the dog Neptune led to finding allergy cures.

Conservationists often prophesy that someday man will have to farm and mine and chemically process the oceans. "Someday" is getting nearer, as many land resources near exhaustion. "Someday" is here for certain maritime industries.

Fish protein is not all caught by trawls and hooks. Thailand consumes five thousand tons a year of savory pastes made from plankton, tiny drifting animals and plants seined in silk nets. Plankton is the diet of the biggest mammal that has ever lived, the blue whale which grows to a hundred feet long. It lives on animals one could line up 3,000 strong and cover with a thumb. In one day two men can haul enough plankton to feed 350 people that day. Plankton gumbo is about 60 per cent protein and the rest fats, carbohydrates and minerals, a satisfying and balanced regimen.

In the submerged mussel farms of France, which have been cultivated for seven hundred years, the annual yield is 10,000 pounds of edible meat per acre. A land acre produces about two hundred pounds of beef in a year. The sea requires no tillage, no fertilizer, no vermin sprays and no rain. It is a culture broth, endlessly creating.

Those most starved for protein live in Islam and the Orient, and especially in Japan, China, India and Israel, totaling at least a billion people. The Carnegie Institute in Washington, D.C., exceeded its "pure" research status to run a pilot plant in Cambridge, Massachusetts, to seek the production economics of a promising species of algae, *Chlorella*, a minute green vegetable rich in protein. The Cambridge center multiplied *Chlorella* in tanks to a thick green soup. When dehydrated, the alga left a 56 per cent weight of protein. Dried alfalfa contained only 15 per cent protein and hay only 12 per cent. *Chlorella* has been used in experimental diets of lepers. At the Milford, Connecticut, shellfish station of the U.S. Fish and Wildlife Service, Dr. Victor Loosamoff fed the alga to oysters, which fattened to a fine succulence. Another experiment in algae production for human consumption is underway at the University of Texas.

An historic statement, forgotten by most, was issued on September 25, 1945, by President Harry S. Truman. He claimed as additional territory of the continental United States an area four times as large as Texas, namely the seabed subsoil and waters of the continental shelf into the high seas and gulfs to the drop-off line, legally defined as a depth of six hundred feet where the shelf generally declines into the deep. Off New York it is over a hundred miles to the drop-off line, in Western Florida nearly two hundred, and a good hundred miles from Galveston, Texas.

The Shelf Doctrine was urged on Truman as a far-sighted definition of U.S. offshore oil rights. Test drilling at sea off California, Louisiana and Texas had already proven rich oil deposits beneath the seabed. Soon metal islands, "Texas towers," were to be towed out and anchored as well platforms. But Truman had claimed a lot more than oil. The water itself was included, which meant fishing rights. By long tradition they did not extend beyond a three-mile limit from a nation's shores. The President's proclamation started something. Everybody wanted in on the act: Persia laid claim to its Persian Gulf shelf. Since the Gulf is at no point as deep as six hundred feet, Persia's new territory ran right across to three miles of Arabia. Peru, which owns a narrow shelf due to the inconsiderate manner in which the Andes Mountains drop into the sea, seems to have claimed everything west except the Caroline Trench. This nation seized five whalers owned by Aristotle Socrates Onassis, the laird of Monte Carlo, two hundred miles at sea, and Lloyd's of London was obliged to pay three million dollars to bail them out.

Iceland drove British trawlers out of sight of land; gunplay broke out between American and Mexican shrimping fleets in the Mexican Gulf. The states of California, Texas and Louisiana resisted federal claims to their watery real estate. No one knew where international boundaries were any more. The drop-off line was forty miles off the mouth of the Rio Grande, the Mexican-United States border, in a shelf full of oil. Between Maine and Nova Scotia there is no drop-off line and the international border dribbled off vaguely in the Bay of Fundy. Texas towers were soon clanking far out of sight of land, with helicopter commutation for the crews. A hundred miles southeast of Cape Cod, the U.S. Air Force planted a Texas tower as a radar station, the first post of an expensive early warning fence to be planted at sea up and down the east coast.

Military and economic exploitation of the continental shelf was a reality ten years after Truman's proclamation. Free divers led the way. Geologist John Zeigler and Chief Underwater Photographer David Owen, of the Woods Hole Oceanographic Institution, dived with air lungs to survey for the foundations of the radar island on George's Bank. In the Gulf of Mexico, oil geologists were taking diving lessons. Humble Oil established a diving team, and Magnolia Oil sponsored a Recent Sediments Study off eastern Texas with a team of six divers, including four geologists led by Dr. Daniel Feray.

Among the products of the sea, petroleum is a mystery. Most geologists believe it is made of decayed marine animals, but nobody knows exactly how. Until recently, exploration aimed entirely for structural traps, or underground domes containing oil. These were detected by using a gravimeter, an electronic device which is placed level on the ground, or sea floor, as the case may be. It gives a recording of the gravity attraction of the earth at that point. If the reading differs from the known attraction of that latitude, it may be caused by an oil-bearing cavity. The next piece of evidence the explorers look for is limestone of the oil-making Eocene Period, seventy to forty-five million years ago. They know it is Eocene if they find an imbedded shell of the great limestone mason, *Nummulites*, a flat, round-shelled, single-celled animal which existed by the trillions of tons and built the crests of the Swiss Alps when sharks swam over London and Rome. One tiny shell of *Nummulites* will start a dance in a petroleum laboratory. It is an almost certain proof of oil. You must bet a good deal more money to make sure by test drilling.

Domes were all the rage until wildcatters, innocent of the geological verities, brought in the fabulous East Texas field with no domes at all. In the Pembina field in Alberta, Canada, test drills were grinding away for a cavity estimated to be 6,000 feet down, when they struck oil in a sand layer at 3,500 feet. It was the biggest reservoir found in 1953 in North America. Geologists called this new freak a "stratographic trap." It did not respond to gravimeters because there were no appreciable cavities. The oil was saturated in porous limestone or sand and sealed in by oilproof sediments.

Dr. Feray's team dived for information on existing life and sediments on the Gulf floor, which might give clues to the formation of stratigraphic traps in the Eocene epoch. Some clams and sea snails have changed little since then and probably choose similar homesteads, in either sand, mud or coral. The Texas geologists were checked out on U.S. Navy diving tests. They sailed on a converted shrimp boat, the *Cavalier*, equipped with dredges and drop corers. These devices collected bottom samples, but the investigators added a living dimension to the research. They dived to observe and collect sedentary animals and those living under the floor. They bottled natural gas bubbles from the floor and dug with geological hammers and dandelion spades for creatures burrowed in the bottom. In the bright reflected light of the floor and good water visibility, Feray's team experienced the real environment of petroleum-building. They took notes with wax crayons on plastic tablets strapped to their thighs, shot stills and movies, and bagged starfish, sand dollars, snails and clams. Their greatest depth attained was sixty-five feet. They reported, "The fish were friendly." Red snappers, angelfish, sheepsheads and triggerfish nuzzled their masks. Once another survey party twelve miles away set off dynamite in the water to make seismic records of the bottom structure. At the first shock, the divers thought someone was hitting their air bottles with a hammer. Otherwise the sea floor was silent, except when clams closed their shells with a click.

Before the Texas forays, Cousteau's *Calypso* oceanographic expeditions carried out an extensive geological survey in the Persian Gulf with its ten-man free-diving team, led by Frédéric Dumas and Albert Falco. The area off the coast of Trucial Oman, the former Pirate Coast of Arabia, was an oil-prospecting concession awarded to an Anglo-French consortium by the Sheikh of Abu Dhabi. The white French research ship carried four geologists and surveyors of the d'Arcy Exploration Company, the leader of which, a red-headed Australian named Allen Russell, took a couple of diving lessons and finned down to the floor with his little hammer. Cousteau's task was direct exploration with a marine gravimeter and rock cores taken from the floor in water depths to two hundred feet.

Drop coring is a method of obtaining samples from the floor without resorting to the heavy expense of drilling. One type of sediment corer is a weighted pipe with a sharp mouth which is dropped and drives into the bottom, sometimes boosted by an explosion on contact. It brings up a cross-section of the bottom soils. The most advanced pipes do not compress the layers, but are fitted with relieving pistons which bring up true vertical sections. Dr. Maurice Ewing, of Columbia University's Lamont Geological Observatory, has obtained sixty-foot cores from the Atlantic floor. One time he was coring the Caryn Sea Mount, halfway between New York and Bermuda, a mile-high cone already charted by sonar. It seemed peculiar to Ewing. His pipe came up full of lava. He had discovered a volcano right in the middle of a circle two thousand miles in diameter considered devoid of them.

The British Discovery Expedition once dropped a coring pipe in the Atlantic which came up with a top layer of pure soft coal. Startled at the phenomenon, the expedition took more cores in the same place. None contained coal. The scientists had scored a bull's-eye on a lump of coal dropped by some old steamer. Pipes have often come up with sections of unlucky fish which were slumbering on the bottom.

The coring pipe used on the *Calypso* was a rock sampler eighteen inches long, sticking down from a half-ton bomb-shaped weight. The first drop was in forty feet of water. The boatswain swung the bomb over the stern on a crane. The corer hung from a manila hawser with another long loose line attached to haul it up. Skipper François Saôut cut the hawser and the bomb whizzed down. When winched up, the pipe was missing. The *Calypso* divers, who had been watching the employment of this brutal device without enthusiasm, went down and found the pipe lying on the floor, surrounded by an inquisitive group of fish. The pipe was bent into a Z and the supertempered cutting mouth was crumpled like a paper napkin. Yet the bottom appeared to be level sand.

The divers dug into it with their hands. An inch beneath was a smooth rock surface, which seemed as hard as granite. (This rock has not yet been identified.) Here and there the rock was pierced by the burrows of fragile-shelled mussels, which have a coring trick better than steel pipes: they manufacture a body secretion which dissolves rocks. One of the rock-eaters, the Mediterranean *datte de mer*, a finger-sized bivalve with a dainty shell that cracks if you drop it on a deck, digs into marble and granite to twice its own length. It is the diving gourmet's greatest delicacy. The sea date turns hardstone piers and jetties into Swiss cheese and harbor divers finish the destruction with hammers as they raid piers for the mussels. The boss never knows what happens under the surface.

Wearing sarcastic grins, the *Calypso's* divers climbed the ladder holding up the ruined coring pipe. They returned with geological hammers and chipped rock samples from the edges of the mussel holes. With one diver holding a chisel against the floor and another hanging in space and pounding it with a maul, the *Calypso* team secured samples from four hundred stations in two months.

Other riches of the floor are now being exploited. In Malaya a company is prospecting tin ore on the sea bottom. The cement used in the reconstruction of the French naval base at Toulon was mixed with sand dredged from underwater quarries located by G.E.R.S. divers. Thousands of tons of sand fill for a New Jersey highway was pumped from the floor of New York Harbor in 1955. Slabs of manganese have been found on the bottom. Phosphates and glauconite are plentiful off the United States east coast and in the Agulhas Bank, where the amount of pure calcium phosphate in a dredging is up to 50 per cent of the volume. The phosphates were formed by vast tragedies among marine animals which occur when a current shifts its course. The water temperature changes suddenly, and all the animals in an area die and fall to the floor. The decomposing bones form ammonium phosphate which reacts with the calcium carbonate of the bottom to make calcium phosphate. It is used as fertilizer, in the manufacture of ceramics and enamel and in medicine. These thermal massacres included one in the Western Atlantic in 1882, in which dead fish floated six feet thick on the ocean between Boston and New York. How many more deaths there were may be guessed by the fact that when fish are killed in an underwater explosion, only about 10 per cent rise to the surface. The rest sink to the bottom.

Apart from the mineral riches of the floor, ocean water itself is a chemical bonanza. It contains all the known elements, including gold. The yellow stuff is one-billionth part of salt water. In 1935, an Australian named George Duncan built a sea-gold refinery, which pumped fifty tons of sea water a day through a chemical extraction process, and yielded ten ounces of gold. The fixed market price of gold was $35 an ounce, so Duncan grossed $350 a day. His plant cost $40,000 and he had to hire people and power to run it. Duncan did not get rich. The weirdest quest for ocean gold was the German *Meteor* Expedition of 1924–28, led by the Nobel Prize chemist, Fritz Haber. He won his backing by claiming Germany could pay her war debts with gold refined from sea water. Carrying a gold filtration plant and excellent conventional oceanographic resources, the *Meteor* plied the North and South Atlantic for three years, amassing immense data on oceanography. Of course, the gold process was much too expensive to pay off, but the gains for science were historic. Many oceanographers believe Haber's gold was a satirical disguise for the real purpose of the expeditions —to reconnoiter the Atlantic for U-boats. Certainly Doenitz's World War II *Unterzeebooten* marauded in the Atlantic as if it were their private lake.

The chemical resources of ocean water are inexhaustible. A single cubic mile of sea water weighs about 4,000 million tons and contains 166 million tons of dissolved salts. And how many cubic miles are there to work on? The *Canadian Mining Journal* estimates 300 million. This ore body is as handy as the nearest shore line. The oceans also contain a lot of water, a substance that is becoming rare. In the oil fields of Arabia, on the edge of the Persian Gulf, drinking water costs more than high octane gasoline. The water table in the United States, particularly the West, is receding at an alarming rate. In 1955, sixty-five United States research projects were striving to convert saline water to potable standards, and there were at least that many in the rest of the world. One of these, on the French Riviera, was a sea-water converter constructed by Henri Coanda, a tall, worldly, French scientist. Using no other power source than the sun, Coanda produces cold fresh water with its natural bacteria undisturbed: "living water," as he calls it. Coanda collects heat with parabolic mirrors, which run steam turbines that pump sea water into gravity tanks and circulate it through a solar furnace and heat exchangers. The water never reaches the boiling point so that healthy bacteria are not killed. For one square yard of mirror surface in a twelve-hour day of sunshine, Coanda produces twenty-five gallons of fresh water. He has enough excess solar energy to run an irrigation pumping system. He has demonstrated, in the two years that his pilot plant has been operating, that his system may produce water at the quantity, quality and cost of a metropolitan watershed operation. At the heart of the system are jet nozzles which work by the Coanda Effect, his discovery in manipulating jet streams. The Effect increases the volume and velocity from a jet pipe six to twenty times without further power intervention of moving parts, as shown by tests at Purdue University in 1948. In the solar still, sea water is shot up from Coanda nozzles with such force that it pulverizes into water vapor and brine. The water vapor passes from the top into heat exchangers and the brine runs off at the bottom.

Sea water contains a small amount of copper, which we may have to extract in the near future. The world's known high-grade copper deposits will be exhausted in sixty years. Then more expensive production will be needed on low-grade ores. At present copper can be refined from sea water at about the same cost as from low-grade ore. The reason why oysters are cultivated off river estuaries is that rivers have a larger percentage of copper than the sea, and oysters love it. The oyster pumps a barrel of sea water through its digestive system each day. French oysters are pale and English and American oysters are greenish because of the different ration of copper in the water. The sewers of greater New York liberate two thousand tons of copper into the sea each year. "The people of New York," said E. Frankland Armstrong and L. Mackenzie Miall in *Raw Materials From the Sea*, "provide ample copper for their oysters."

Sir John "Challenger" Murray and his convivial colleague, the Belgian Abbé Renard, two great oceanographers of the nineteenth century, studied thousands of bottom sediments collected on the H.M.S. *Challenger* expedition in the 1870s, and arrived at remarkable glimpses of the involved chemical interactions in the oceans. Consider the making of glauconite, one of the most common silicates found on the continental shelf. The pair were convinced that it is formed when animal planktons die and their shells rain down into mud containing iron. Sulphates and bacteria in the water react on the dead organic matter to make iron sulphide. Then oxygen in the water gets to work and translates it into ferric hydroxide, which combined with silica and potassium in the water, produces glauconite. The sea is a mysterious retort, a vast challenge to chemistry. Dr. H. K. Benson, a chemist, said, "Marine animals and plants can concentrate the life-vital elements

found in the sea far better than physical and chemical processes humans
now know."

A cubic mile of sea water contains over 25 million tons of magnesium
salts. Magnesium was first commercially produced in France in 1857 to
make photographic flash powder. The first bar of magnesium refined from
the sea was a British feat. An American firm operates two gigantic refineries
at Freeport and Velasco, Texas, which drink from the Gulf of Mexico 90
million pounds of magnesium a year. The process brings the chemistry of
the sea out into factory tanks, for the precipitant is milk of lime, made from
oyster shells dredged in Galveston Bay. The biggest British plant making
metal out of water pumps ten million gallons a day, using as a precipitant
milk of calcined dolomite quarried on land. It produces twice the Texas
amount of magnesium per water volume, for the dolomite already contains
magnesium. The airplane is what is making the sea so busy. About a half
ton of magnesium in alloys goes into each plane. Magnesium is fired into
the air in star shells and tracers and came down on houses in incendiary
bombs during the old-fashioned wars. The original use in flash photography, now a hundred years old, is still enormous. The metal is alloyed with
aluminum to improve resistance to marine corrosion. It also prevents caking
in table salt. It is embodied in rubber diving masks and Epsom salts, and is
mixed in the ink of this page.

When General Gaius Julius Caesar came back from the conquest of Gaul
he was given a triumph, the Roman equivalent of the grand opening of a
Los Angeles supermarket. Crowds turned out to see Julius' new gown, the
special Tyrian purple number reserved for emperors, victors, knights and
those politicians who could promote it. The purple toga was like a mink
coat; many elusive animals had to die to make it. The animal that paid was
Murex brandaris, a bristling rock shell of the Mediterranean, whose decayed
flesh yielded imperial purple dye. The conchological poet, Professor Josiah
Keep, has mused over *Murex* in the following passage: "How beautifully
the different sciences are joined together! Cities of the Mediterranean come
trooping past us, their inhabitants clothed in strange garments, which reflect
the bright colors of the summer sunshine." Roman dressmakers also kept a
lot of chaps busy diving to get the rock shell. Slaves were pressed into
service as divers. When Christianity took up headquarters in Rome, the
Popes mixed old with new. To our day His Holiness wears Tyrian purple,
now known as *dibromoindigo*.

It is a kind of iodine, a nonmetallic element of the sea, discovered by a
French gunpowder maker during the Napoleonic wars. Bernard Courtois
could not get saltpeter because of the English blockade (while England was
hiring Robert Fulton to blow up the French blockade). Courtois had to
make saltpeter by mixing manure with pounded mortar from old walls and

boiling it with wood ashes. His works was near the sea, from which farmers dragged kelp, dried it and burned it to make a soil conditioner. The gunpowder maker found that seaweed ashes could be used in his process instead of pulverized limestone, and were cheaper.

One day, while cleaning his copper kettles with strong sulphuric acid over heat, Courtois saw lilac vapors rising and condensing on the top of the vessels in hard, dark crystals. This was iodine, named by Joseph Louis Gay-Lussac in 1813. It is a nomadic element residing in earth, air and ocean, and skipping from one to another as it pleases. Iodine is washed from the sky by rain, impregnates soil and rides silt down rivers to the ocean where it builds seaweed and imperial *Murex* and climbs on top of the storm combers to be hurled to the sky again in spray.

Those are a few of the vast riches of the sea and the shelf that have been exploited. The scouts of this modern wilderness are free divers. They have reached less than halfway down the continental shelf on compressed air. Commandant Tailliez believes that helium-oxygen and other gaseous mixtures will open the entire shelf for swimming prospectors. However, to give divers security on the drop-off line six hundred feet down requires physiology and equipment research that cannot be brought to bear by the small forces and pitiful sums now exerted on the problem. There are less than fifty diving physiologists active in the world today, and only a handful of them are working on the shelf attack, often without effective liaison with each other.

There is hope in the fact that wealthy oil companies are aware of what diving has achieved. Air-lung manufacturers may be able to gain enough profits on the leaping amateur market to begin basic investigation of man on the drop-off line.

Yet before this is even underway, the vanguard is on its way to the abyss.

16

To the Abyss

IN 1951 the grand adventurer, film artist and story-teller, Robert Flaherty, saw Captain Cousteau's first undersea films and was as excited as a boy. Flaherty, who looked like one of Hogarth's eighteenth-century squires, said, "Captain, you must meet Will Beebe!" He brought them together at a dinner party at his local, The Coffee House Club of New York. Cousteau showed the junior's deference to a master that characterizes the relations of French men of learning. Dr. William Beebe was an inspiration to the new generation of underwater men in Europe.

Dr. Beebe, unlike Cousteau, was an academically trained scientist, a curator of birds at twenty-two, author of a mammoth monograph on pheasants, explorer of South America, the Himalayas and Borneo—a famous man before he went under water with a bucket helmet in the early twenties. That switched his interests to marine life. He knew how to fire others with his enthusiasm. Films, lectures, *National Geographic* articles and a long line of best-selling books had come from his expeditions to a great audience. Not the least of Beebe's talents was his knack for charming wealthy men into sponsoring researches and providing ships. Explorers regard the hardships of the field as a holiday after their ordeals to raise the money.

After several years of helmet walking and photography, Beebe looked down a reef edge "into the green depths where illuminations like moonlight showed waving sea fans and milling fish far beyond the length of my hose." He had netted strange creatures from the unknown below, and had one time discussed with President Theodore Roosevelt how to visit them. Beebe sketched a cylindrical depth chamber, while "T.R." preferred a sphere. Beebe built a cylinder in 1926 and announced his plans to dive a

mile. The newspaper story agitated a foot-loose young geologist and engineer from New England named Otis Barton, who had been designing a
sphere to go two miles down. Barton tried to tell Dr. Beebe his ball was
superior to a cylinder. He wrote letter after letter without reply and felt
Beebe "was as unapproachable as an Indian potentate and twice as wary."
Beebe had received a flood of eccentric designs for depth vehicles and Barton later found that he "was not instinctively fond of mechanical gadgets."
Through a mutual friend, Barton at last met the scientist in December,
1928. Beebe looked at the blueprints and said he would be willing to test
Barton's sphere. Barton rushed to construct it with his own money. He
fitted it with four fused-quartz windows, "chunks of melted sand (that)
cost me five hundred dollars apiece," said Barton in his fascinating auto-
biography, *The World Beneath the Sea*. Barton joined Beebe's field camp
on Nonsuch Island near Bermuda to organize a tender and lowering gear
for the "Bathysphere," as Beebe named it. Barton said, "Life on the island
revolved around Dr. Beebe, who spent his free moments on a ledge studying the heavens through a telescope. Before dinner he gave each of us one
whiskey and soda, and later, in his bunk, he read us *Barrack Room Ballads*."

Barton chartered an old hulk, the *Ready*, as tender for the Bathysphere.
Then he discovered the *Ready's* winches could not lift his five-ton sphere.
Barton simply melted it down and built another half as heavy. He said it
looked like "an enormous, inflated and slightly cockeyed bullfrog." The
first test dive was made off Nonsuch in June, 1930. Beebe and Barton
squirmed through the fifteen-inch hatch and were bolted in by seamen
driving sledge hammers on the big nuts. It was nerve-wracking for the
hydronauts inside. They turned on the oxygen rebreathing system and
watched Gloria Hollister, a tall, beautiful blonde assistant of Beebe's, bait
the outside to attract deep-sea animals.

As they sank into the green water, Barton felt the seat of his pants getting wet. Water was squirting in under the hatch. "Beebe," he cried,
"there's a leak. Shall I phone John to pull us up?" Beebe replied, "No, I
think not. Don't frighten them on deck." Having looked after the morale
of John Tee-Van, Beebe's able assistant, and the others safe on the boat,
they continued on down to eight hundred feet, shipping only five gallons
or so of water. Both were semi-intoxicated by oxygen. "We felt warm and
peppy, overoptimistic and ready to welcome any adventure," Barton reported.

At the observation window, Beebe busied himself making notes of what
he saw, and passing them to Barton who phoned them up to Miss Hollister.
Later Beebe was to phone an international broadcast from the Bathysphere
2,200 feet down.

For their second dive, the leak was daubed shut with white lead and they went deeper. They also reduced the oxygen flow to stay sober. At a thousand feet Barton interrupted his entranced shipmate with a mechanical problem. The inch-thick electric cable, an unstretched line which entered the sphere through a stuffing box, was slowly intruding the cramped ball, forced by sea pressure. The cable settled on Barton. Beebe turned from the window and said, "Reminds me of the death of Laocoön and his sons in the coils of the serpent," and went back to fish-watching. Fourteen feet of rubber snake squeezed through on the shrinking Barton before they surfaced. Gloria Hollister went down with Barton and took photos of phosphorescent fish. The thousand-watt lamp on the outside nearly cooked them inside, and had to be turned too low to light photos. Barton experimented on the sphere and lowered it without occupants for tests.

On one of these trials without people, the ball was terribly heavy coming up, laying a heavy strain on the winch. They guessed it was full of water. On deck the sphere squirted. Beebe started opening a wing bolt on the hatch. The pent-up water pressure exploded with a roar, as he leaped aside. The bolt screamed down the deck like shrapnel and mist puffed from the bolt hole. Beebe stuck a thermometer in and judged from the water temperature the Bathysphere had flooded at two thousand feet.

Otis Barton presented the Bathysphere to the New York Zoological Society, Beebe's parent organization. Barton wanted to be a big underwater movie producer. He had expensive picaresque adventures with crazy boats and odd associates, including Floyd Crosby, the cinematographer of *Taboo*; Count Ilya Tolstoy; a shark-fighting girl diver; an Arkansas cowboy diver; banana boats; pregnant sharks; and a Choctaw Indian who smoked marihuana and thought he was a Filipino. Barton worked five years and distributed his substance on this grand enterprise. His second submersible leading lady, a Powers model, lost her bucket helmet during the unplanned entrance of a manta ray. It became Barton's best thrill sequence.

In the meantime, Beebe was pressing into greater depths in the Bathysphere. In September, 1932, he and Barton reached seventeen hundred feet, beyond the furthest penetration of light. "From here down, for two billion years there had been no day or night, no summer or winter, no passing of time until we came to record it," wrote Beebe in his vivid book, *Half Mile Down*. They keep the lights off inside and outside the sphere so that Beebe could concentrate on observing phosphorescent animals. He saw saber-toothed viperfish and dull golden siphonophores—colonies of microorganisms strung in weird string forms. He sighted dragon-fish with a double line of lights along their bodies, and at 1,850 feet, Beebe saw the first deep squids *in situ*. "Their great eyes, each illumined with a circle of colored lights, stared at me—those unbelievably intelligent yet reasonless eyes backed by no brain and set in a snail," he said.

At 1,950 feet they had a scare. The Bathysphere began to pitch, banging them about. "For a fraction of a second, which seemed an exceedingly long time to us, it felt as if we had broken loose and were turning over," Beebe wrote. Every two or three minutes the bouncing started up again. It was an unavoidable part of going into the depths like a yoyo on a string. As the tender rolled, the Bathysphere bounced.

They continued to 2,200 feet. There Beebe saw a fish never seen before. It was an elongated animal with no visible illumination organs, yet it was bathed in sepulchral light. The fish turned toward the window and the light went out. Another onset of pitching threatened to smash up their oxygen system, so they phoned to be hauled up. A hundred feet higher Beebe saw two unknown six-foot fish, shaped something like barracudas. They held their mouths open and their fangs were luminous. Pale blue lights ran along their sides and from their chins and tails there hung threads with red and blue lights on the ends. Beebe named these apparitions Untouchable Bathysphere Fish.

Beebe had put a live lobster in a cheesecloth bag outside above his window, thinking that it would be crushed by pressure and give off tasty matter to attract fish. The lobster came up alive and kicking from eight tons total pressure on its shell.

The original equipment of the Bathysphere was rather makeshift. Several individuals and corporations contributed excellent new fittings for dives in 1934. Beebe carried with him on every descent a copy of the classic *The Depths of the Ocean*, by Sir John Murray and Johan Hjort.

Beebe was not primarily interested in breaking depth records, nor were the depth argonauts who came afterward. These machines were built to make scientific observations in the depths of the sea. It did not matter if you went three hundred feet or a mile, if intelligent use was made of the privilege. Greater depths were important only because of what could be learned of life in these zones, which may not dwell in higher levels. Beebe prepared for his third dive of 1934 to three thousand feet, the limit of his cable. It would be over four times the greatest depth attained in Galeazzi's butoscopic turret.

Barton left his interminable underwater film epic to join Beebe on the big dive. On August 15, the tug *Gladisfaden* towed the barge out to sea. Beebe gave the drama of departure short shrift in his report: "Three hours later Mr. Barton and I were dropped overboard far out at sea."

At 1,680 feet Beebe strained his eyes intently on a disconcerting phenomenon he had seen on previous dives and could never understand. A vague, colorless creature came out of the night, turned in front of his window and flared so bright red that it lighted his face. Previously Beebe simply reported that it "exploded," for he could not see it after the flash. This time he kept his eyes sharply on it. It was a big red shrimp, which used the stunning flash as a defense against hungry types that came too near. At 2,450 feet Beebe saw an oval fish twenty feet long, perhaps a whale or whale shark. It was too far away to make out any details. He regretted that he could not realize this monster for the benefit of the "size-conscious human race." He felt that at least it showed "what still remains for the pioneer explorer of the depths of the sea."

The Bathysphere came to a soft stop 3,028 feet down. "I knew this was my ultimate floor," said Beebe. "The cable on the winch was very near its end." They were in a pressure of more than a ton per square inch. They were hanging a mile over the floor and there were only a few turns of the cable to hold them there. Beebe studied the black space which no man was to reach again for fifteen years. He watched the lamps of passing creatures for only five minutes. Captain Sylvester and John Tee-Van sounded anxious on the phone. A heavy vibration struck the globe and it began to rise. The primitive winch drum was made of wood, and the people above were anxious for them. A beam swell was rocking the lighter. The men a half mile below heard a sharp "plunk" and wondered if they were falling free to the floor, where, Barton said, "We would have had an awfully long time to make observations." It was a bad moment for the party on the tender. They looked for steel cable to come writhing out of tension from the sea. But it was only the snapping of the line that guided the cable on the winch drum. The men in the ball were sorry for the anxiety they caused Tee-Van's people. Beebe said, "Truly we in the Bathysphere had the best of it at all times."

The next attempt to take observers to the abyss was a vehicle called the "bathyscaphe," from the Greek for "deep boat." It was a free submarine vehicle, a depth dirigible with a pressure-resisting ball like Barton's, suspended from a metal envelope containing a lifting fluid, high-octane gasoline, which was much lighter than water and almost incompressible.

The man who proposed the idea was the Swiss physicist, Auguste Piccard, the adventurer of pressure extremities. He went 55,557 feet up in a balloon and 10,395 feet down in the sea in another balloon, the bathyscaphe. I called on 71-year-old Professor Piccard last year in his hotel across from St. Germain-des-Pres in Paris. He was a tall man with a large frame, a high-domed head and silky, white hair that touched his shoulders. He had a long face, a well-modeled nose and the rosy lips of a young girl. Hinged to the tops of his spectacles were powerful magnifying lenses, which he snapped into place to read print. With him was his dark, towering son, Jacques, the pilot of the third bathyscaphe, the *Trieste*.

Three bathyscaphes have been built. The first was the *FNRS-2*, standing for *Fonds National de la Recherche Scientifique*, the Belgian government scientific research fund. The number two meant that it was the second balloon the fund had provided for Piccard. The *FNRS-1* was the stratosphere balloon. Piccard and his associate, the Belgian nuclear physicist, Max Cosyns, started building the first depth balloon before World War II, and had actually cast the pressureproof steel ball when war stopped the project. Dr. Cosyns, an enemy of Hitler, survived several years in the German genocide factories, came home and revived the deep-boat scheme. He

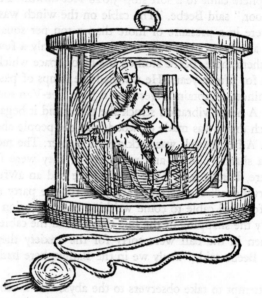

An early diving-sphere design by Nicolo Tartaglia, 1554. It could not have worked.

and Piccard completed the *FNRS-2* in 1948 and took her to a deep off West Africa for the first dives. The sphere was designed to resist the pressure of 13,000 feet, the average depth of the oceans. The ball was well engineered, but the thin metal envelope containing the gasoline was not seaworthy. After a 4,600-foot automatic dive without men, the bathyscaphe was wrecked in mild surface swell while the mother ship tried to recover her.

Commandants Tailliez and Cousteau had joined the test with the French Navy Undersea Research Group. They believed fervently in the principle and fought to continue bathyscaphe experiments. Tailliez was posted to Indo-China, which left Cousteau to champion the vehicle. In 1951 Cousteau induced the Belgian and French governments to sign a treaty to build a second deep boat, using the pressure ball from the first model, new generous Belgian money and the engineering facilities and diving knowledge of the G.E.R.S. The second bathyscaphe was built at the Toulon arsenal under the direction of Piccard, Cousteau and a naval engineer named André-Joseph-Marie Gempp. There were many improvements in design. Gempp designed an envelope shaped like a submarine. It had a vital new feature, the *sas*, an entrance shaft leading down from the conning tower through the envelope to the entrance of the ball, so that the two-man crew could enter the machine while it was afloat. In the previous model, the crew had to enter the ball while the bathyscaphe was held out of the water by a crane. Piccard and a companion, Dr. Théodore Monod, had to spend twelve hours inside the ball in the only piloted dive of the former Bathyscaphe— to eighty feet. The *sas* would be flooded with water after the men were inside, so that it did not need to be pressurized. On the return to the surface the crew would blow the water out of the *sas* with compressed air.

The Indo-Chinese War pulled Commandant Gempp off the job. Professor Piccard grew impatient. There was a certain amount of friction between himself and the French Navy group. Jacques Piccard told me it came from a Navy lack of appreciation of civilian scientists and foreigners to boot. The G.E.R.S people felt that Professor Piccard was trying to rush the construction of a revolutionary submarine which needed testing of each feature and great deliberation in construction. The situation came to a head late in 1951 when Professor Piccard pulled out of the committee and went to Switzerland and Italy to raise money for a third bathyscaphe solely under his control. He and son Jacques got the steel foundry, Acciaierie di Terni, to forge a new ball and the Cantieri Riuniti dell' Adriatico, a dockyard in Trieste, to build an envelope resembling the Gempp design. Final assembling was by the shipbuilding firm of Navalmeccanica in Naples. The Italian Navy weighed in with escort vessels and docking courtesies. The third bathyscaphe, the *Trieste*, was achieved in less than two years by a retired professor and his thirty-one-year-old son, educated as an economic historian. However, it turned out that the Toulon bathyscaphe, the *FNRS-3*, went into the water before the *Trieste*.

In August, 1953, Jacques and his father dived to 3,500 feet off Naples, short of Otis Barton's 4,500-foot descent on a cable in 1950 in his benthoscope, the third depth sphere he built. Jacques Piccard described the dive to me: "We go down smoothly. I look out the window. We have our outside searchlights on, shining down into the dark. I see the ground beautiful and clear. I tell my father, 'We are landing.' Instantly we are in complete darkness. We feel no shock. The voltimeter and ampimeter are normal, indicating the lights are still on. What is this? There is a faint glow outside, and I see what has happened. We are buried over the window in mud. The bathyscaphe has plunged into the bottom. We hope to see the ground, but not the underground. Outside it looks like *farine*, how you say—wheat flour? There are very interesting little shells mixed with it. We do not fear anything. If we enter so peacefully, we could go out. After fifteen minutes, I touch the button which releases the iron pellets in the ballast tubes. We do not come out. I give another shot and the *farine* disappears. We are too light and go fast to the surface."

The Piccards made fifteen dives in the first two years. "We never see sharks or great fishes," Jacques said, "just siphonophores, plankton, jellyfish, crabs and starfish. On the ground are little beasts swimming at great speed, perhaps blennies. They are lovely to watch in the shadows of the projector. These fish, living in total darkness, seem indifferent to our bright lights. There are many animal holes, *comme ça*." Piccard made a one-inch circle with his fingers. "We watch the holes for a long time and see the head of a fish come out. He swims and others come out. If we move the *Trieste* along the floor, whist! they are all back in their holes."

The positive buoyancy of the bathyscaphe was created by four silos loaded with iron-shot pellets, held in a wet tube by electromagnets. The pilot touched a button which cut the electricity to jettison pellets. There were many situations in which very delicate adjustment of trim was necessary to slow the descent and stop in midwater, or, as the vehicle cooled in the depths and became heavier. Young Piccard told me the expenditure of pellets into the sea was their greatest operating expense. "They cost about 25 cents a yard for a dive," he said sadly. The deepest dive of the *Trieste* in 1954 cost them $866.25 in iron shot. The sum may sound silly to an organization like the U.S. Navy, but it was a vast amount to the professor and his pilot.

This dive, to 10,395 feet off Naples in September, 1953, more than doubled the greatest previous depth reached by man. The attempt was not to "break the record." From its very inception the bathyscaphe design was intended for this medium range, just as Barton's Bathysphere was limited to 3,000 feet and his benthoscope to 5,000. The depth on the big dive was determined by the geography of the Mediterranean, where there have been found only two depths greater than the 13,000-feet range of the bathyscaphes, deeps charted by the *Calypso* expeditions off Zante Island, and Cape Matapan, Greece. The Piccards dived to a vast sandy submarine plateau south of Ponza Island, where soundings showed depths from 9,600 to 10,400 feet.

The *Trieste* was towed out to Ponza by the Italian Navy tug *Tenace*, accompanied by the corvette, the *Fenice*, which was to police the area of the dive. It was thick with fishermen, rowboats, sightseeing yachts and even water skiers. They stayed overnight in Ponza. The Professor got indigestion on a lobster, while the Mayor of Ponza boasted of the island's economy, which was based on lobsters, tourists and Ponzans in New York. There were five thousand on the island and eight thousand in New York.

The next day they went out again. The corvette chased the sightseers, and under a gray sky, the *Trieste* went down with her Italian and Swiss flags flying into "the realm of eternal calm," as Professor Piccard put it. In the cramped ball the big Piccards adjusted themselves. Father crouched at the window and six-foot, five-inch Jacques stooped over the controls. When they passed the 6,900-foot level reached by the *FNRS-3* on a test dive near Toulon the month before, Professor Piccard was in virgin space. He felt a calm elation like the one he had nine miles in the stratosphere in a balloon, but "here there was no sun, no moon, no stars, only night and mystery." Jacques triggered the electromagnet and dropped a quantity of pellets. It slowed their falling speed. The manometer showed they were in the pressure of 10,300 feet. They touched bottom gently this time and did not enter it. Professor Piccard thought of Akleh-ben-Nafy, the ninth-century zealot of Islam, who rode as far west as he could in Africa, continued into the Atlantic surf, reined up, waved his scimitar and shouted toward Mecca, "Allah is my witness that only the sea prevents me from riding on and converting other peoples to the Prophet by fire and sword." In Piccard's case only the earth prevented him from going deeper. He was at an impasse. The Italian Navy no longer had bases in the Atlantic from which it could tow him to greater deeps.

The Piccards did not stay long. Soon they were soaring for the surface. Above, the corvette fussed back and forth, clearing a wide area for the emergence of the bathyscaphe. As the *Trieste* neared the surface, a speedboat roared into the open area, towing an Italian movie starlet on water skis. Cameramen were making publicity shots of her nibs. The corvette screamed at them through the loud hailer, but the publicity outfit continued to circle round. The captain of the *Fenice* thought of firing a warning shot over them. But he got a better idea. He turned a fire hose on the movie expedition. The *Trieste* popped up safely.

The French bathyscaphe was, in the meantime, methodically test-diving off Toulon. The program called for ten dives, stepping down by stages. Each major increase in depth was preceded by an automatic dive without passengers. The commander of the *FNRS-3* was another of those beanpoles, like Beebe and the Piccards, who somehow got into a line of work requiring them to spend hours inside balls with much less than six feet of headroom. He was Commandant Georges S. Houot, six feet four inches tall, a bashful, quiet man with large dark eyes. Houot had been posted in 1952 to succeed Cousteau as commander of the A.E.R.S. research and diving vessel, the *Élie Monnier* and to take over the *FNRS-3*. After Cousteau had showed him over the diving tender, Houot confessed that he was the last man in the world to lead an underwater team. After a mild polio attack a couple of years before his doctor had forbidden him to go swimming. Cousteau and Commandant Tailliez begged the Navy to relieve Houot, but he was confirmed in the job.

Later Georges Houot was to dive deeper than anyone had ever gone in the ocean. His engineer and crewmate was a theatrically handsome, resourceful young man named Pierre-Henri Willm. The two saw the *FNRS-3* through to completion and dived her on all tests. Much more equipment went into the French boat than the Piccards had been able to afford, such as an ultrasounder to accurately gauge her landings and exact depths. The National Geographic Society sent from America the services and deep automatic flash cameras of Dr. Harold E. Edgerton. Another advantage over Piccard's vehicle was the fact that France had a naval base at Dakar, French West Africa. Southwest of Dakar there was a deep of 13,300 feet, 36 hours out at the towing speed of a seagoing tug.

One winter morning I went out to see one of the last test dives off Toulon, aboard the *Élie Monnier*, which towed the bathyscaphe. The tender, a big captured German sea tug, hauled the little submarine on a 550-foot line. The maximum speed was four knots and it took a long time to pass the harbor *digue*, and a lot longer in the choppy sea outside. The bathyscaphe rode evenly with her decks awash and occasional spray over the bathtub, or conning tower. I went into the hot wardroom, where Houot, Willm and Commandant Georges Ortolan, the rugged skipper of the research ship, were gathered with a vehement conversational band over a morning *casse-croûte* of bread, *pâté* and authoritative red *pinard*, the French Navy wine issue. Ortolan made room for me on the banquette.

The *Élie Monnier* vibrated under the tow and pitched in a most peculiar fashion in the whitecaps. Ortolan took an experienced look at my complexion and, with a sympathetic smile, silently gave way, so I could take the breeze. I sheltered near a door where I could lean out in the cold and take deep breaths. One of the *Élie Monnier's* junior officers was leaning halfway over the rail, which made me feel less mortified but still embarrassed. The naval correspondent of *Le Figaro*, Pierre Dubard, stayed at table, swallowing and turning alternately red and green like a traffic light, but would not give up on the yarns.

Six miles out the *Élie Monnier* hove to and a noisy convention was held on the afterdeck around the towering Houot and Ortolan, who surveyed the pitching submarine. Divers waddled out on deck in slick black suits and threw out a rubber raft, which bobbed up to rail level and fell eight feet down. Houot said to me, "The meteorologist says the weather may turn bad. We will not dive. We will have an exercise for the divers, putting the crew aboard the submarine, making the underwater checks and taking the crew off." The divers vaulted the rail, holding their masks in place, and dropped seatfirst into the waves. They struck out underwater for the *FNRS-3*. Midshipman André Michaudon, in a windbreaker, stepped deftly into the rubber boat. Two seamen, bulging with life jackets, paddled him out to the bathyscaphe. The waves tended to obscure the view, so I went to the bridge deck to watch.

Michaudon leaped to the narrow deck of the *FNRS-3* and ran up into the bathtub. He disappeared into the *sas*. Below in the rolling ball, he watched the divers flipping about, fending themselves off the swaying envelope. They went through the motions of removing the security dogs from the electromagnets and saw that the guide chain was hanging properly from the ball. If one of the clamps were left on the shot silos in an actual dive, the crew might be trapped, too heavy, on the floor. At length the practice was over and the sea party returned. The *Élie Monnier* dragged the submarine back to Toulon and eased her into a narrow berth surrounded by barbed wire and armed sentries. The precautions were not for military security; the bathyscaphe was not a secret. She was protected against smokers; she held twenty thousand gallons of gasoline.

Houot and Willm sent the bathyscaphe to Dakar in a freighter in January, 1954, and flew there in a Comet jet liner for dives number nine and ten of the test program. After that scientific utilization of the depth vehicle would begin. Why did Houot and Willm want to fall into pressure of almost six thousand pounds per square inch? They were confident of the vehicle, but pressure could kill them a hundred ways, so fallible are man's mechanisms. Many people saw little importance to the bathyscaphe, including some marine experts, whose business was inquisitiveness about the sea. Harold Edgerton was checking his electronic flash installations on the lower envelope of the *FNRS-3* one day in the Toulon arsenal, when a French officer strolled by and said, "Ah, that is the kodak for sharks, *ne c'est pas?*" Edgerton grinned and the visitor said in sincere curiosity, "Actually, what *are* you hoping to find in the pictures?" Edgerton said, "If I knew what, brother, I wouldn't bother looking."

Houot and Willm were not themselves scientists. They were breaking in a tool of science. They knew the tiny submarine promised much for learning, and they were proud of their duty to prove her. They were to be rewarded by the same emotion as Tensing and Hillary atop Mount Everest, two men reaching the uttermost accomplishment after a history of team effort, organization and self-reliance. Practically nothing was known about the depths, except that life exists in the deepest trenches. In 1951 the Danish *Galatea* expedition took soil and water samples from the floor over thirty-four thousand feet down in the Mindanas Trench in the Philippines. The *Galatea* brought up seventeen anemones, sixty-one cucumbers and three shellfish in the bottom trawl. The night of the abyss is the Ultima Thule of earth science.

As Houot and Willm waited on diving weather in Dakar, Professor Piccard gave an interview in Italy in which he stated that the *FNRS-3*'s sphere was defective. After all, he had built it in 1938. He recommended that the automatic dive should be to twenty thousand feet to be sure of the ball. He wrote to the French Admiralty that X-rays would show minute air bubbles in the castings of the sphere. Willm said the letter caused "a rather discouraging interlude," while Navy engineers went to the Belgian steel works that had cast the ball and went over the original X-rays. There were minute flaws in the X-rays. The Admiralty assured Houot and Willm that the ball would be safe for a thirteen thousand-foot dive and left it to their discretion how to proceed. They elected to go ahead on plan.

During the long, rough voyage to the diving grounds, the bathyscaphe broke her tow and went adrift at night in 12-foot waves. The *Élie Monnier* kept the little submarine in a searchlight all night and restored the towing cable in the morning. Willm went to her in a rubber boat and set the automatic ballast release for 13,500 feet. Then he locked himself out and she went down empty. The dive was figured to last three hours. The escort vessels moved five miles off to avoid collision when she came up. A Navy flying boat patrolling the diving area spotted her surfacing almost exactly on time and radioed the ships. Houot and Willm got aboard with two tanks of compressed air and blew the *sas*. They worked the conning tower hatch open and found the entry tube still half full of water. They bailed out 500 gallons with a tool bag and entered the ball. The diving graph showed the *FNRS-3* had reached 13,450 feet.

Houot said, "Now all that remained was for Willm and me to go there ourselves."

The big dive, two and a half miles down, began in a heaving sea, February 15, 1954. Houot and Willm transferred to the bathyscaphe in shorts and pullovers, with a brief case containing sandwiches and a bottle of wine. The divers carried shark billies on wrist thongs as they moved around under the bathyscaphe, making her ready. One of them came out of the water and reported the safety clamp was jammed on No. 4 ballast silo. It closed the magnetic field, and to remove it meant a quarter of the shot ballast would fall into the sea. To leave it on and carry this dead weight would be too dangerous. Usually the *Élie Monnier* carried only about 500 pounds of extra shot, which was used to tip the scales just before a dive. But Willm smiled —he had put an extra ton of shot on the *Élie Monnier* before leaving Dakar. They could empty the silo, adjust the magnet and refill from the top of the envelope. Seamen started ferrying 125-pound sacks of shot in a rubber raft and Houot lifted them aboard. The sea was running high; two of the first four sacks fell out of their grasp and into the water. They saved the rest of the shot and the *FNRS-3* was ready to go. They had lost an hour in the reballasting.

The two tall men entered the sphere and bolted the hatch. They were thrown about in the rolling ball. Willm phoned the topman, "Michaudon, the hatch is closed. Cast off and let's go!" Commandant Ortolan called on the radio-telephone from the *Élie Monnier*, "Final reading of the echo-sounders 4,050 meters (13,365 feet). Your towline has been cast off."

Willm: "Michaudon, open the vents of the air tanks."

Michaudon: "All vents open."

Willm: "Open the safety valve of the airlock."

Michaudon: "Open."

Willm: "Good. *A bientôt.* Get off in the dinghy."

Michaudon unplugged the conning tower phone and got off.

Willm on the R-T: "Hello, *Élie Monnier*, we're ready to dive. Let us know when all personnel is off."

Ortolan: "Hello, bathyscaphe. You can dive."

Willm said to his skipper, "Valves one and two." They flooded the *sas*, and that was enough water to sink the *FNRS-3*. They heard the last of Ortolan's play by play, "Your deck is going under. Water halfway up the bathtub. Your antennae is . . ." Silence. The rocking stopped. Houot wrote in the log, "10:08 hours—communication with surface cut." The *FNRS-3* fell softly, in the green photosynthetic zone, which rapidly flushed with aquamarine and turned indigo blue. "From now on, no human being could do anything to help us," Houot wrote in his and Willm's stirring account, *2,000 Fathoms Down.* "It was with a slight sense of intoxication that we felt ourselves the sole masters of our fate."

The bathyscaphe sank one foot per second. Houot sent ultrasound signals every half hour to the surface, the letter A for *Je vous Appelle* (Bathyscaphe calling), v for *Tout Va Bien* (All's well) and a number, indicating depth in hundreds of meters. At 1030 hours, Houot sent: "A A A, V2, V2"—660 feet down. He got no answer from the research ship, which was supposed to send the letter R as an acknowledgment.

At 1100 Houot sent: "AAA V7 V7." No answer.

Willm, crouched at the porthole, felt something dripping on the back of his neck. The stuffing box on a pressure gauge had given way slightly. Since they were headed for pressure four times greater, Willm picked up a heavy monkey wrench and swung the nut tighter. The bathyscaphe was going down at the speed of a hundred feet a minute. Outside, "stars" of plankton gleamed in the lights. At 1130 Houot tapped out "AAA V20 V20"—6,560 feet.

Willm held his finger on the shot release button for a hundred seconds and a ton of shot poured out and drummed on the sphere like rain. This slowed the bathyscaphe. At noon they reached 9,900 feet, and sent up "AAA V30 V30." They decided to stop and make observations. Willm jettisoned another ton of shot, but she was still too heavy. He squirted shot for another twenty seconds. The bathyscaphe was now about as deep as the *Trieste's* lowest dive. The machine stopped and hung. Every square inch of the gondola bore a load of 4,370 pounds. Bright red shrimps swam past the window. "All control apparatus functions perfectly," Houot wrote in the log. In order to start down again, they had to valve some precious gasoline from the envelope. "It was like losing blood," said Houot. The gasoline volume was by now slightly contracted by pressure, but the bathyscaphe was designed to compensate for the shrinkage. Under the envelope were hatches open to the sea, so that salt water could take up the space.

Willm said, "It's about time we heard the frames cracking." The Duraluminium framework which held the ball to the gondola was under such stress that, according to his prior calculation, it should shrink about .04 inch. The frames made no noise. 1230: "AAA V33 V33," and still no acknowledgment from the *Élie Monnier*. Fifteen minutes later, Houot switched on the echo-sounder and the stylus began drawing a picture of the floor. When they had come within 660 feet of the bottom, they lightened ship again to land very gently. Houot took the porthole in the climactic moments.

1300 hours: "AAA V40 V40." Houot shouted, "I see the bottom!" The droplights fell in a bright circle on dazzling yellow sand, scored with low ripples and small mounds with animal holes in them. The guide chain dangled below the car, touched bottom and relieved enough weight to bring the bathyscaphe to a stop, floating on a chain 13,287 feet down. The column of water that rested on them weighed 68,000 tons, and could have contained ten Empire State Buildings standing on top of each other, without reaching the *Élie Monnier*.

The gasoline cooled further and they sank until the gondola touched earth. Fine sand bloomed around the car. On the sand grew a delicate sea anemone, like a tulip, but actually a cluster of tiny animals. Houot gave the window to Willm. "Shark!" he yelled. "Fine big head. He's quite different from the ones of the surface." The shark was over six feet long. It swam into the beam of lights and looked at their window with large popped-out eyes.

The plan of Dive No. 10 called for three hours on the bottom, so they started up the twin electric motors on the top of the envelope, motors that ran in oil baths. The *FNRS-3* nosed along the floor and they got ready to make photographs and movies. Suddenly a tremor shook the bathyscaphe and there was a rumbling noise overhead and the crash of a heavy object very near them on the floor. The performance was repeated. The exterior lights went out. The two thirteen-hundred-pound batteries on skids atop the envelope had cut loose from their electromagnets. They were emergency ballast that would drop off automatically if anything went wrong. The fuse had blown for some miserable reason. After a half hour in the new realm, the *FNRS-3* hauled them off to the surface at top speed.

Houot took the ultrasound key and sent M for *Je Monte* (I ascend). They were terribly disappointed, Willm the more so. Houot got out the sandwiches and wine and tried to console him. The young engineer said, dolefully, "And it had to happen on my *last* dive." Now that the test program was over he would give up his place to scientists. Houot said, "Courage, old man, I shall want you along in the Red Sea and the Pacific to drop a few batteries." At 1500 hours he sent "V13 M. V13 M." At 1522, after 5 hours and 14 minutes under the sea, the porthole flooded them with green light and the ball started to rock. They looked at each other and sighed. They said simultaneously, "It was so nice down there." Willm switched on the radio-telephone, "Hello, *Élie Monnier*, bathyscaphe calling." Ortolan's hearty voice boomed, "Hello, bathyscaphe. Receiving you loud and clear. All your signals received. The flying boat is overhead and the Admiral wants to say hello." From the circling Sunderland, Rear Admiral Jean Georges Gayral came in with his congratulations. On the escorting weather frigate *Beautemps Beaupré*, the radioman sent the news stuttering on the fleet radio frequency. I was on the *Calypso* in the Persian Gulf when our radioman picked it up. He posted the bulletin in the mess, under the heading, *"Gloire à la Marine Nationale!"*

Willm stepped aside for Théodore Monod, the marine biologist who made two dives with Houot off Dakar. Dr. Monod is the only man who has been down in both the *FNRS-2* and the *FNRS-3*. Houot was astonished at the way Monod called off the species of the strange animals he and Willm had been sighting. There were quite a few animals Monod had never seen before. In Toulon, in the two years since the big dive, Houot has taken down a dozen scientists, Commandants Tailliez and Cousteau, three reporters, including Kenneth MacLeish, of *Life* magazine, and Dr. Edgerton, the first foreigner to be honored with a dive. These dives have not exceeded 7,600 feet. The *FNRS-3* will not be taken to her record depth again. Houot and Willm, when I last saw them, were full of plans for the next bathyscaphe, which will be designed to reach the bottom of the Challenger Deep, between Guam and the Carolines. It is 35,640 feet deep.

Since the bathyscaphe there has been revived interest in the exploration of *inner* space, as contrasted with the fantasies of outer space that weigh so heavily on engineering resources and the public purse. It is no accident that bold creative spirits started out with flight problems and graduated to depth exploration, the earth science. Paul Bert was the founder of aviation medicine; J. S. Haldane was an alpinist; Beebe was an aviator; Papa Piccard beat all the airplanes of his time with balloon ascensions; Georges Houot was a mountaineer, and both Tailliez and Cousteau were fliers. Then they went into the sea.

Cousteau finished *The Silent World* by saying, "The Aqualung is primitive and unworthy of contemporary levels of science," Houot and Willm ended their chronicle, *2,000 Fathom Down,* with "F.N.R.S. *3* is only a prototype, a blind, clumsy, limping monster." In his final lecture at the University of Brussels, when he retired in 1954, Professor Piccard described the "mésoscaphe," a diving helicopter. The term means medium-range-boat. The sea imposes a modesty on those who try her.

Appendices

Appendices

Events in Underwater History, 415 B.C. to 1955

The author invites readers to send additions and corrections with sources of information, care of the publisher, Harper & Brothers, 49 East Thirty-third Street, New York, New York.

415 B.C.	Greek divers destroy booms at Syracuse
333 B.C.	Divers destroy boom defenses of Tyre: Alexander the Great
196 A.D.	Divers cut ships' cables, siege of Byzantium
375	Diving hoods with air pipes described: *De Re Militari*, Vegetius
1203	Divers cut ships' cables, siege of Les Andelys, France
1250	Air reservoirs for wreck divers described: *Novum Organum*, Sir Roger Bacon
1472	Hand-propelled wooden submarine, came apart in 3 pieces for portage: Venice, Roberto Valturio
1500 (circa)	Leather diving lungs with air hoses, submarine boats, described: Italy, Leonardo da Vinci
1535	Diving bell used to explore sunken Roman galleys: Lake Nemi, Italy, Guglielmo de Lorena
1538	Diving bell demonstrated by Greeks to Charles V: Spain
1559	Samuel Champlain describes 70-foot dives by West Indians
1565	Turkish divers attack Malta, met by local divers
1578	Submarine with ballast tanks operated by jack screws: England, William Bourne
1620	Submarine galley with air purifying system in Thames: Cornelius van Drebbel
1640	Diving bell used in wreck: Dieppe, France, Jean Barrié
1643	Cossack 40-man cowhide submersibles attack Turkish ships: Black Sea
1644	Fish-shape metal submarine designed, with surface air pipes: France, Père Marin Mersenne
1648	Speculation on future submarines: England, *Mathematickal Magick*, Bishop John Wilkins
1660	Studies of physical properties of compressed air: England, Robert Boyle
1665	Diving bell used in wreck: Tobermory, Scotland
1677	Arab divers employ bell on wrecks: Cadaqués, Spain
1679	Design for self-contained diving dress: Italy, G. A. Borelli
1687	Galleon treasure recovered by Indians and diving bell: Grand Bahama I., William Phips
1690	Diving bell reaches 60 feet for 90 minutes: England, Edmund Halley
1692	Submersible chamber: France, Denis Papin
1715	Leather diving suit used to 60 feet on salvage: England, John Lethbridge
1728	Air-supplied bell used on many salves: Sweden, Martin Triewald
1729	Submarine boat dives 45 minutes: River Dart, England, Nathaniel Symons
1754	Helmet suit with pumped air used on salvage: Yarmouth, England

1772   Self-contained helmet dress demonstrated, Académie des Sciences: France,
            Dr. Freminet

1773   Wooden submarine *Maria* lost in 132 feet with inventor, John Day:
            Plymouth, England

1774   One-hour descent to 50 feet in helmet dress fed by submerged compressed
            air tank: Le Havre, France, Freminet

1776   First authenticated attack by military submarine—American *Turtle* vs. H.M.S.
            Eagle: New York harbor, U.S.A., David Bushnell, Sgt. Ezra Lee.

1790   First modern diving bell used: Ramsgate harbor works, England, J. Smeaton

1793   Divers cut ships' cables, siege of Mayenne: France

1797   Helmet dress with pumped air tested: Oder river, Germany, Klingert

1798   Helmet dress in one-hour dive: Toulon, France, Burlet (convict), Sardou
            (prison guard)

1800   Practical submarine, hand-propelled *Nautilus*, dives 6 hours: Brest, Robert
            Fulton

1803   Elgin marbles salved from wreck: Kythera I., Greece

1815   *Mute*, 100-man submarine, built in New York: U.S.A., Robert Fulton

1819   Practical open helmet with pumped air: England, Augustus Siebe

1825   Five submarines with compressed-oxygen air supply: England, Capt. John-
            son

1827   Submarine, *Le Dauphin*, dives 44 minutes: Les Andelys, France, Beaudouin

1831   Diving sphere lost on test: Spain, Cervo
            Recovery of £120,000 from wreck H.M.S. *Thetis*, 50 feet deep, near Rio de
            Janeiro: Capt. Thomas Dickinson, R.N.

1832   Submarine boat dives 20 minutes: France, Villeroi

1834   Submarine sinks with inventor: France, Jean Baptiste Petit

1837   Prototype modern helmet diving dress: England, Augustus Siebe

1839   Beginning of *Royal George* salvage, Spithead, founding of salvage diving
            techniques, first navy diving school (to 1843): Col. Charles Pasley,
            A. Siebe, Corp. R. P. Jones

1841   Compressed air caissons used on Chalonnes-sur-Loire bridge piers: river Loire,
            France, Triger

1844   First scientific dives: Sicily, Prof. H. Milne-Edwards

1845   Diving chamber *Hydrostat* used to recover 100-foot bronze cannons in *Ré-
            publicain* wreck: Brest, France, Dr. Payerne
            Voyage au fond de la Mer by Capt. Mérobert, undersea novel: France

1850   Sheet-iron submarine *Brandtaucher* makes military sortie from Kiel: Germany,
            Wilhelm Bauer

1851   First submarine escapes from *Brandtaucher*, Kiel: Bauer, Witt, Thomsen
            Submarine dives 10 hours: Lake Michigan, U.S.A., Lodner D. Phillips

1855   *The Physical Geography of the Sea* by Lt. M. F. Maury, U.S.N.
            Submarine *Le Diable-Marin* makes 134 dives: Kronstadt, Russia; photographs
            attempted from portholes: Wilhelm Bauer
            French Navy adopts helmet dress used to 130 feet: Cabirol

1862   Submarine *El Actineo*, oxygen-regenerating breathing supply dives 54 times,
            up to 5-hour submersions with 10 men: Spain, Narciso Monturiol
            35-foot submarine built for U.S. Navy by Villeroi

1863   First proven powered submarine (compressed air) *Plongeur*, 420 tons: France,
            Siméon Bourgeois, Charles-Marie Brun
            Semi-independent compressed-air diving dress (*aérophore*) with first diving
            mask: France, Benoît Rouquayrol, Auguste Denayrouze

1864   The submarine boat sinks its first ship. Confederate *David IV* destroys U.S.S.
            Housatonic, herself destroyed: Charleston, S.C., U.S.A., Lt. Dixon, Hunley,
            Alexander

1864   U.S. hand-propelled, 16-man submarine with oxygen regeneration system
            sinks in Hatteras storm

1865	Steel sphere, exterior lamp, electric signals to surface, reaches 245 feet: Belle Isle, France, Ernest Bazin
1866	*Aérophore* helmet suit introduced Greek sponge fishery: France, Rouquayrol and Denayrouze
	Physician dives to study physiology: France, Alphonse Gal
	First automobile torpedo: England, Whitehead
1868	Compressed-air-driven submarines built in Russia
	Voyage sous les Flots by Aristide Roger, undersea novel: France
1869	*20,000 Leagues Under the Sea* by Jules Verne
1870	Salvage effort on galleons of Vigo: Spain, Magen, Sicard, Bazin
1871	Observation chamber *Talpa Marina* attains 230 feet: Bay of Naples, Italy, S. Torelli
1872	Proposal of optical periscope for submarine; photography through periscope foreseen: Belgium, Maj. Daudenart
	Intelligent Whale, 26-foot submarine with airlock: U.S. Navy, Oliver Halstead
1873	*The Depths of the Sea* by Wyville Thomson: Britain
	Decompression chamber used on Brooklyn Bridge pier workers: U.S.A., Dr. Andrew H. Smith
1875	First fully independent compressed-air lung used on salvage, *Magenta* wreck: Toulon, A. Denayrouze
	Dallmeyer lenses used on camera "beaneath the waters of San Francisco Bay" —report by Eadweard Muybridge
1878	Steam submarine *Holland I* built Paterson, N.J.: U.S.A., John P. Holland
	Steam submarines built for Greece, Turkey, Russia: Rev. G. W. Garrett (England), Theodore Nordenfelt (Sweden)
	Cave dive in helmet suit: Fountain of Vaucluse, France, Ottonelli
1879	*La Pression Barometrique*—basic researches in altitude and pressure physiology: France, Paul Bert
	First independent oxygen lung, regenerating system: Britain, Henry Fleuss
	One-man submarine, oxygen system, pedaled propeller, optical periscope, suction cup time bomb—52 built in Russia: Stephan Drzewieki
1880	Experiments with submerged camera: Sturbridge, Mass., U.S.A., George C. Moore
1881	First practical electrically-driven submarine, 11-ton *Goubet I*, with net cutters and torpedoes; sold to Brazil: France, Goubet
	Fenian Ram, 4-HP gasoline-engine submarine: U.S.A., John P. Holland
1884	*Peace Maker*, 30-foot electric submarine with exit lock, descends 65 feet: New York, Josiah H. L. Tuck
1885	60-ton steam submarine, *Nordenfelt I*, with steam reservoir for running submerged, sold to Greece: Garrett and Nordenfelt
	Naked diver swims 500 feet horizontally underwater, stays down 4 minutes: Hungary, James
	Small electric submarine tested: West Indies Docks, London, Andrew Campbell and James Ash
	Recovery of £90,000 from *Alphonso XII* wreck, 162 feet down: England, Alexander Lambert
1886	35-foot electric submarine *Porpoise* demonstrated: England, J. F. Waddington
	Precursor of modern submarines, 60-foot steel-hulled electric *Gymnote*; still in service 1907: France, C. H. L. Dupuy de Lôme and Gustave Zédé
	Scientific dives: France, Louis Boutan
1887	73-foot electric submarine *Peral* dives 30 feet: Cadiz, Spain, Lt. Isaac L. Peral
	Bronze electric submarine, 16-foot *Goubet II*, draws from Drzewieki's ideas, operates four years: France, Goubet

125-foot, 160-ton 1,000-HP submarine, *Nordenfelt IV*, shown in Naval Review, Portsmouth, sold to Russia, wrecked on passage

1888 — U.S. Navy competition for submarine design won by J. P. Holland

1890 — 160-foot bronze electric submarine *Gustave Zédé* in French naval service (to 1901): Toulon, Ramazotti

1891 — "Spectacles to Be Used in Diving," article in *American Journal of Ophthalmology*: D. W. Stevenson

1892 — 80-foot steel electric submarine *Pullino*, 3 propellers: Italy, Pullino

1893 — First underwater photographs: Banyuls-sur-Mer, France, Louis Boutan

1894 — Wooden submersible with airlock and wheels, *Argonaut Junior*: U.S.A.. Simon Lake

Proposal that submarines be propelled on surface by gasoline engines, which also charge batteries for diving: Italy, Giulio Martinez

1896 — French submarine competition won by 116-foot steam electric *Narvak*: Laubeuf

1897 — Steel sphere *La France*, electric lights, telephone, external claws, lowered 165 feet: Piatti del Ponzo (Italy), A. Delisle (France)

35-foot iron electric submarine *Argonaut*, with wheels and airlock, travels 2,000 miles on bay floors: U.S.A., Simon Lake

1899 — Photographs by artificial light to 165 feet: France, Louis Boutan

Photographs from submerged *Argonaut*: U.S.A., Simon Lake

1900 — *La Photographie Sous-Marine* by Louis Boutan; describes 3 underwater cameras, submarine optics, light penetration in sea, amateur cameras, artificial lighting systems

First U.S. Navy submarine commissioned—*Plunger*: J. P. Holland, Isaac D. Rice

Royal Navy submarine flotilla founded with 5 Holland boats built by Vickers

1901 — Undersea archeological expedition, Antikythera I., Greece, recovers bronze masterpieces of Periclean Age: Capt. Demetrios Kondos

Seabed samples dredged from 19,900 feet: Prince Albert of Monaco

1902 — Wheeled salvage chamber with mechanical claws: Italy, Giuseppe Pino

66-foot steel gasoline-electric submarine *Protector*: Simon Lake

1903 — Submarine escape lung, oxygen regenerating: England, Sir Robert Davis

1904 — Greek and Swedish helmet divers reach 190-foot deep wreck, destroyer *Chamois*: Patras, Greece

1905 — German U-Boat flotilla founded with Krupp *U-1*, which torpedoes moving target in demonstration

Echo-sound experiments: Norway, Berggraf

French submarine *Farfadet* sinks: Bizerte, Africa

Lake submarine dives 138 feet: Germany

1906 — British Admiralty Deep-Diving Committee establishes diving tables to 200 feet: J. S. Haldane, A. E. Boycott, G. C. C. Damant, A. Y. Catto

1907 — Greek sponge divers discover Roman 1st Cent. B.C. wreck, Mahdia, Tunisia; excavated 1908–13 for classic sculptures: France, Alfred Merlin, Jean Baehme

Submarine escape lung, oxygen regenerating, adopted by Royal Navy: S. S. Hall and O. Rees

Artificially lighted underwater photographs: France, Étienne Peau

1908 — "Fishing submarine" with mechanical tongs, wheels, searchlight, telephone, tested to 325 feet: Toulon, France, Abbé Raoul

1909 — Naked free escape through torpedo tube, U.S. Submarine *Porpoise*, down to 26 feet: Manila, Lt. Kenneth Whiting

1910 — Royal Navy submarines cruise 10,000 miles to Hong Kong with tender

German U-boats standardized with interchangeable parts

1911 — Ultra-sound detection of dived submarine: Paul Langevin (France), Chilovsky (Russia)

1912	Cylindrical observation chamber: England, Sir R. H. Davis

1912   Cylindrical observation chamber: England, Sir R. H. Davis
The Depths of the Ocean by Sir John Murray and Johan Hjort (Norway)
Recovery of £700,000 from *Oceana* wreck, 90 feet down: English Channel
1913   Articulated diving armor: Germany, Neufeldt and Kuhnke
Photographs from chamber 30 feet down: U.S.A., J. E. Williamson
Underwater robot camera, time-lapse: H. Hartman, Monaco
Attested naked dive to 200 feet: Greece, Stotti Georghios
Modernization of U.S. Navy diving: George D. Stillson and G. W. French
1914   First undersea motion picture, *Williamson Submarine Expedition*, made from
       Photoscope chamber, Nassau: U.S.A., John E. Williamson
U-boat 9 sinks H.M.S. *Aboukir, Hogue and Cressy*: Lt. Otto Weidingen
Echo-sound detects icebergs, sounds 8,000-foot bottom: U.S.A., Reginald A.
       Fessenden, Harold W. Fay
1915   Sinking of U.S. Submarine *F-4*, Hawaii, 304 feet; helmet divers reach
       wreck: Crilley, Loughman, Drelishak. Raised by Comm. J. A. Furer,
       deepest recovery of entire vessel
Full-length film, *Twenty Thousand Leagues Under the Sea*: J. E. Williamson
U-boat blockade of Britain; sinking of R.M.S. *Lusitania*
1916   Robot camera with floodlamps locates German booby traps in flooded Bel-
       gian coal mines: England, Siebe, Gorman, Sir Frederick Young
German cargo submarine *Deutschland* arrives U.S.A., Capt. Koenig
Robot depth camera tested U.S. Navy: H. Hartman
Attested naked dive to 198 feet by sponge diver; Kastellorizo I., Greece
1917   U-boats sink 6 million tons of British shipping in one year
Russia orders 4,000-ton submarine, not completed
Photos; focus, speed and trigger controls underwater: U.S.A., W. H. Longley
$25 million in gold recovered from *Laurentic* wreck, N. Ireland (to 1924):
       Britain, G. C. C. Damant, E. C. Miller
Raising of 24,000-ton battleship, *Leonardo da Vinci*: Taranto, Italy, Ferrati,
       Gianelli
German government declares unrestricted submarine warfare
H.M. Submarine *K-13* accidentally sunk, Gareloch; 46 crew men saved by
       hauling bow to surface
1918   *U-57* mined off Dover; crew escapes from 125 feet with Draeger oxygen lungs
"We are sinking U-Boats faster than Germany can build them, and building
       ships faster than the U-Boats can sink them" (May 23)—British Prime
       Minister Lloyd George
Italian underwater chariot attack sinks battleship *Viribus Unitis*: Yugoslavia,
       Raffaele Paolucci, Raffaele Rossetti
Two giant M-Class, aircraft-carrying submarines launched in Britain, later lost
       in accidents
1919   Proposal that deep divers breathe helium, prediction of 50 per cent greater
       depths: U.S.A., Elihu Thomson
Dive in armor to 608 feet: Mexico, Victor Campos
1920   Scientific dives to study coral reefs: Samoa, A. G. Mayor
1923   First underwater color photos: Dry Tortugas, U.S.A., W. H. Longley
1924   Independent compressed air lung, manually valved: France, Yves le Prieur
First rubber foot fins: France, Louis de Corlieu
First helium-oxygen experimental dives: U.S. Navy and Bureau of Mines
1925   Raising of U.S. Submarine *S-51*: Edward Ellsberg and Ernest J. King
Scientific dives: Denmark, C. G. J. Petersen; Galapagos I.: William Beebe,
       (U.S.A.)
Bronze statue of youth (4th Cent. B.C.) recovered: Bay of Marathon, Greece,
       Evangelos Leonidas
Underwater television experiment: Capri, H. Hartman
La Perle by Louis Boutan

1926   Raising scuttled German fleet at Scapa Flow, including 6 battleships averaging
            26,000 tons each (to 1933). Britain, Thomas McKenzie, E. F. Cox
            Lake Nemi, Italy, drained to recover 1st Cent. A.D. pleasure galleys
            First artificially-lighted color photos (magnesium flash on surface): U.S.A.,
            W. H. Longley, Charles Martin

1927   Rescue bell for sunken submarines: A. R. McCann, U.S.N.
            U.S. Submarine S-4 sunk off Cape Cod, raised 1928, described in classic *On
            the Bottom* by Edward Ellsberg, 1929

1928   Submarine escape lung, oxygen rebreathing system, adopted U.S. Navy:
            C. B. Momsen
            Archeological expedition recovers off Cape Artemision, Greece, "Thundering
            Zeus" bronze (c. 450 B.C.) and "Boy Jockey" (c. 220 B.C.): George Karo,
            Alexander Benakis
            Submerged movies, Haiti: U.S.A., William Beebe, Mark Barr, John Tee-
            Van
            Emergence of goggle diving and undersea hunting in Mediterranean, Florida,
            California: Guy Gilpatric et al.
            Beginning of 7-year salve of $6 million in gold from wreck of S.S. *Egypt*,
            426 feet down; Bay of Biscay: Sorima Co., Giovanni Quaglia

1929   Founding of Experimental Diving Unit, U.S. Navy
            Recovery of marble "Venus of Rhodes"

1930   Butoscopic Turret reaches 700 feet: Italy, Roberto Galeazzi
            Bathysphere reaches 1,400 feet, Bermuda: U.S.A., William Beebe, Otis
            Barton
            Admiralty committee establishes diving tables to 300 feet: Leonard Hill,
            R. H. Davis, G. C. C. Damant, F. A. Buckley
            Navy helmet divers on compressed air reach 344 feet; one dies: Britain
            North Pole Expedition in submarine *Nautilus*: U.S.A., Sir Hubert Wilkins
            Marble reliefs (2nd Cent. B.C.) recovered: Piraeus harbor, Greece, George
            Karo

1931   Commercial 16 mm underwater camera marketed: U.S.A., E. R. F. Johnson
            Five escape from H.M. Submarine *Poseidon*, 125 feet down, China Sea, with
            Davis oxygen lungs

1932   Bathysphere attains 2,170 feet: Bermuda, Wm. Beebe, Otis Barton
            Underwater spear gun: France, Alexander Kramarenko

1933   First sport diving club, the Bottom Scratchers: California, Glenn Orr
            First use of echo-sound for fish detection: Britain, Capt. Ronald Balls
            Depth camera housing reaches 18,000 feet; lost on first camera test: U.S.A.,
            E. R. F. Johnson

1934   Relics of British warships sunk 1781 recovered from York River, Virginia:
            Mariners Museum, Newport News
            Amateur diving group, Club des Sous-l'Eau, founded Paris: Yves le Prieur
            Recovery of 6th Cent. B.C. Greek sculptures from Sele river: Italy, Umberto
            Zanotti-Bianco, Paola Montuoro
            Bathysphere reaches 3,036 feet: Bermuda, Beebe and Barton
            Half Mile Down by William Beebe
            Scientific dives: Plymouth, England, Marine Biological Assn. of U.K.,
            Kitching, Macan, Gilson
            Underwater gun with rubber cables: France, Georges Beuchat
            Cave dives: Swildon's Hole, England, Graham Balcombe, Jack Sheppard

1935   Cave dives with helmet suits: Wookey Hole, England, Balcombe and Shep-
            pard
            Underwater movies: Baja California, Mexico, John D. Craig
            Archeological survey port of ancient Tyre with underwater photos (to
            1937): France, Père A. Poidebard

1936   First underwater chariot: Italy, Teseo Tesei, Elias Toschi

1937   Film of escape exercise from submarine, *Redoutable*: France, Le Prieur, Jean
        Painlevé
        Helium-oxygen dive in helmet suit to 420 feet: Lake Michigan, U.S.A.,
        Max Gene Nohl, Edgar End
        Simulated 500-foot helium-oxygen dive, U.S. Navy Experimental Diving
        Unit: A. R. Behnke, O. D. Yarbrough

1938   Patent on mask covering eyes and nose: France, Maxim Forjot
        The Compleat Goggler by Guy Gilpatric, first book on amateur diving and
        hunting
        Diving team formed: Philippe Tailliez, Frédéric Dumas, Jacques-Yves
        Cousteau
        Dives in Adriatic Sea: Austria, Hans Hass
        Construction begun of depth vehicle, Bathyscaphe *FNRS 2*: Belgium, Auguste
        Piccard, Max Cosyns

1939   Sinking of U.S. Submarine *Squalus*; 33 crew men escape from 240 feet in
        McCann bell. First use of helium-oxygen on deep diving operations
        16 mm hand-held motion pictures: France, P. Tailliez; W. Indies, H. Hass
        (Austria)
        16 mm cinécamera lowered to 4,200 feet: U.S.A., E. N. Harvey, E. R.
        Baylor
        Sinking of H.M. Submarine *Thetis*

1940   Hand-held 35 mm movies: Cousteau, Tailliez and Dumas
1941   £2 million in gold recovered from *Niagara*, 438 feet down: New Zealand,
        J. P. Williams, J. C. Johnstone
        Bottom photos, 16,200 feet: U.S.A., Maurice Ewing
        Italian chariots sink tanker at Gibraltar: J. V. Borghese, Visintini, Magro
        Underwater combat team with Lambertsen oxygen-rebreathing lungs formed
        U.S. Office of Strategic Services: Christian J. Lambertsen
        British "underwater working parties" defend Gibraltar anchorage: William
        Bailey, L. P. K. Crabbe
        Five Japanese midget submarines assault Pearl Harbor, damage U.S.S.
        Arizona
        Italian charioteers disable H.M.S. *Queen Elizabeth* and *Valiant*: Alexandria,
        Egypt, Luigi de la Penne
        First confirmed sinking by U.S. submarine—*Atsutusan Maru* by U.S.S.
        Swordfish: Comm. C. C. Smith

1942   Biggest ship-raising, 79,280-ton U.S.S. *Lafayette* (ex-*Normandie*); largest
        navy diving school formed on operation, New York: Commodore William
        Sullivan, Capt. B. E. Manseau, Merritt-Chapman and Scott
        Japanese midget subs attack Diégo-Suarez, Madagascar; sink tanker, damage
        H.M.S *Ramillies*. Also attack Sydney harbor, Australia

1943   "Kaitens"—Japanese suicide torpedo group—formed; later sink many ships
        Japan launches 24 torpedo-plane-carrying submarines
        Free air lung dive to 166 feet: France, Georges Comheines
        Fully automatic compressed air "Aqualung" (*Scaphandre-autonome*) "opens
        age of undersea exploration": France, J.-Y. Cousteau and Emile Gagnan.
        (Marketed France 1946, Britain 1950, Canada 1951, U.S.A. 1952)
        203-foot Aqualung dive: Frédéric Dumas
        British midget subs disable German battleship *Tirpitz*: Kaafiord, Norway,
        B. C. G. Place, D. Cameron
        Call for volunteers, U.S. Navy underwater demolition teams

1944   British and Italian charioteers sink 10,000-ton cruiser *Bolzano*: La Spezia,
        Italy
        Nazi underwater team attacks Nijmegen Bridge, Holland
        Eight Japanese one-man submarines attack U.S. fleet anchorage, Ulithi Atoll,
        West Caroline Is., sink tanker *Mississinewa*; all midgets lost

1945 U.S.A. claims territory of Continental Shelf to 600-foot "Dropoff Line"; many nations follow: Harry S. Truman

French Navy Undersea Research Group (G.E.R.S.) founded: Tailliez, Cousteau, Dumas

Helmet dive in flexible dress, breathing hydrogen-oxygen, to 528 feet: Sweden, Arne Zetterstrom

Two largest submarines in history launched by Japan—each 3,500 tons and carrying 3 torpedo planes—designed to attack Panama Canal. War ends before mission

1945

> ### OFFICIAL SUBMARINE WARFARE TOTALS IN WORLD WAR II
>
> BRITAIN, with 218 submarines, sank 1,257 merchant ships with a loss of 76 submarines
>
> U.S.A. with 288 submarines, sank 1,113 merchant ships, with a loss of 52 submarines
>
> GERMANY, with 1,072 submarines, sank 2,606 merchant ships, with a loss of 705 submarines
>
> JAPAN, with 181 submarines, sank 147 merchant ships, with a loss of 130 submarines

British midget sub XE-4 cuts telegraph cables, Saigon-Singapore and Saigon-Hong Kong: Lt. M. H. Shean

Soviet submarines sink two shiploads of Nazis fleeing East Prussia; 8,000 drowned

British midget H.M.S. XE-3 sinks cruiser Takao: Singapore, Lt. Ian Fraser, Leading Seaman J. J. Magennis

1946 Archaeological investigation Phoenician port at Sidon (to 1950): France, Père Poidebard

U.S. Navy adopts free escape for submariners

Dives in Vaucluse Fountain: G.E.R.S.

1947 Experimental Aqualung dives to 297 feet: G.E.R.S., Toulon (Cousteau, Tailliez, Dumas, Georges, Fargues, Morandière)

First underwater television chain: Bikini I., U.S. Navy (to 180 feet)

Cave dives: Chartreux Spring, France, G.E.R.S.

Color movies (35 mm) in natural light, 125 feet down, off Tunisia; artificially lighted sequences at 160 feet: G.E.R.S.

1948 Helmet dive on helium-oxygen to 540 feet by W. Bollard, R.N.: Loch Fyne, W. O. Shelford

Bathyscaphe FNRS2 tested West Africa: A. Piccard, M. Cosyns, G.E.R.S.

Aqualung dive on compressed air to 307 feet: F. Dumas

Samples dredged from 26,500 feet, Albatross expedition: Sweden, Hans Pettersson

Classic wreck found, Anthéor, France: Henri Chenévée, Henri Broussard, Dr. Dénereaz; another discovered nearby, 1953, by Dr. Jean Piroux (excavated 1955 by G.E.R.S., Tailliez)

Excavation of Roman port at Fos-sur-Mer: France, Dr. Beaucaire (continues)

Founding French Federation of Submarine Clubs: Jean Borelli

First Italian amateur club, Genoa: D. Gonzatti, Dr. L. Stuart-Tovini

1949 La Plongée en Scaphandre by Phillippe Tailliez et al., established tables for successive Aqualung dives (Revised 1955 by Dumas)

Simulated helium-oxygen dive to 561 feet: Boatswain's Mate Harold Weinsbraud, U.S.N.

Otis Barton lowered in his benthoscope to 4,500 feet: California

British cave divers in France—subterranean river Labouiche: Dr. Robert E. Davies

Bronze panther of Hellenistic age found off Monaco: Giordano

1950   Mechanical excavation of Roman wreck (c. 90 B.C.), 130 feet deep: Albenga, Italy, Nino Lamboglia, Giovanni Quaglia

Photos from unoccupied Benthograph 4,050 feet: U.S.A., Robert Dietz, Hancock Foundation

Cave dives: St. Georges Fountain, France—Guy de Lavaur, Club Alpin Sous-Marin—and in the Lirou Siphon, Lombard

International Underwater Spearfishing Association founded: California, Ralph N. Davis

Hand-held color-corrected photoflash shots 150 feet down: *Calypso* Expeditions

First scientific diving team formed at Scripps Institution of Oceanography, California: Conrad Limbaugh

Sunken submarine H.M. *Truculent* located by Aqualung diver: Comm. H. J. Hodges, R.N.

The deepest photograph—18,000 feet down: David Owen, Woods Hole Oceanographic Institution, Massachusetts

1951   Hand-held underwater color shots by electronic flash: France, Dmitri Rebikoff

Bottom samples, 34,000 feet, Philippine Deep: *Galatea*, Denmark

Huge carrara parts of Roman temple recovered: Saint-Tropez, France, Henri Broussard

Pyrotechnic torch to light underwater films: France, Ruggieri, Dumas

Naked dives to 115 feet: Portofino, Italy, Alberto Novelli, Ennio Falco

Deepest echo-sounding—35,847 feet in Philippine Trench: H.M.S. *Challenger*

Wreck (c. 3rd Cent. A.D.) discovered Anse St.-Roch: France, Louis Lehoux, Club de la Mer

Television locates sunken H.M. Submarine *Affray*; R.N. Experimental Laboratory

The Sea Around Us by Rachel Carson

1952   Keel-laying U.S. Atomic Submarine *Nautilus*: Hyman Rickover, Electric Boat Co.

Excavation begins on 3rd Cent. B.C. Greek wreck, 125 feet deep, near Marseilles (continuing): *Calypso* Expeditions, National Geographic Society

Early U.S. gunboat wrecks recovered: Lake Champlain, Lorenzo Haggulund

Television used for biological study: Scottish Marine Biological Assn., Harold Barnes

1953   Scientific diving team in Pacific: Capricorn Expedition, Scripps Institution of Oceanography, California

Cave dives: Silver Springs, Fla.; recovery of mastodon and Columbian elephant bones: William Ray, Charles McNabb. Bower Cave, Calif.; Jon Lindbergh

The Silent World by J.-Y. Cousteau and Frédéric Dumas

Bathyscaphe *Trieste* dives to 10,400 feet: Ponza I., Italy, Auguste and Jacques Piccard

Turkish fishermen net 4th Cent. B.C. bronze Demeter at Bitez

Hand-held television to 125 feet: *Calypso* Expeditions, Thomson-Houston Co.

1954   Caribbean archeological expedition: U.S.A., Edwin Link, Mendel Peterson

Diving geodetic survey, Persian Gulf: *Calypso* Expeditions, British Petroleum

Diving sedimental study, Gulf of Mexico: D. E. Feray, Henry Nelson, Magnolia Petroleum Co.

Diving search for U.S.S. *Monitor* wreck, Cape Hatteras: Monitor Historical Society, Raynor T. McMullen

Bathyscaphe *FNRS3* in man's deepest descent—13,287 feet off Dakar: France, Georges S. Houot and Pierre Willm

Archeological survey, Chios I., Greece: Richard Garnett, London *Sunday Times*

Observation chamber "Aquascope" in Chesapeake Bay: Gilbert Klingel, Willard R. Culver.

Free dive on helium-oxygen to 350 feet: U.S.A., Jean Clarke-Samazan

Television lowered to 600 feet to locate wreckage of Comet jet liner Elba I.: Royal Navy

1955   First Congress on submarine archeology: Cannes, France, Henri Broussard, Fernand Benôit

Cave dives: Murray Hamilton and Donald Gerue, Radium Springs, Ga. *Union Rhodanienne* and Lyon *Tritons*, subterranean river, La Balme, France. Anglo-French Expedition, Norbert Casteret and R. E. Davies, subterranean river, Labouiche, France

Jet injector air lung, *Le Mistral*: Cousteau and Gagnan

Launching Atomic Submarine *Nautilus*

Archeological searches for Greek ships sunk 415 B.C., Syracuse: Sicily, Arthur W. Baker

Undersea Bibliography

OCEANOGRAPHY AND DIVING HISTORY
Armstrong, E. F., and Miall, L. M., *Raw Materials from the Sea*, Brooklyn, 1946.
Boutan, Louis, *La Perle*, Paris, 1925.
Carson, Rachel, *The Sea Around Us*, New York, 1951.
Chapman, V. J., *Seaweeds and Their Uses*, New York, 1952.
Davis, Sir Robert H., *Deep Diving and Submarine Operations*, London, 1951.
De Quatrefages, A., *Ramblings of a Naturalist on the Coasts of France and Sicily*, London, 1857.
Herdman, Sir William A., *Founders of Oceanography*, London, 1923.
Hervey, A. B., *Sea Mosses*, Boston, 1882.
Lee, Henry, *The Octopus*, London, 1875.
Meunier, V., *Les Grandes Pêches*, Paris, 1878.
Murray, Sir John, and Hjort, Johan, *The Depths of the Oceans*, London, 1912.
Pohl, Lucien L., "Understanding the Cultured Pearl," *Natural History*, June, 1955.
Portier, Paul, "Naissance de l'Anaphylaxie," *Acta Allergologica*, 1952.
Pratt, R., *et al.*, "Report on the Antibiotic Activity of Seaweed Extracts," *Journal of the American Pharmaceutical Association*, November, 1951.
Résultats Scientifiques des Campagnes de la Calypso, Vol. 1, Paris, 1955.
Romanovsky, *et al.*, *La Mer*, Paris, 1953.
Siebe, Henry, *The Conquest of the Sea*, London, 1873.
Smith, Maxwell, *World-Wide Sea Shell Catalogue*, Windermere, Florida, 1953.
Stoloff, Leonard, "Irish Moss," *Economic Botany*, October, 1949.
Sverdrup, H. U., *et al.*, *The Oceans*, New York, 1942.
Winchester, Clarence, *Shipping Wonders of the World*, 2 vols., London.

SALVAGE

Benham, Clarence, *Divers' Luck*, Sydney, 1949.
Connolly, T. W. J., *History of the Royal Sappers and Miners*, London, 1855.
Eadie, Tom, *I Like Diving*, Boston, 1929.
Ellsberg, Edward, *Men Under the Sea*, New York, 1939.
Ellsberg, Edward, *On the Bottom*, New York, 1929.
Grossett, Harry, *Down to the Ships in the Sea*, London, 1953.
Magen, H., *Les Galions de Vigo*, Paris, 1873.
Masters, David, *Epics of Salvage*, London, 1953.
Masters, David, *When Ships Go Down*, London, 1932.
Masters, David, *Wonders of Salvage*, London, 1944.
Salvage of the U.S.S. Lafayette (ex-S.S. *Normandie*), U.S. Navy Bureau of Ships, Washington, 1946.
Salvage Operations on the Comet G-ALYP, Admiralty, London, 1954.

DIVING PHYSIOLOGY

Bert, Paul, *Barometric Pressure,* Translated by M. A. and F. A. Hitchcock, Columbus, Ohio, 1943.
Diving with Self-Contained Apparatus, U.S. Navy Experimental Diving Unit, Washington, 1954.
Douglas, C. G., "John Scott Haldane," *Obituary Notices,* Royal Society, London, 1936.
Haldane, J. S., *Report of a Committee Appointed by the Lords Commissioners of the Admiralty to Consider and Report upon the Conditions of Deep-Water Diving,* London, 1907.
Hoff, E. C., et al., *A Bibliographical Sourcebook of Compressed Air Diving and Submarine Medicine,* Washington, 1948.
Nitrogen-Oxygen Mixture Physiology, U.S. Navy Experimental Diving Unit, Washington, 1955.
Physics and Physiology for Divers, Scripps Institute of Oceanography.
Report on Use of Helium-Oxygen Mixtures for Diving, U.S. Navy Experimental Diving Unit, Washington, 1942.
Tailliez, Philippe, et al., *La Plongée en Scaphandre,* Paris, 1949.
Zetterstrom, Arne, "Deep-Sea Diving with Synthetic Gas Mixture," *Military Surgeon,* August, 1948.

FREE DIVING

Bradner, Hugh, and Dietz, Robert S., *Recent Developments in Scuba Diving in Europe,* Technical Report ONRL 55-55, U.S. Navy, 1955.
Clarke, Eugenie, *Lady with a Spear,* New York, 1952.
Cousteau, Jacques-Yves; Tailliez, Philippe; and Dumas, Frédéric, *Par Dix-Huit Mètres de Fond,* Paris, 1946.
Cousteau, Jacques-Yves, and Dumas, Frédéric, *The Silent World,* New York, 1953.
Drach, Pierre, "Lacunes dans la Connaissance de Peuplement des Mers et Utilisation des Scaphandres Autonomes," *La Revue Scientifique,* Paris, 1952.
Gibb, H. A. R., trans., *Ibn Battuta, Travels in Asia and Africa,* London, 1929.
Gilpatric, Guy, *The Compleat Goggler,* New York, 1938.
Hahn, Walter A., and Lambertsen, Christian J., *On Using Self-Contained Underwater Breathing Apparatus,* National Academy of Sciences, Washington, 1952.
Hass, Hans, *Diving to Adventure,* New York, 1952.
Owen, David M., *A Manual for Free Divers,* London, 1955.
Rebikoff, Dmitri, *L'Exploration Sous-Marine,* Paris, 1952.
Revelle, Roger, et al., "Free Diving, a New Exploratory Tool," *American Scientist,* Vol. 41, No. 4.
Ribera, Antoni, *Els Homes Piexos,* Barcelona, 1954.
Schenk, Hilbert, Jr., and Kendall, Henry, *Shallow Water Diving and Spearfishing,* Cambridge, Maryland, 1954.
Tailliez, Philippe, *La Plongée sans Câble,* Paris, 1953.
"Underwater Mapping by Diving Geologists," *Bulletin of the American Association of Petroleum Geologists,* Vol. 38.

UNDERSEA WARFARE

Beach, Edward L., *Submarine!,* New York, 1952.
Borghese, J. Valerio, *The Sea Devils,* Chicago, 1954.
Chalmers, W. S., *Max Horton and the Western Approaches,* London, 1954.
Chatterton, E. Keble, *Gallant Gentlemen,* London, 1931.
Edwards, Kenneth, *We Dive at Dawn,* London, 1939.
Frank, Wolfgang, *The Sea Wolves,* London, 1955.
Guam: Operations of the 77th Division, U.S. War Department, Washington, 1946.
Hashimoto, Mochitsura, *Sunk,* London, 1954.

Omaha Beachhead, U.S. War Department, Washington, 1946.
Utah Beach to Cherbourg, Department of the Army, Washington, 1947.
Waldron, T. J., and Gleeson, James, *The Frogmen*, London, 1950.
Warren, C. E. T., and Benson, James, *Above Us the Waves*, London, 1953.

SUBMARINE VEHICLES AND ENGINEERING

Barton, Otis, *The World Beneath the Sea*, New York, 1954.
Beebe, William, *Half Mile Down*, New York, 1934.
Blair, Clay, Jr., *The Atomic Submarine*, New York, 1954.
Delpeuch, Maurice, *Les Sous-Marin è Travers les Siècles*, Paris, 1907.
Domville-Fife, Charles W., *Submarine Engineering of Today*, London, 1914.
Falck, N. D., *A Philosophical Dissertation on the Diving Vessel Projected by Mr. Day and Sunk in Plymouth Sound*, London, 1775.
Hichborn, Philip, "The Demonstrated Success of the Submarine Boat," *Engineering Magazine*, June, 1900.
Houot, G. S., and Willm, Pierre, *Le Bathyscaphe*, Paris, 1954.
Lake, Simon, and Corey, Herbert, *Submarine*, New York, 1938.
Parsons, W. B., *Robert Fulton and the Submarine*, New York, 1922.
Pesce, G.-L., *La Navigation Sous-Marine*, Paris, 1906.
Piccard, Auguste, *Au Fond des Mers en Bathyscaphe*, Paris, 1954.
Sasaki, Tadayoshi, "The Submarine Research Apparatus, 'Kuroshio,' " *Senpaku* (Tokyo), Vol. 25, No. 1.
Tartaglia, Niccolò, *Queseti et Inventioni Diverre*, 1554.

UNDERWATER ARCHEOLOGY

Action d'État: Fouilles Archéologiques, Paris, 1951.
Cary, M., *The Geographic Background of Greek and Roman History*, London, 1949.
Cousteau, Jacques-Yves, "Fish Men Discover a 2,200-Year-Old Greek Ship," *National Geographic Magazine*, January, 1954.
Diole, Philippe, *Promenades d'Archéologie Sous-Marines*, Paris, 1952.
Graves, Robert, *The Greek Myths*, 2 vols., London, 1955.
Karo, George, "Art Salvaged from the Sea," *Archaeology*, Winter, 1948.
Lamboglia, Nino, and Benôit, Fernand, *Fouilles Sous-Marines en Ligurie et en Provence*, Bordighera, Italy, 1953.
Merlin and Poinssot, *Cratères et Candélares de Marbre Trouvé en Mer près de Mahdia*, Tunis, 1930.
Peterson, Mendel L., *History Under the Sea*, Smithsonian Institute, Washington, 1954.
Philadelfeus, A., *The Museums of Athens*, Athens, 1935.
Poidebard, A., and Lauffrey, J., *Sidon: Aménagements Antiques du Port de Saida*, Beirut, Lebanon, 1951.
Poidebard, A., *Un Grand Port Disparu: Tyr*, 2 vols., Paris, 1939.
Salvaging Revolutionary Relics from the York River, Mariners Museum, 1939.
Smith, A. H., *Lord Elgin and His Marbles*, London, 1916.

UNDERWATER PHOTOGRAPHY

Boutan, Louis, *La Photographie Sous-Marine et Les Progrès de la Photographie*, Paris, 1900.
Craig, John D., *Danger Is My Business*, New York, 1938.
Dieuzeide, R., *Le Professeur Louis Boutan*, Algiers, 1934.
Du Pont, A. Felix, *Under Sea with Helmet and Camera*, New York, 1940.
Edgerton, Harold E., "Photographing the Sea's Dark Underworld," *National Geographic Magazine*, April, 1955.
Hommage à Louis Boutan, L'Institut Océanographique d'Indochine, 1936.
Johnson, E. R. F., "Undersea Photography," *Journal of the Society of Motion Picture Engineers*, January, 1939.

Moncrief, Henry S., "Historical Developments in Underwater Photography," *PSA Journal*, November, 1951.
Owen, David M., "Deep Sea Underwater Photography," *Photogrammetric Engineering*, March, 1951.
Peau, E., "Le Cinématographe Sous-Marin," *Bulletin d'Hygiène*, Le Havre, 1917.
Peau, E., "La Photographie Sous-Marine," *Annuaire Général et International de Photographie*, Paris, 1908.
Schenk, Hilbert, and Kendall, Henry, *Underwater Photography*, Cambridge, Maryland, 1954.
Williamson, John E., *Twenty Years Under the Sea*, London, 1935.

BIOGRAPHY, ETC.

Cullingford, C. H. D., *et al.*, *British Caving*, London, 1953.
De la Fuÿe, Marguerite Allotte, *Jules Verne*, London, 1954.
Fessenden, Helen M., *Fessenden, Builder of Tomorrows*, New York, 1940.

PERIODICALS CONSULTED

All Hands, Washington.
L'Appel de la Mer, Juan-les-Pins, France.
L'Aventure Sous Marine, Paris.
Bulletin Officiel du Club Alpin Sous-Marin, Cannes, France.
De Havilland Gazette, Hatfield, Herts.
L'Eau et la Vie Sous-Marine, Paris-Tanger.
FAO Fisheries Bulletin, Rome.
Journal of the American Society of Naval Engineers.
Letter of the Cave Diving Group, London.
Marine Review, London.
National Geographic Magazine, Washington.
Natural History, New York.
Neptune, London.
Neptunia, Paris.
Neige et Glace, Paris.
Penguin Science, London.
Scientific American, New York.
The Skin Diver, Lynwood, California.
Soundings, Boston.
The Sunday Times, London.
Le Trident, Paris.
The UNESCO Courier, Paris.
U.S. Naval Institute Proceedings.
The Waterbug, Clearwater, Florida.

Index

323

Set in Intertype Garamond
Format by Katharine Sitterly
Manufactured by The Haddon Craftsmen, Inc.
Published by HARPER & BROTHERS, *New York*

ρ